Principles
of
Surveying

Principles
of
Surveying

Charles A. Herubin

Hudson Valley Community College
Troy, New York

RESTON PUBLISHING COMPANY, INC., RESTON, VIRGINIA 22090
A Prentice-Hall Company

c.1

Library of Congress Cataloging in Publication Data

Herubin, Charles A.   1931-
   Principles of surveying.

   1. Surveying.   I. Title.
TA 545.H47   526.9   73-15796
ISBN 0-87909-618-7

Copyright © 1974 by
Reston Publishing Company, Inc.
A Prentice-Hall Company
Box 547
Reston, Virginia 22090

10   9   8   7   6   5   4

Printed in the United States of America.

Preface

This book is intended for colleges and technical schools and is designed to facilitate self-study.

I believe that the purpose of a surveying course should be to impart basic knowledge plus training in the use of traditional surveying equipment—tape, transit, and level. The use of this equipment requires thorough understanding and much practice for success, while the use of more sophisticated equipment requires less understanding and less practice. Since the surveyor may be called on to use any type of equipment, it seems advisable that he or she be well versed in the use of traditional equipment and have sufficient knowledge of basic principles to learn quickly the use of more modern equipment. This book is written in accordance with this philosophy.

The following procedures are employed throughout the book to enhance its clarity to the student reader:

1. Logical progression from easier topics to more difficult ones. The book is designed to be studied in order from start to finish.
2. Consistent use of terms as defined in this text.
3. Complete explanation of each operation as it is introduced, without trying to relate it to other operations not yet understood by the student.
4. Avoidance of reference to historical methods, involved theory, or lengthy introductions which, while providing smoothness of transition, I believe often hide from the student what it is he or she should master.
5. Explanation with words and diagrams of the way work is actually performed in the field, so that the reader with no previous experience can duplicate the operations.
6. Inclusion of enough theory so that understanding it will enable the student to reconstruct proper procedures rather than memorize them.

The book includes enough material for two semesters of instruction, including several lectures and one field period per week. It is not intended primarily as a reference book; but I think the sample field notes and descriptions of certain methods of operation will be valuable as references.

Contents

CONTENTS

Principles
of
Surveying

INSTRUCTIONAL OBJECTIVES OF CHAPTER 1

1/ *Given several bearings and azimuths, the student should be able to convert bearings to azimuths and azimuths to bearings.*

2/ *Given çoordinates of two points in the first quadrant, the student should be able to compute bearing and distance of one from another.*

3/ *Given the bearing and distance of a point from the origin, the student should be able to compute the coordinates of the point.*

4/ *Given the bearing and distance of a second point from a point of known coordinates, the student should be able to determine the coordinates of the second point.*

5/ *Given station and offset of a point, the student should be able to demonstrate by sketch that station and offset positions are actually coordinate positions.*

chapter one

Introduction

No one can work long in the fields of civil engineering, architecture or construction without becoming involved with surveying. Planning and design are based on the results of surveys and construction is controlled by surveying. The persons employed in these fields will work with plots made from surveys and will build in accordance with surveyors' marked stakes. In addition, a high percentage will find themselves surveying occasionally, even though they are not primarily surveyors.

1–1 DEFINITIONS

Surveying is the art of determining and establishing large measurements of the required accuracy in an economical way. Determining the positions of existing objects is called **preliminary surveying** since this is done as a first step so that a design may be prepared based on the existing situation. Establishing positions so that construction will conform to design drawings is called **construction stakeout** since it is done by positioning stakes at key points to control construction.

Plane Surveying is that type of surveying in which the curvature of the earth is not considered. This book deals with plane surveying.

Geodetic Surveying is that type of surveying in which the curvature of the earth is considered. This consideration is not necessary except for surveys of great length requiring a high degree of accuracy.

1–2 REASONS FOR SURVEYING

Surveying is the first step (except for early planning) in all but the smallest engineering or architectural projects and is often the last step before the finished construction is accepted by the owner.

A typical case follows to illustrate reasons for surveying. Notice that, in addition to the large number of persons involved in the surveying work, many more are involved to the extent that they must understand and depend on the surveying results.

1. A large company decides to build a new manufacturing plant. Its development department locates suitable land and a price per acre is agreed upon to purchase it from the present owner.

2. A surveyor hired by the company determines the location of the property's boundaries and the area of the property. He prepares a map of the property boundary and a written legal description of the property boundary, which includes the area in acres. An agreement is made to transfer ownership of the property, as defined by the legal description, from its present owner to the company, and the total price is computed according to the area determined by the surveyor.

3. A designer is selected by the company to prepare construction plans for the new plant. The designer then hires a surveyor who obtains locations of all existing objects of importance to the designer, such as ground surface elevations; nearby roads, railroads, water lines, gas lines, electric lines and sewers; streams, swamps or ponds; and adjacent buildings, and prepares a map called a plot plan which the designer can use to situate the plant for economy of construction and efficiency of operation.

4. During the preliminary stages of design, a soil investigation will be made to determine suitability of the soil to carry the weight of the plant buildings. Borings must be made in the soil to extract samples of soil for examination and testing. The borings must be accurately located at the points where building weight on the soil is critical. A surveyor hired by the designer will locate with stakes the points where the soil borings are to be made.

5. When the design drawings are completed, an agreement will be made between the company and a builder to construct the plant in accordance with the design drawings and specifications for a certain price. The designer will inspect the work of the builder as an agent of the owner and must approve the work before the owner will pay the builder.

    The builder must construct each building or other improvement in the proper location as shown on the plot plan on which the designer has superimposed the buildings and other improvements. A surveyor hired by the builder will provide construction stakeout for the builder. The stakeout involves setting stakes and other controls on a continuing basis as various portions of the construction require them. A surveyor hired by the designer will check the stakeout before the builder uses it.

6. As a portion of the work is completed, the builder will apply for payment

for that portion. In many cases, such as construction of earth embankment or excavation, a surveyor hired by the designer measures the quantity of work completed and the builder is paid for this quantity. A surveyor hired by the builder will check the measurements of the designer's surveyor.

7. Some changes are usually made to the original plans while construction is taking place. A surveyor hired by the designer measures these changes in the field and the construction plans are then revised to show the construction "as built."

The surveyors referred to in this hypothetical case may be independent contractors specializing in surveying who are engaged for any one of the surveying projects; they may be surveyors who are full time employees of the company, designer or builder; or they may be employees who perform surveys in addition to other technical duties.

The group doing the field work is called a *survey party* and the man in charge is called the *party chief*. Other members are named according to the equipment each one uses.

In all cases, the surveyor should realize that surveying is not an end in itself, but is a service performed to assist someone else to achieve a goal, in this case the construction of a manufacturing plant. He should, therefore, perform his work to best achieve the aims of his client or employer.

1-3 SURVEYING REFERENCE

Horizontal and Vertical

Surveying measurements are made in a vertical direction and in a horizontal direction, using the earth itself as a framework. The *vertical* direction is toward the center of the earth and is indicated by the pull of gravity. A string with a weight on it will hang in a vertical line, since it is pulled by gravity. The points on a vertical line have no horizontal displacement from each other.

The *horizontal* direction is perpendicular to the vertical direction. The points on a horizontal line have no vertical displacement from each other.

A vertical line is called *plumb* and a horizontal line called *level*. Lines from two points on the earth's surface to the center (vertical lines) cannot be parallel. However, at the relatively short distances involved in plane surveying, they are so nearly parallel that they are assumed to be so with no significant error. In addition, the perpendicular (horizontal line) to one vertical line cannot be perpendicular to any other vertical line; but in plane surveying a horizontal line is assumed to be perpendicular to all vertical lines. Again, no significant error is introduced by this assumption. This system assures that

Figure 1-1 Plumb bob and hand level

each surveying project is consistent within itself, being controlled by the framework of vertical and horizontal directions.

The *plumb bob* (shown in Fig. 1-1) is used to establish a vertical line, specifically to transfer a point from one elevation to a higher or lower elevation with no horizontal displacement. The weight of the bob on the string holds it plumb and all points on the string are on a plumb line through the point of the bob.

The *hand level* (shown in Fig. 1-1) is used to establish a horizontal line. It contains a glass vial in the shape of a circular arc which contains fluid. An air bubble in the fluid stays at the high point of the curve. The vial is marked and aligned so that the line of sight through the hand level is horizontal when the bubble is centered on the mark. The hand level is held up to the eye by hand and used for approximate work. The transit and engineer's level, even though of far greater accuracy, are also aligned with level vials constructed according to the same principle.

Relationship Between Survey Sites

An individual survey must often be referenced to another site by a more specific framework. Some examples follow:

1. A water supply project must be accurately related in elevation to the source of water which may be miles away.

2. A rocket launching pad must be oriented with great accuracy in the proper direction to reach a particular location a great distance away.

3. A conveyor belt leading from one building to another must be manu- factured at a distant plant to fit accurately between buildings when delivered to the site.

Surveying

Definitions + Terminology

The hand level - is used to establish a horizontal line. It contains a glass vial in the shape of a circular arc which contains fluid. An air bubble in the fluid stays at the high point of the curve. The vial is marked and aligned so that the line of sight through the hand level is horizontal when the bubble is centered on the mark, the hand level is held up to the eye and by hand and used for aproximate work, the transit and engineers level, even though of far greater accuracy are also aligned with level vials constructed according to the same principal

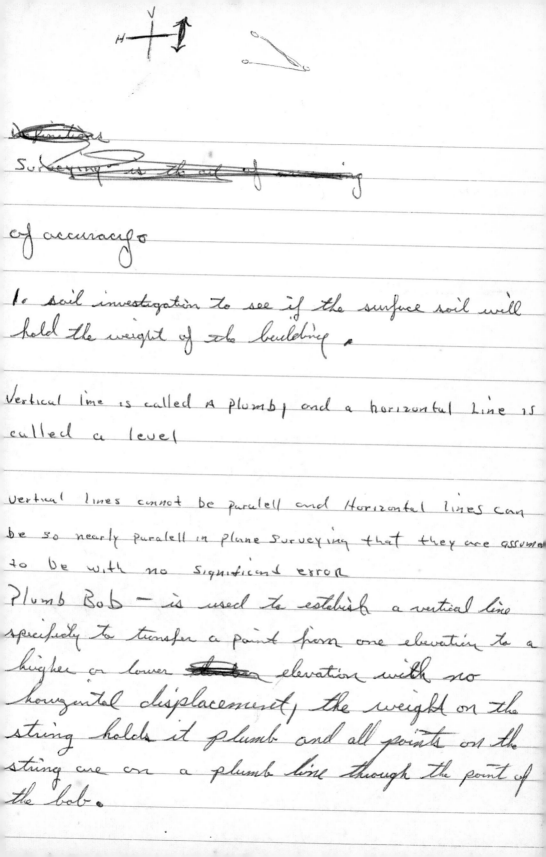

~~Definitions~~

~~Surveying is the art of ~~

of accuracy.

1. soil investigation to see if the surface soil will hold the weight of ~~the~~ building.

Vertical line is called a plumb, and a horizontal line is called a level

Vertical lines cannot be paralell and Horizontal lines can be so nearly paralell in plane Surveying that they are assumed to be with no significant error

Plumb Bob — is used to establish a vertical line specifically to transfer a point from one elevation to a higher or lower ~~elevation~~ elevation with no horizontal displacement, the weight on the string holds it plumb and all points on the string are on a plumb line though the point of the bob.

Definitions

Surveying - the art of establishing large measurements of the required accuracy in an economical way.

Preliminary Surveying - Determining the positions of existing objects. This is the first step so that a design may be prepared based on the existing situation

construction stakeout - Establishing positions so that construction will conform to design drawings, since it is done by positioning stakes at keypoints to control construction

Plane Surveying - is that type of surveying in which the curvature of the earth is not considered.

Geodetic Surveying - is that type of surveying in which the curvature of the earth is considered. This consideration is not necessary except for surveys of great length requiring a high degree

4. A new section of highway must be designed to run from one existing highway to another many miles away and must join each existing highway at the proper location.

Each example points out two or more objects whose locations must be known with reference to each other. If both are located with reference to a common system, their locations with respect to each other can be determined.

Sea Level

Average sea level is used as a reference, called a *datum*, for elevations. The average sea level is designated as zero and the elevation of any other point can then be designated by a number of feet above sea level or below sea level. The sea level datum is a curved line parallel to the average surface of the earth. It is a horizontal line; therefore its use as a reference is consistent with our vertical and horizontal reference system.

A *bench mark* is a permanent or semi-permanent point of known elevation which can be used to establish other elevations. Bench marks with elevations referred to average sea level have been established throughout the United States by the *National Geodetic Survey*. This organization is a branch of the U.S. Department of Commerce and is responsible for establishing and maintaining surveying control networks in the United States.

Some areas, such as cities or industrial plants, have all elevations referenced to an assumed datum assigned to a bench mark in the immediate area. Therefore, all elevations in the area are referenced to the same datum and to each other, but not to elevations outside the area. A small survey may be made from a datum assumed for that one project and unrelated to any other.

North Pole

The direction to the north pole is used as a reference to establish horizontal direction from one point to another. Any direction may be indicated as an *azimuth* or angle clockwise from north and any direction may be indicated as a *bearing* or angle east or west from north or south. In Fig. 1-2 the direction from A to B may be designated as an azimuth of 045° or a bearing of N 45° E, the direction from A to C may be designated as an azimuth of 210° or a bearing of S 30° W, and the direction from A to D may be designated as an azimuth of 330° or a bearing of N 30° W.

An azimuth may be any angle from zero degrees to 360 degrees. A bearing may be any angle from zero degrees to 90 degrees.

An assumed north is often used as a reference to serve as a starting direction for calculations when the true direction is not needed.

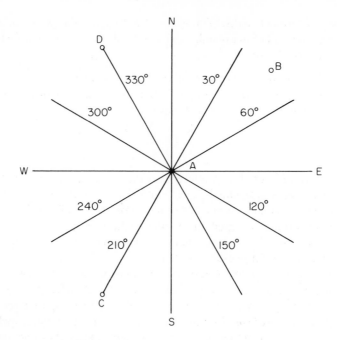

Figure 1-2 Azimuths and bearings

Coordinates

A *coordinate system* can be used to locate a point on a plane. Points are located with reference to a point called the origin. Two axes, called x and y, are established through the origin. Distances up or to the right are positive and distances in the opposite directions are negative.

A coordinate system is shown in Fig. 1-3. The distance north or south of the origin is called *latitude* and the distance east or west is called *departure*. Coordinate systems used for surveying are usually located so that only the first quadrant is used. The y axis runs north from the origin and the x axis runs east from the origin.

Coordinate locations are given by two numbers, the first being the distance from the origin in the north direction (latitude) and the second being the distance from the origin in the east direction (departure). In Fig. 1-4, point A has coordinates (10, 20) and point B has coordinates (50, 50).

The relationship between points A and B can be established once their coordinates are known. The distance $\overline{AB}$ can be found by the Pythagorean Theorem as follows:

$$\overline{AB}^2 = x^2 + y^2$$
$$\overline{AB}^2 = 30^2 + 40^2$$
$$\overline{AB} = 50$$

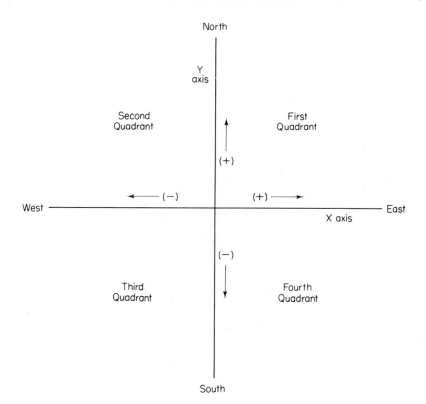

Figure 1-3 Coordinate system

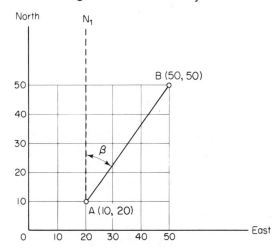

Figure 1-4 Coordinate system as used in surveying (first quadrant only)

The direction of $\overline{AB}$ can be found by trigonometry as follows:

$$\text{Angle } N_1 \, AB = \arctan \frac{30}{40} = \arctan .75$$

$$\text{Angle } N_1 \, AB = 36° - 50' \text{ (nearest } 10');$$
$$\text{or the bearing from } A \text{ to } B$$
$$\text{is } N \, 36° - 50' \, E$$

Thus, the distance and direction of A and B from each other are established.

The distance can also be found by trigonometry using the bearing angle. The line $\overline{AB}$ is the hypotenuse of a right triangle with the difference in latitude between A and B as the side adjacent to the bearing angle and the difference in departure between the two as the side opposite the bearing angle. Therefore:

$$\cos \text{ bearing angle} = \frac{\text{adjacent side (diff. in lat.)}}{\text{hypotenuse } (\overline{AB})}$$

$$\sin \text{ bearing angle} = \frac{\text{opposite side (diff. in dep.)}}{\text{hypotenuse } (\overline{AB})}$$

Therefore, $\overline{AB}$ equals difference in latitudes divided by the cos of the bearing angle or difference in departures divided by the sin of the bearing angle. Mathematically:

$$\overline{AB} = \frac{(l_B - l_A)}{\cos \beta}$$

$$\overline{AB} = \frac{(d_B - d_A)}{\sin \beta}$$

For Fig. 1–4:

$$\overline{AB} = \frac{40}{.80} = 50$$

or

$$\overline{AB} = \frac{30}{.60} = 50$$

Coordinates can be computed for a point if the bearing and distance from the origin to the point are known. The formulas from the previous paragraph are used with the differences in latitudes and departures being the unknowns. When the starting point has coordinates $(0, 0)$ the differences in latitudes and departures are equal to the latitude and departure. Therefore, as demonstrated in Fig. 1-5:

$$l_c = L \cos \beta$$

and

$$d_c = L \sin \beta$$

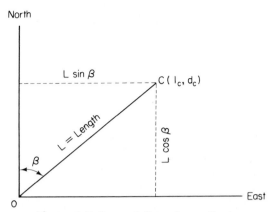

Figure 1-5 Computation of coordinates

It follows that coordinates can be computed for a point of known bearing and distance from a point of known coordinates other than (0, 0). The bearing and distance are converted to differences in latitude and departure which are added algebraically to the latitude and departure of the point of known coordinates. See Fig. 1-6 for a realistic application using coordinates

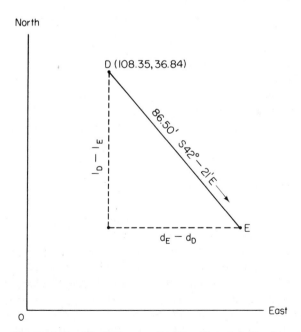

Figure 1-6 Finding coordinates of point E when coordinates of point D and bearing and distance from D to E are given

to the nearest hundredth of a foot and bearings to the nearest minute.

$$
\begin{aligned}
l_D - l_E &= L \cos \beta \\
&= 86.50 \times .73904 \\
&= 63.93
\end{aligned}
$$

$$
\begin{aligned}
l_E &= l_D - 63.93 \\
&= 108.35 - 63.93 \\
&= 44.42
\end{aligned}
$$

$$
\begin{aligned}
d_E - d_D &= L \sin \beta \\
&= 86.50 \times .67366 \\
&= 58.27
\end{aligned}
$$

$$
\begin{aligned}
d_E &= d_D + 58.27 \\
&= 36.84 + 58.27 \\
&= 95.11
\end{aligned}
$$

Stationing

Stationing is a variation of the coordinate method which is used for long, narrow projects such as pipelines and highways. A line, which may be straight or have angles or curves in it, is established from an origin of zero. Points on the line are designated by stations 100′ apart. Station 1 + 00 is 100′ from the origin, station 2 + 00 is 200′ from the origin, and so on. Points on the line between full stations are also called stations and are designated to the hundredth of a foot, for example: station 1 + 20.00 or station 2 + 55.29. Points not on the line are designated by station and offset distance right or left at a perpendicular to the line. Examples are shown in Fig. 1-7.

1–4 NOTEKEEPING

Measurements and sketches are kept in pencil in a field notebook as the work progresses. Measurements are entered as soon as they are made to lessen the chance for a mistake. The notebook is a field record and ordinarily no change or addition should be made after the party has left the field. A field entry that must be changed in the office should be changed in such a way that the original can still be read and there is a clear indication that the change is an office change. Colored pencil can be used for an office change or addition; otherwise a note should be added stating that the correction was made in the office.

    Notes must be complete, legible, self-explanatory, logically arranged and,

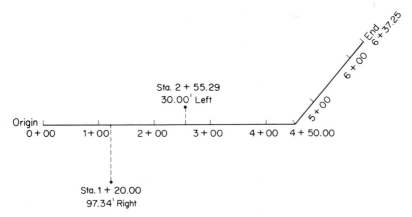

Figure 1-7 Locations by station and offset

in many cases, arranged according to recognized practice. The reasons are that notes may be used by another surveyor some years later; they may be used by office personnel who do not see the field site; and they may be used as evidence in court.

Because of the possibility that field notes may become court evidence, many surveyors do not allow erasing in the field book. An erasure could cause suspicion that the field record was altered after the field work was finished. Instead, mistakes are crossed out in the field so that they can still be read, and the correct entry is made while still in the field.

The following information must be included in the field book for each day:

1. Name of project and location.
2. Date.
3. Weather conditions, especially those that can affect the type of work being done.
4. Names or initials of party members and their positions in the party.
5. Identification of equipment used.

This information is helpful when a mistake is made in the field and is not discovered until field work is finished. Often the mistake can be traced to weather conditions or faulty equipment and a correction can be made without redoing all the field work.

An index should be kept at the front of each book showing the name of the project and page numbers for each project. Each page, consisting of the two facing sheets, should be numbered and a new page should be used for a new date. The note keeper should use a straightedge for sketches and should not crowd notes.

PROBLEMS

1/ Convert the following bearings to azimuths:

a. N 30° E	e. S 84°–17′–30″ W
b. S 43° E	f. S 18°–56′–15″ W
c. S 26° W	g. S 31°–19′–45″ E
d. N 27°–31′–20″ W	h. S 76°–14′–06″ E

2/ Convert the following azimuths to bearings:

a. 073°	e. 094°–10′–02″
b. 136°	f. 299°–42′–13″
c. 201°	g. 311°–19′–00″
d. 277°–18′–30″	h. 172°–27′–40″

3/ In each case, compute bearing and distance of the second point from the first by trigonometry. All points are in the first quadrant.

a. (900.00, 1000.00)	(1000.00, 918.20)
b. (1000.00, 1000.00)	(1196,80, 1034.52)
c. (1190.99, 876.83)	(1175.22, 1053.01)
d. (1433.37, 1319.84)	(1408.48, 1035.11)

4/ Point A has a bearing of N 60° E and distance of 300 ft from the origin. What are its coordinates?

5/ In each case coordinates of a point are given and bearing and distance to a second point are given. Determine the coordinates of the second point:

a. (1000.00, 1000.00); N 30° E; 1000.00 ft
b. (1000.00, 1000.00); N 10° E; 188.92 ft
c. (974.89, 725.58); N 84°–58′–50″ E; 275.47 ft
d. (1175.43, 880.92); N 82°–55′–20″ W; 171.79 ft

INSTRUCTIONAL OBJECTIVES OF CHAPTER 2

1/ *Given an explanation of a source of error, the student should be able to decide whether or not measures should be taken to eliminate it based on whether it is systematic or accidental.*

2/ *Given the magnitude of an accidental error and the number of operations, the student should be able to determine probable total error.*

3/ *Given total horizontal and vertical errors and length of circuit for each, the student should be able to determine orders of accuracy.*

chapter two

Accuracy and Error

The surveyor's job requires him to control errors, not eliminate errors. In fact, he cannot eliminate them. The mark of a skilled surveyor is that he knows the difference. He obtains the necessary accuracy and no more; and he does so efficiently.

2-1 DEFINITIONS

Errors are inaccuracies in any one measurement due to the type of equipment used or the way in which the equipment is used.

Systematic Errors are errors that occur in the same direction, thereby tending to accumulate so that the total error increases proportionally as the number of measurements increases.

Accidental Errors are errors that occur randomly in either direction, thereby tending to cancel one another so that, although the total error does increase as the number of measurements increases, the total error becomes proportionally less, and the accuracy becomes greater as the number of measurements increases.

Note: It is not always possible to identify each error as systematic or accidental although most fall under one type or the other.

Mistakes are inaccuracies in any one measurement because some part of the surveying operation is performed improperly.

Total Error is the sum of the inaccuracies in a completed job. Since inaccuracies are either positive or negative, it is an algebraic sum.

Surveying accuracy is determined by completing a circuit to the point of beginning (or another known point). The **Error of Closure** is the difference between the actual position of the finishing point (either horizontally or vertically) and the location of the same point determined mathematically as a result of the circuit.

Accuracy is the ratio of error of closure to the total distance of the survey or, in some cases, to the square root of the total distance.

Order of Accuracy is the range of accuracy acceptable for particular surveys.

2-2 ACCURACY AND SPEED

Accuracy is of primary importance in surveying — not maximum accuracy, but accuracy of the required order. Speed is also important. However, achieving proper accuracy must always take precedence over working at the utmost speed.

Delay causes the surveying work to be more expensive; and design, construction, or transfer of ownership of land may be delayed at extra expense to those waiting and depending on the survey for information.

However, by hurrying, the survey party may allow excessive total error, make a mistake, or forget to perform some part of the work. A return visit to the field may then be required, which makes the surveying work more expensive. If design, construction, or property transfer have proceeded based on inaccurate or incomplete surveying information, redesign or reconstruction may be required at extensive expense, or a lawsuit may be initiated because of an erroneous property transfer. The surveyor will certainly be named a party to such a suit. Obviously, excessive haste can have more disastrous results than excessive effort to achieve high accuracy.

2-3 ERRORS AND MISTAKES

To control errors so that the total error is not excessive, sources of error must be understood; and methods and equipment must be chosen which will reduce the total errors to allowable levels without wasting time. Sources of error are instrumental, personal (physical abilities and concentration of the surveyor), and natural (weather and ground conditions).

Size of total error depends on the precision of the equipment and the way in which the equipment is used. More precise equipment often requires more time to operate and normally costs more to buy or rent. More accurate field methods nearly always require more time. On the other hand, extremely precise equipment is available which takes less time for certain operations. In this case, additional cost of expensive equipment must be weighed against cost of extra time spent using less expensive equipment. With identical equipment and methods, some surveyors consistently achieve more accurate results than others and all will achieve poorer results with adverse weather conditions.

Systematic errors are generally caused by imperfections in the manufacturing of equipment — not mistakes in the manufacturing process, but an inability to achieve absolute perfection. Equipment may also cause systematic errors because of being damaged or out of adjustment. Systematic errors may sometimes be due to field methods or weather conditions. Since systematic errors build up to larger values as the work progresses, some means must be taken to compensate for them whenever they can be identified and their magnitude determined.

Accidental errors are due to field methods and conditions of the work site. They are small, partially compensating errors which cannot be eliminated but can be reduced by choice of field methods.

Accidental errors tend to accumulate in proportion to the square root of the number of possibilities for their occurrence.

Mathematically:

$$\frac{E_n}{E_1} = \frac{\sqrt{n}}{\sqrt{1}}$$

Where

E_n = error in n measurements
E_1 = error in 1 measurement
n = number of measurements

and

$$E_n = \pm E_1\sqrt{n}$$

Example:

A tape measurement can be made to the nearest 0.01′. Therefore, the maximum probable error in one operation, E_1, is 0.005′. If the taping operation is repeated 36 times in measuring a line*, the probable total error is found as follows:

$$E_n = E_1\sqrt{n}$$

where

$$n = 36$$
$$E_n = 0.005' \times 6$$
$$= \pm 0.03'$$

Note that the direction of the probable error is not known and therefore no corrective measure can be taken.

Mistakes cannot be permitted. To avoid mistakes, proper field methods must be made habitual. These methods must include checks of all steps. Succeeding chapters will explain the usual methods and checks. When a mistake is not caught in the field, it usually requires a return trip to the field to correct it.

---

* The beginning and end of the line are such a distance apart that the measuring tape must be stretched step–by–step 36 times to cover the distance.

2-4 ORDER OF ACCURACY

Horizontal accuracy is computed by dividing the error of closure by the total measured distance of the survey, for example:

$$\text{Accuracy} = \frac{0.40' \quad \text{(error of closure)}}{3500.00' \text{ (total measured distance)}}$$

$$= \frac{1}{8750} \text{ or } 1:8750$$

Solve this way

$$\frac{0.40'}{3500.00'} = \frac{1}{x}$$

$$x = \frac{3500.00'}{0.40'} \text{ or } 8750$$

Accuracy need not be computed beyond the nearest whole number and is properly shown as a ratio with one as the numerator. Allowable horizontal accuracy is shown in Table 2-1, which indicates that 1:8750 is third order accuracy.

If systematic errors are eliminated and no mistakes are made, accuracy will increase as the length of the survey increases. The reason for this is that accidental errors (the only ones present) increase as the square root of the number of measurements (assumed to be proportional to total distance) which is a lower rate than the increase in total distance. Therefore, error of closure (numerator) increases at a lower rate than total distance (denominator), making the fraction smaller as the total distance increases.

For this reason, the National Geodetic Survey relates the allowable accuracy of horizontal surveys of great length (10 miles or more) to the square root of the distance. In these cases, the minimum allowable accuracy equals the square root of the total distance in miles multiplied by a factor.

Allowable vertical error of closure is also shown in Table 2-1. The allowable error of closure is proportional to the square root of the distance of the level circuit which is approximately proportional to the number of measurements. Assume that a survey is required to be completed with second order accuracy. If the length of the level circuit is four miles, the minimum acceptable error of closure is:

$$0.035' \times \sqrt{4} = 0.070'$$

If the error of closure is 0.070 ft or less, the survey is accurate enough to qualify as second order work.

Note that required vertical accuracy varies directly with the square root of the total distance (approximately proportional to the number of measurements) so that it is properly related to the probable total error. In other words, the accuracy required to qualify as second order work is 0.035 ft error times the square root of the number of miles in the circuit.

The required accuracy must be known before a surveying project can be carried out properly. The agreement to provide surveying services might specify an order of accuracy. In another case, the surveyor might determine how accurately to place stakes for construction from his own knowledge of construction methods. In each case, the required accuracy will indicate which equipment to use and what procedure to follow. The greater the accuracy required, the higher the precision of the equipment and the more time-consuming and painstaking the procedures must be to reduce errors. Specific examples are given in succeeding chapters.

2–5 ERROR IN LOCATING A POINT

In the field, objects are located in the horizontal position by angles, distances, or a combination of both. Any combination that can be used to plot a point on paper with compass and protractor can be used in the field. The location will not be mathematically exact, either on paper or in the field. The surveyor should appreciate the relative accuracy of the combinations of angles and distances that can be used.

Method 1. A point can be located in relation to one other point by a direction and a distance.

Method 2. A point can be located in relation to two other points by a direction from each of the two points or by a distance from each of the two points.

Method 3. A point can be located in relation to two other points by a direction from one point and a distance from the other point.

Any of the preceding methods will result in an intersection of two lines. While this is sufficient to locate a point, in practice a third line is often established for greater reliability. The least probable error will be obtained in any case if the angle between intersecting lines is 90°. The more the angle varies from 90°, the greater the probable error becomes.

Examples are shown in Figs. 2-1 and 2-2. Known points are shown as solid dots and points being located are shown as circles. Lines used to locate points are shown in heavy weight.

TABLE 2-1

National Geodetic Survey:
Standards of Accuracy for Traverse and Leveling

Order	Minimum Horizontal Accuracy Normal Traverse	Minimum Error of Closure	
		Long Traverse 10 miles or more	Level Circuit
First:	1 : 25,000	0.66 ft. $\sqrt{M}$	0.017 ft. $\sqrt{M}$
Second:	1 : 10,000	1.67 ft. $\sqrt{M}$	0.035 ft. $\sqrt{M}$
Third:	1 : 5,000	3.43 ft. $\sqrt{M}$	0.05 ft. $\sqrt{M}$

M is distance of circuit in miles

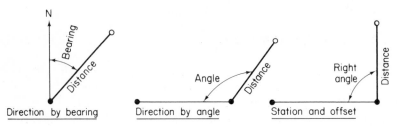

Method 1— Direction and distance

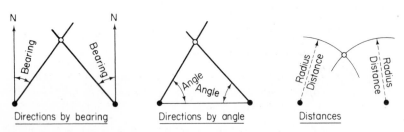

Method 2— Two directions or two distances

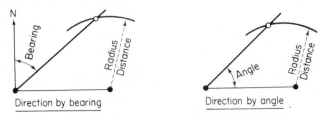

Method 3—Direction from one point, distance from another

Figure 2-1 Methods of locating a point

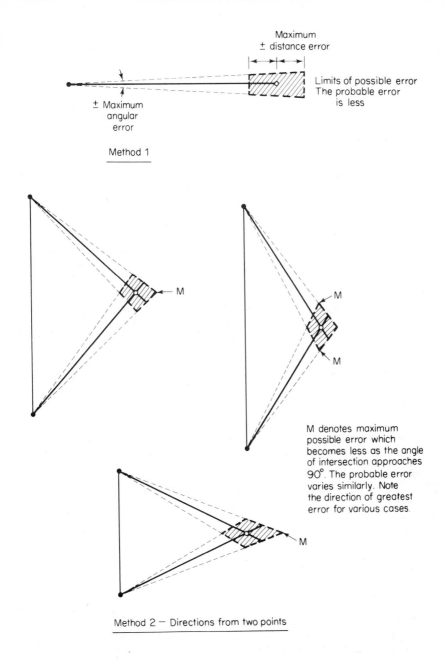

Method 1

M denotes maximum
possible error which
becomes less as the angle
of intersection approaches
90°. The probable error
varies similarly. Note
the direction of greatest
error for various cases.

Method 2 — Directions from two points

Figure 2-2 Relative accuracy of the methods

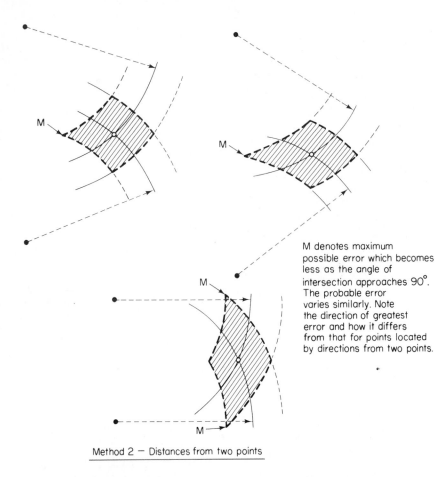

M denotes maximum
possible error which becomes
less as the angle of
intersection approaches 90°.
The probable error
varies similarly. Note
the direction of greatest
error and how it differs
from that for points located
by directions from two points.

Method 2 — Distances from two points

Figure 2-2 (Cont.) Relative accuracy of the methods

PROBLEMS

1/ An accidental error of 0.01 ft is likely in each one of 50 separate measurements which are to be added to get the desired total. What is the probable
total error? What is the probable total error if the individual accidental
error is 0.02 ft? If it is 0.04 ft?

2/ If the accidental error is 0.002 ft and there are 31 separate measurements,
what is the probable total error?

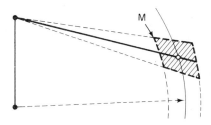

M denotes maximum possible
error which becomes less as the
angle of intersection approaches
90°. Note that the angle of
intersection will be 90° (and
error will be the least) if
direction and distance are
measured from the same point.

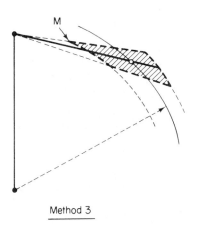

Method 3

Figure 2-2 (Cont.) Relative accuracy of the methods

3/ A circuit is completed with a horizontal error of closure of 0.26 ft in a circuit of 6974.28 ft length. What are accuracy and order of accuracy?

4/ If the horizontal error is 0.17 ft and the length 2784.94 ft, what are accuracy and order of accuracy?

5/ A circuit is completed with a vertical error of 0.10 ft in 36 miles. What is the order of accuracy?

6/ If the vertical error is .09 ft and the length is 6300 ft, what is the order of accuracy?

INSTRUCTIONAL OBJECTIVES OF CHAPTER 3

1/ *Given the necessary equipment, the student, with a partner, should be able to tape on sloping ground, holding the tape and plumb bob in the various positions required for taping horizontally, employing voice signals, and recording entries in the field notebook. Distances should have an accuracy of 1:3000.*

2/ *Given a tape correction, the student should be able to correct a given measured distance to the nearest one-hundredth of a foot.*

3/ *Given an average temperature, the student should be able to correct a given measured distance to the nearest one-hundredth of a foot.*

4/ *Given a slope angle or difference in elevation between two points and the slope distance between the points, the student should be able to compute the horizontal distance to the nearest one-hundredth of a foot.*

5/ *Given any of the sources of error listed in the chapter, the student should be able to tell whether the resulting error is plus or minus or could be either plus or minus and should describe methods to control the error where appropriate.*

chapter three

Horizontal Distances

Horizontal distances are fundamental because plane surveying is based on the two mutually perpendicular directions — horizontal and vertical. There are two operations involving horizontal distances — *measuring a distance* and *setting a point*.

A *distance is measured* between two points that are there before the distance is measured: i.e., an unknown distance is determined.

A *point is set* from an existing point at a predetermined distance: i.e., the distance is known beforehand and the location of the point is determined.

3-1 INTRODUCTION TO EQUIPMENT AND METHODS

Horizontal distances are ordinarily measured in the following ways:

1. *Taping* or measuring between two points with a tape calibrated in feet to the nearest one-hundredth. Steel tapes are commonly used although cloth tapes with or without metal wire reinforcing are used where high accuracy is not important. The tape may be marked in hundredths continuously from the zero mark to the opposite end, commonly a distance of 100, 200 or 300 ft. It may be marked only at each ft from zero to the opposite end with one ft before the zero mark calibrated in tenths or hundredths. See Fig. 3-1.

2. *Electronic distance measuring.* An accurately positioned transmitter sends an electromagnetic wave of known velocity to a reflector which returns the wave. The total time of travel at the known velocity provides a means of determining the distance between transmitter and reflector.

3. *Subtense bar.* The subtense bar of known length is set up horizontally at one end of a line to be measured and aligned perpendicular to the line. The angle at one end of the line subtended by the known length

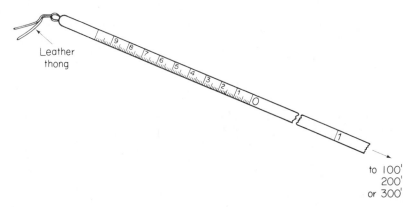

Leather
thong

to 100'
200'
or 300'

Figure 3-1 Tape

at the other end of the line is used to determine the length of the line. See Fig. 3-2.

4. *Stadia.* The principle is the same as that of the subtense bar except that a constant angle is subtended by a length which varies in proportion to the length of the line to be measured. The stadia principle and procedure are covered in Chap. 7.

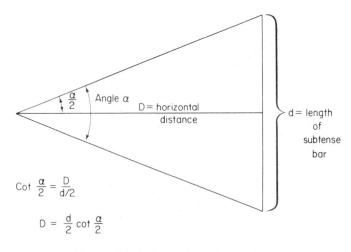

Angle α

$D =$ horizontal
distance

$d =$ length
of
subtense
bar

$$\text{Cot } \frac{\alpha}{2} = \frac{D}{d/2}$$

$$D = \frac{d}{2} \cot \frac{\alpha}{2}$$

Figure 3-2 Distance by subtense bar

3-2 TAPING OPERATION

Taping is the simplest of the methods in theory, but requires more skill and practice than any of the others because accuracy is dependent on the surveyor himself, rather than properties built into the equipment.

Terminology

Certain terminology is customary. The point at which measuring begins is toward the *back* and measurements proceed *forward* to the other point. The *tapeman* at the back is the *rear tapeman* and the one at the front is the *head tapeman*. Any point on the straight line between the two points is *on line* and if not on line it is *right* or *left*, looking forward from the back.

A *range pole* (see Fig. 3-3) may be stuck into the ground just beyond the point ahead to enable the rear tapeman to keep the head tapeman on line by line of sight. Points for measurement are often marked by driving into the ground $\frac{1}{2}$ in. to $\frac{3}{4}$ in. steel reinforcing rods, 1 in. to $1\frac{1}{2}$ in. pipe, or wooden stakes with nails in the tops. Temporary points are marked with nails or *surveyor's pins*.

Use of Plumb Bob

Tape measurements are usually not made with the tape held on the points. Normally, each end is held above a point and is located vertically over the

Figure 3-3 Range pole and surveyor's pins

Figure 3-4 Tape and plumb bob

point by means of a plumb bob and string. See Fig. 3-4 for one proper method of holding the tape and plumb bob.

Proper Tension

A steel tape stretches when pulled. Its length changes if the tension changes. For this reason, it should be pulled with the tension for which it is designed. Only at this tension can its actual length be expected to be the same as its calibrated length. The proper tension is normally 20 lb for a 100 ft length of tape suspended at the two ends and is increased or decreased in proportion to the length used. For example, the proper tension for a 50 ft length is

$$\frac{50}{100} \times 20 = 10 \, \text{lb}$$

and for a 120 ft length

$$\frac{120}{100} \times 20 = 24 \, \text{lb.}$$

If the tape is supported throughout its length, as when lying on a level sidewalk, the tension should be one half as much. In the case of full support, it is necessary to pull just hard enough to straighten the tape. With the tape suspended, its actual length is on a curve which is longer than a straight line; the tape must be elongated enough by the tension so that the length along the curve is longer than the tape reading and the level distance under the tape is the same as the tape reading. Thus, with proper tension, the tape reads the correct level distance.

There is a tendency for the inexperienced surveyor not to pull hard enough. Thus the error due to improper tension is likely to be a plus error because the end of the tape being read is not stretched far enough and will indicate a greater reading than the correct level distance.

Proper tension may be maintained by attaching to the zero end of the tape a spring balance which indicates the tension in pounds. In ordinary work with experienced personnel the tension is usually estimated by the head tapeman; the rear tapeman resists the tension by holding over the point.

In measuring the distance from A to B, the first measurement is 100 ft. and is 6 in. off line. Therefore, the distance on line is shorter than 100 ft. In accordance with the Pythagorean Theorem, the straight line distance is found as follows:

$$D^2 = 100^2 - 0.5^2$$

and

$$D = 99.999$$

and

the error due to being off line is $+0.001$ ft.

The second measurement is on line forward but off line the same distance at the rear and contains the same error. Error due to misalignment for the entire distance is only $+0.002$ ft. in 300 ft. This is an accuracy of 1:150,000. The error due to a misalignment of 6 in. in 100 ft. is not significant because the accidental errors in measuring the distance are of greater magnitude.

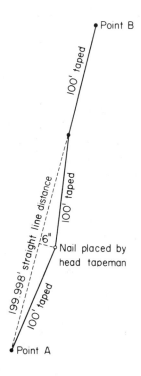

Figure 3-5 Error in six-inch misalignment

Proper Alignment

In order to measure the distance accurately from one point to another, the distance must be measured in a straight, level line. When the tape is not as long as the distance, the tape must be stretched to one intermediate point and then from that point to the next until the entire distance is covered. The full distance is the total of the partial distances.

Some means must be devised to stay on line. Usually lining up the head end of the tape with the end of the line by eye from the rear tapeman's position will be sufficiently accurate. See Fig. 3-5 for an example of the error caused by being *off line*. This misalignment is seldom a source of significant error. A range pole may be used as a guide in staying on line. A good method is to hold a plumb bob by the string over the back point and line the string by eye with the range pole. The rear tapeman can easily see whether the forward end of the tape is on line with the string and range pole.

Taping on a Level Line

It is necessary to hold both ends of the tape on the same horizontal line in order to measure a level distance. This often requires one tapeman to hold his end of the tape higher than the other end. Except for short distances of 30 or 40 feet, the tape can be held steadily only by bracing the hand on some part of the body. Figure 3-6 shows several common holding positions. These or other comfortable positions should be used whenever possible. The tapeman must be well balanced and solidly in position to resist tension on the tape with a minimum of movement.

The head tapeman* or downhill tapeman* should call for a particular holding position which will keep the tape approximately level with his holding position (see footnote). The proper position may be determined with a hand level (shown in Fig. 1-1) or by eye.

The principle by which accuracy can be estimated is the same as shown in Fig. 3-5. The error caused by being six in. too high or too low is the same as that caused by being six in. right or left. However, it is more difficult to line up the tape accurately in elevation and not keeping the tape level is a source of significant error. Another way of analyzing the error in a tape measurement which is not on line or not level is illustrated in Fig. 3-7.

This means that if the tapemen are off 1.4 ft right, left, high, or low in a distance measured as 100.00 ft, the distance is really 99.99 ft and there is a plus error of 0.01 ft. The accuracy will be the same (1/10,000) if one end of the tape is 0.7 ft. off in a taped length of 50.00 ft.

Taping Operation Described

Surveyor's pins or nails may be used to mark intermediate points. Surveyor's pins should be stuck into the ground at an angle of 45° with the ground and

---

* The more experienced tapeman or the party chief acts as head tapeman on most work and directs the operation. However, on a steep slope it is easier for the tapeman downhill to estimate a horizontal line and much easier for him to use a hand level for alignment.

Figure 3-6 Positions for holding tape

33

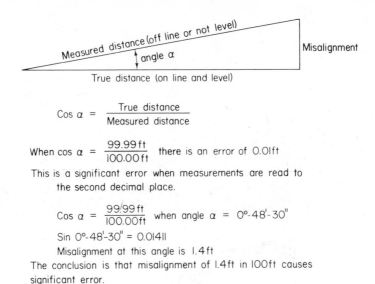

$$Cos \; \alpha \; = \; \frac{True \; distance}{Measured \; distance}$$

When cos $\alpha \; = \; \dfrac{99.99 \, ft}{100.00 \, ft}$ there is an error of 0.01ft

This is a significant error when measurements are read to
    the second decimal place.

$$Cos \; \alpha \; = \; \frac{99.99 \, ft}{100.00 \, ft} \quad when \; angle \; \alpha \; = \; 0°\text{-}48'\text{-}30''$$

Sin 0°-48'-30" = 0.01411

Misalignment at this angle is 1.4ft

The conclusion is that misalignment of 1.4ft in 100ft causes
significant error.

Figure 3-7 Significant error caused by tape misalignment

perpendicular to the tape. The spot at which the surveyor's pin enters the
ground is the point for measurement. See Fig. 3-3 for an illustration of
surveyor's pins.

A set of surveyor's pins contains eleven pins. They can be used for long
distances or where stations are being marked. A pin is placed at the starting
point and the head tapeman goes forward with the other ten pins. He marks
hundred ft stations with pins and when the rear tapeman leaves each point,
including the first point, he picks up and keeps the pin after the measurement
is made and checked. Thus the number of pins the rear tapeman has as he
comes up to a new point is the number of the station of the new point from
the beginning. This is a check on the notekeeping. Nails stuck into the
ground at each point are left behind where they can be referred to again,
but do not provide a running check on the number of the station.

When taping on pavement, the head tapeman can write the station
number next to each point. After a new point is marked by the head tapeman,
the rear tapeman calls the number of the point he is on and the head tapeman
adds one station mentally and calls the new station number as he writes it.
The rear tapeman repeats the new station as a check.

When stations are being marked, a full 100 ft distance is taped whenever
possible. This means the tapemen must *set a point* 100 ft from an existing
point. If stations are not needed, a nail is set on line at a convenient point and
the tapemen *measure a distance* from the previous point to it. Measuring a

distance is generally simpler than setting a point, so surveyors usually do not count stations without a good reason.

It is sometimes impossible to tape a full 100 ft because of the slope of the ground. A process called *breaking tape* may be used when stations are being counted. A point is set by the head tapeman at a convenient number of whole ft from the back point. The rear tapeman comes forward and holds that ft mark over the newly set point and the head tapeman goes forward and sets another point at a convenient number of whole ft. The rear tapeman holds the new ft mark over the new point. The process is repeated until 100 ft are accumulated and then a station is set. If surveyor's pins are being used, one is placed at the station.

The term *breaking tape* is often loosely used to mean measuring short, horizontal distances up or down a slope whether stations are counted or not.

Teamwork is required to tape efficiently and accurately. Voice and hand signals are needed. Each measurement must be checked and immediately recorded. Good systems for measuring a distance and setting a point are described here step by step. Refer to Fig. 3-8 while following the method for measuring a distance.

Mistakes can be made for several reasons when reading the tape. If the tape is viewed so that the numbers are upside down a two digit number may be read backwards. With certain digits such as 1, 3, 6, 8 and 9 this can easily happen. Certain numbers look alike when the tape is worn, especially 3, 8 and 0; they can be mistaken one for another. The man reading the zero end can mistake the direction in which the hundredths increase and misread the tape as shown in Fig. 3-8. These mistakes can be prevented if the number on either side of the number being read is checked.

Note that every measurement is checked by three means:

1. Reading it a second time
2. Saying it aloud
3. Hearing it repeated.

STEP BY STEP PROCEDURE
FOR
MEASURING BETWEEN TWO EXISTING POINTS

Rear Tapeman (holding reel)	Head Tapeman (holding zero end of tape)
	1. Holds zero approximately over point and calls "holding zero."
2. Holds plumb bob on point and observes where tape lines up with point. Either a number will	

Head Tapeman (Starting)

Rear Tapeman (Starting)

Head Tapeman (Final)

Rear Tapeman (Final)

Figure 3-8 Holding numbers on both ends of tape

be over the point or the tape must be moved toward the rear tapeman so that the lower number is over the point. In Fig. 3-8 the point is approximately half way between 96 and 97. The tape must be held with the 96 over the point so that tenths and hundredths can be read over the other point. Calls, "give me half a foot."

3. Slacks off on tape, until 0.5 is held approximately over his point.

4. Holds plumb bob string on 96 over point, braces self, and calls "mark" while plumb bob is over point or is silent if it swings away from point.

5. Applies proper tension (20 lb), and with the tape pulled tighter the distance read is a little less. Slides plumb bob string until plumb bob is over point at same time rear tapeman is calling "mark."

6. Resists tension. Repeats "mark, mark" while on point.

7. When satisfied the number is correct, slacks off on tape, holding string on tape with thumb and forefinger while checking number on both sides of string and reading number under string.

8. Checks number on each side of 96. Calls "nine six."

9. Looks at .32 to verify it. Calls "nine six point three two" and records it in notebook while saying it.

10. Looks at 96 to verify it. Repeats "nine six point three two."

                                                11. Signals to move on.

12. Picks up surveyor's pin if used.

13. The measurement may be taken again as a further check.

STEP BY STEP PROCEDURE
FOR
SETTING A POINT 86.30 FEET FROM EXISTING POINT

Rear Tapeman (holding reel)	Head Tapeman (holding zero end of tape)
1. Puts head tapeman on line with hand signals or by calling "left" or "right." Holds 86 roughly over point.	
	2. Roughly locates .30 on line. Clears surface of grass and other interfering objects within area where he expects point to fall. Calls "hold eight six".
3. Holds 86 over point after checking adjacent numbers on tape. Calls "holding eight six."	
	4. Calls "holding point three oh" after checking adjacent numbers. Holds plumb bob string on .30 with thumb and forefinger and applies proper tension.
5. Resists tension, and calls "mark" while plumb bob is over point or is silent if it swings away from point.	
	6. While rear tapeman is over his point and he himself is on line, the head tapeman drops the plumb bob so that it sticks into the soil. He places a nail in the hole.

The procedure must be repeated to verify the position of the nail.

Figure 3-9 Setting a point on pavement

If the point is to be set on a hard surface such as pavement, the plumb bob is dipped until the point touches the surface. It is held in that position by the string until it can be reached with the other hand and a scratch made at the point (see Fig. 3-9).

Hand signals are sometimes needed when conditions are poor for voice communication, such as on noisy city streets or construction sites. Signals to "take a foot" or "give a foot" are the hand motions that come naturally — a waving of the hand in the direction of desired movement. A signal to move right or left to get on line is a waving motion of the hand in the appropriate direction. A large, slow motion means a long distance and a short, quick motion means a short distance.

3–3 CORRECTIONS

Significant errors should be corrected whenever their magnitude and direction can be determined. A *significant error* is one which could reduce the accuracy below that required. Accidental errors cannot be corrected because the direction is not known. Some systematic errors can be corrected and may have to be corrected to obtain the required accuracy.

Temperature Correction

Steel, like other solid material, expands or contracts with changes in temperature. The coefficient of expansion is an index of the amount of change in size a material will undergo because of a change in temperature. Each material has its own coefficient of expansion. The coefficient of expansion indicates the percent any length will expand or contract with a change in temperature of one degree. A coefficient of .01 indicates a one percent change in length for a one degree change in temperature. Thus one ft would expand to 1.01 ft with a one degree rise in temperature, and to 1.05 ft with a five degree rise. A length of 100 ft would increase to 101 ft with a one degree rise in temperature. A lowering of the temperature will cause a proportional decrease in length.

Steel tapes have a coefficient of expansion of 0.00000645 ft per ft per degree. In other words, a steel tape lengthens 0.00000645 ft for each ft of its original length for each degree increase in temperature and shortens similarly for each degree drop in temperature. The starting point is 68°F, the temperature at which the tape should be of correct length according to manufacturing practice. Two examples follow:

1. A tape which is truly 100.00 ft long at 68°F is used at 95°. A distance is measured as 1308.37 ft. The true distance is greater than the distance read on the tape since the tape increased in length and the inscribed numbers became farther apart. The error is negative, the correction is positive, and the corrected distance is:

Measured distance plus correction

$$= 1308.37' + 0.00000645 \times 1308.37' \times (95–68)°F$$
$$= 1308.37' + 0.22'$$
$$= 1308.59'$$

The correction is negative for temperatures below 68°F.

2. A point is to be set 1308.37 ft from a known point with the same tape at the same temperature. The true distance will be greater than the distance read on the tape. Therefore, the length read on the tape must be less than 1308.37 ft. The distance to be laid out is:

True distance minus correction

$$= 1308.37' - 0.00000645 \times 1308.37' \times (95–68)°F$$
$$= 1308.37' - 0.22'$$
$$= 1308.15'$$

Table III in the appendix can be used to determine temperature corrections directly.

The average temperature during the time a distance is measured may be used or, for highly accurate work, a temperature may be recorded for each tape measurement. The temperature of the tape may not be the same as the air temperature. The tape may be warmer because it has been in the direct rays of the sun or cooler because it has been in wet grass. The appropriate temperature is obtained by using a tape thermometer which is clamped to the tape with the bulb in contact with the tape.

Tape Correction

A tape may be shorter or longer than the dimensions inscribed on it. A new tape, although manufactured with high precision, may have a discernible error. During use, small kinks occur which shorten the tape slightly. Dragging the tape wears it thinner so that it stretches a little longer with standard tension than it did when new. These two sources of error tend to compensate.

If significant error is suspected, the size of error may be determined by comparing the tape with a *standard tape* which is precisely 100 ft long at 68°F when fully supported along its length and under a tension of 10 lb. The standard tape may be made of *invar* or *lovar* metals, which are steel alloys having very low coefficients of expansion. Temperature is not critical with this type of tape.

If the tape being tested reads 100 ft for a length determined to be 99.995 ft by the standard tape, a 100 ft measured length has a true length of 99.995 ft. The error is positive and the correction is negative. The error may be eliminated by greater tension on the tape so that it stretches to the full 100 ft or by applying the correction to each measured distance. See Fig. 3-10 for the method of determining error. Two examples follow:

1. A distance is measured between two points and recorded as 1273.42 ft. The true distance is

$$1273.42' - (.005 \times 12.73)$$

or

$$1273.42' - 0.06' = 1273.36'$$

2. A point is to be set 1273.42 ft from a known point. The tape readings will

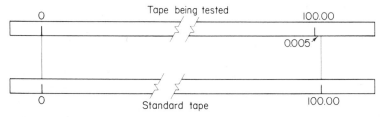

Tape being tested is 0.005 ft short and therefore is 99.995 ft long causing a plus error of 0.005 ft in every 100.00 ft taped.

Figure 3-10 Determining tape error

be greater than the true distance. The distance to be taped in order to establish a true distance of 1273.42 ft is

$$1273.42' + (.005 \times 12.73)$$

or

$$1273.42' + 0.06' = 1273.48'$$

In ordinary surveying and even for short distances (under approximately 100 feet) of high order accuracy a tape correction is not necessary. As indicated in the example, the error is small. It is preferable to replace an old tape with a new one when the error becomes too large.

Slope Correction

In some cases it is faster and more accurate to measure a distance at an angle with the horizontal and calculate the horizontal distance than to measure it with several horizontal steps. The angle up or down from the horizontal is called a *slope angle* and the distance is called a *slope distance*. The slope distance will always be longer than the corresponding horizontal distance.

Two methods of making a slope measurement and calculating the horizontal distance are described here.

METHOD 1

A slope distance may be measured from one point to another, the slope angle determined, and a horizontal distance computed. The slope is along a line that passes through both ends of the tape and does not necessarily follow the ground surface. The horizontal distance (adjacent side) can be calculated by multiplying the slope distance (hypotenuse) by the cos of the slope angle. See Fig. 3-11.

Sometimes a correction, C_s, is subtracted from the slope distance to find the horizontal distance. See Fig. 3-12.

$$C_s = L - L \cos \alpha$$

where

$$L = \text{slope distance}$$
$$\alpha = \text{slope angle}$$
$$L \cos \alpha = \text{horizontal distance}$$

The correction is found in Table IV in the appendix for various slope angles. A correction taken from this table can be combined with tape and temperature corrections to be applied to the taped distance in one step.

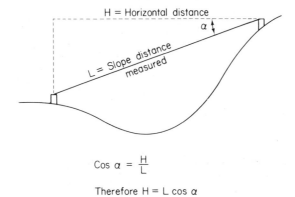

$$\text{Cos } \alpha = \frac{H}{L}$$

Therefore $H = L \cos \alpha$

Figure 3-11 Determining horizontal distance from slope distance and slope angle

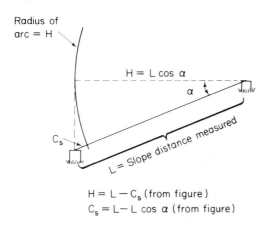

$H = L - C_s$ (from figure)
$C_s = L - L \cos \alpha$ (from figure)

The advantages of using C_s are that it can be taken from a table and it can be combined with other required corrections to make one composite correction.

Figure 3-12 Determining horizontal distance with slope correction, C_s, derived from slope angle

METHOD 2

A slope distance may be measured from a point of known elevation to another point of different known elevation and a horizontal distance computed. The Pythagorean Theorem can be used directly. See Fig. 3-13.

$$H = \sqrt{L^2 - d^2}$$

where

$L =$ slope distance
$d =$ difference in elevation

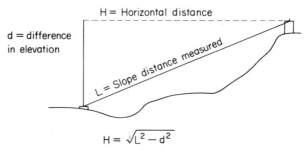

$$H = \sqrt{L^2 - d^2}$$

Figure 3-13 Determining horizontal distance from slope distance and elevation difference

A correction C_s can be computed using the Pythagorean Theorem. The correction is convenient to use and there is little loss of accuracy except at steep slopes where d equals one tenth or more of L. See Fig. 3-14.

$$C_s = L - H$$
$$d^2 = L^2 - H^2 = (L-H)(L+H) = C_s(L+H)$$
$$C_s = \frac{d^2}{L+H}$$
$$C_s = \frac{d^2}{2L}$$

where

L = slope distance
H = horizontal distance
d = difference in elevation

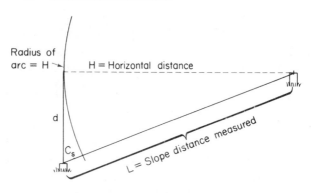

$$H = L - C_s \text{ (from figure)}$$
$$C_s = \frac{d^2}{2L} \text{ (from previous paragraph)}$$

Figure 3-14 Determining horizontal distance with slope correction, C_s, derived from Pythagorean Theorem

Total Correction

When more than one correction is needed all corrections are determined on the basis of the distance as read on the tape, all are added algebraically, and the total is then added algebraically to the distance as read. An example follows.

A distance of 250.00′ is taped with a 300 ft tape on a slope with an angle of 3°. The true length of the tape is 300.03 ft and the temperature is 35°F.

$$C_L = \frac{250}{300}(+0.03)$$

$$= +0.025$$

$$C_T = 250(-0.00021285)$$

$$= -0.033 \text{ from Table III}$$

$$C_S = 2.5(-0.14)$$

$$= -0.35 \text{ from Table IV}$$

$$\text{Total Correction} = -0.36$$

$$\text{Corrected Distance} = 249.64 \text{ ft}$$

3–4 NOTEKEEPING

Notekeeping is shown below for various conditions in Figs. 3-15, 16 and 17.

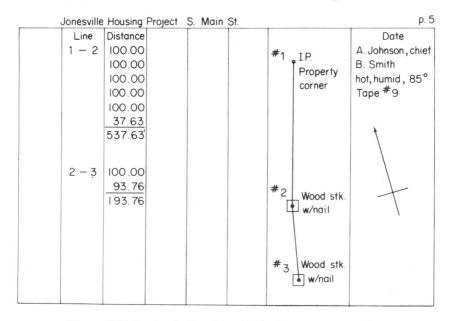

Figure 3-15 Taping field notes—100-foot tape, no corrections

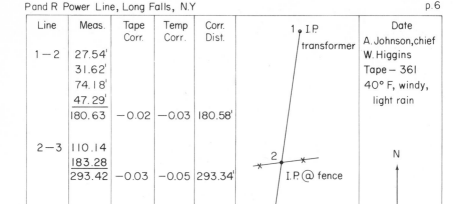

Line	Meas.	Tape Corr.	Temp Corr.	Corr. Dist.		Date
1 — 2	27.54'				1 I.P. transformer	A. Johnson, chief
	31.62'					W. Higgins
	74.18'					Tape — 361
	47.29'					40° F, windy,
	180.63	−0.02	−0.03	180.58'		light rain
2 — 3	110.14				2 I.P. @ fence	N
	183.28					
	293.42	−0.03	−0.05	293.34'	3 I.P.	

P and R Power Line, Long Falls, N.Y   p.6

Figure 3-16 Taping field notes—200-foot tape, temperature and tape corrections

3–5 ERRORS AND MISTAKES

Systematic Errors

The two truly systematic taping errors and their corrections have been discussed. They are:

1. Difference between working tape length and standard tape length.
2. Change in tape length due to temperature variation.

Accidental Errors

The most common sources of accidental errors are:

1. Imperfectly estimating the second decimal place on the tape.
2. Inexact plumbing over a point.
3. Incorrect tension.

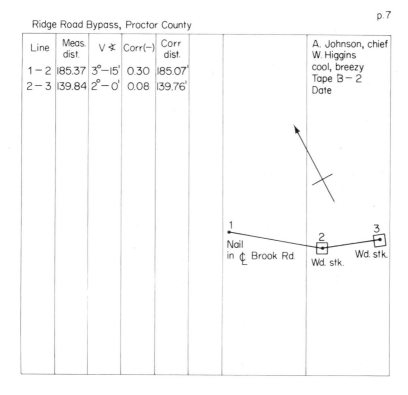

Figure 3-17 Taping field notes—200-foot tape, slope distances

These are truly accidental errors. Neither direction nor magnitude can be determined although incorrect tension is usually too little which results in an error in a plus direction.

Other sources of error are not so readily categorized as systematic or accidental. They always cause error in a plus direction but of an unknown magnitude. Two of the most common are:

1. Misalignment — vertical or horizontal. This source can be controlled as described earlier in the chapter.

2. Wind causing the tape to curve out to the side. This source can be controlled to an extent by applying greater tension and taping shorter distances.

Common Mistakes

1. Misreading a number. This can be avoided by reading the number on each side of the number to be recorded. Look at the distance and estimate

it before measuring. A large mistake like reading 69 ft for 96 ft can be avoided this way.

2. Recording a number wrong. This can be avoided by saying the number out loud while recording it. The other tapeman should listen and verify the number.

3. Using the wrong location for zero. Zero may be at the end of the ring or on the tape. Be sure before starting the work. Verify it with another tape or a ruler if necessary.

4. Omitting a tape length. This is more likely to happen when taping full tape lengths such as 100 ft increments. Each distance should be recorded immediately after being measured. The methods described in this chapter will act as a check.

5. Using the wrong end of the tape. Check this before work begins. It will be noticed as soon as a measurement is made if proper taping procedures are used. However, time is saved if it is noticed and corrected at the start.

6. Allowing the tape to touch brush, a fence, or any other object so that it is not straight and hanging freely between plumb bobs. Look at the tape just prior to making the measurement.

PROBLEMS

1/ A 100-ft tape is determined to be 100.04 ft long when checked against a standard tape. A distance is measured as 149.96 ft. What is the distance after applying the tape correction?

2/ A distance of 1000.00 ft is measured with a steel tape when average temperature is $+18°F$. What is the length when corrected for temperature?

3/ A point is to be set at a distance of 100 ft. The true length of the tape is 99.98 ft and the temperature is $+97°F$. What length should be laid off with the tape?

4/ A distance of 186.73 ft is measured with a slope angle of 3°–05′. What is the horizontal distance?

5/ A distance of 774.86 ft is measured on a slope of 2°–09′ with a 200 ft tape having a true length of 199.99 ft and the temperature is $+102°F$. What is the corrected horizontal distance?

6/ A slope distance of 476.59 ft is measured between two points, one of which is 24.63 ft higher than the other. What is the horizontal distance?

7/ A slope distance of 1200 ft is measured between two points with an elevation difference of 43 ft at a temperature of −15°F with a 300 ft tape having a true length of 300.02 ft. What is the corrected horizontal distance ?

8/ A distance of 396.17 ft is measured at a slope angle of 1°–36′ with a 100 ft tape having a true length of 100.01 ft. What is the corrected horizontal distance ?

INSTRUCTIONAL OBJECTIVES OF CHAPTER 4

1/ *Given the necessary equipment, the student, with a partner, should be able to complete a level circuit of four turning points with an error not greater than .01 ft.*

2/ *Given an engineer's level, the student should be able to demonstrate the proper procedure for setting it up and reading the rod.*

3/ *Given a level rod, the student should be able to select a satisfactory turning point, hold the rod properly, and wave the rod properly.*

4/ *Given a series of rod readings as seen through the engineer's level (either slides or pictures), the student should be able to read them correctly.*

5/ *Given field data, the student should be able to keep complete notes including an arithmetic check.*

6/ *Given an object to be used as a bench mark, the student should be able to write an adequate description.*

chapter four

Vertical Distances

Vertical direction is the second of the two directions on which all plane surveying is based. Its measurement is not straightforward like horizontal measurements and understanding it requires an ability to visualize relationships in space. The study of surveying will assist greatly in developing this ability which is of primary importance in technical work. The necessity to visualize space relationships becomes apparent in this chapter.

4-1 METHOD

The vertical distance between two points can be determined by first finding the vertical distance of each point below a level line as shown in Fig. 4-1. The difference in elevation between the two points can then be calculated. If the elevation of one of the points is known with reference to a datum, then the elevation of the other can be determined with reference to the same datum. The level line could be established with the hand level described in Chap. 1 or with a more precise instrument. The procedure illustrated in Fig. 4-1 is called *leveling*.

4-2 DEFINITIONS

Bench Mark (B.M.) is a permanent or semi-permanent point of known elevation which can be used to establish other elevations. See discussion in Chap. 1. In Fig. 4-1, point A is a bench mark. Each B.M. should be described in field notes so well that someone who has not been in the area before can find it and be certain he has it.

The description should first state the largest area or political sub-division necessary and decrease the area step by step until there can be only one possible point intended. For example, the description of a B.M.

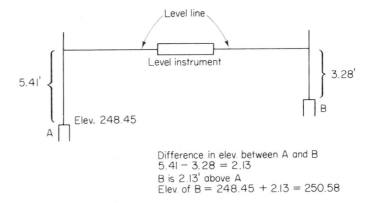

Difference in elev. between A and B
5.41 − 3.28 = 2.13
B is 2.13' above A
Elev. of B = 248.45 + 2.13 = 250.58

Figure 4-1 Leveling procedure

in a statewide benchmark system could begin with the county, then town, then nearest highway intersection, then further details narrowing the location to one point.

Height of instrument (H.I.) is an elevation, established at a known vertical distance above another point of known elevation, from which other elevations can be determined. It is established with a level instrument so that the elevation can be extended in any direction along a horizontal line. In Fig. 4-1, the level line is at the height of instrument.

Turning point (T.P.) is a point of fixed elevation used temporarily in the process of leveling. The point need not be permanent. In Fig. 4-1, point *B* is a turning point.

Backsight (B.S.) is a reading taken with a level instrument on a point of known elevation in order to establish the height of instrument. It is taken in a back direction. In Fig. 4-1, the reading 5.41 ft is a backsight. It is read on a calibrated rod placed on point *A*.

Foresight (F.S.) is a reading taken with a level instrument on a new point in order to establish the elevation of the new point from the height of the instrument. It is taken in a forward direction. In Fig. 4-1, the reading 3.28 ft is a foresight. It is read on a calibrated rod placed on point *B*.

4-3 INTRODUCTION TO EQUIPMENT

The *engineer's level* shown in Fig. 4-2 is used for surveying work of ordinary accuracy. It includes a telescope which defines the line of sight between the eye and the object viewed and magnifies the object. The telescope consists of a metal tube containing four main parts. They are shown schematically in Fig. 4-3.

Figure 4-2 Engineer's level

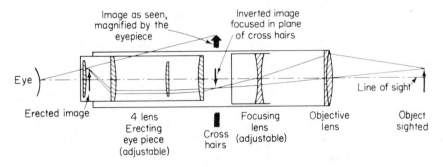

The diagram shows paths of two representative rays from a point at the top of the object sighted. Rays from this point and from every other point on the object are distributed across the entire face of the objective lens. Where rays from a point on the object are brought to a point within the telescope that point is in focus and a visible image of it is formed. The lenses are designed to bring the object into focus by bending (refracting) rays from all points on the object to a focus in the same plane. For accurate sighting this must be the plane of the cross hairs. The instrument man sees the image enlarged because of the wide angle at which the refracted rays come to his eye.

Figure 4-3 Internal focusing telescope with erecting eyepiece

The *objective lens* is fixed at the end toward the object being sighted (object end). Its purpose is to admit light rays into the telescope to form an image. This image is upside down.

The *focusing lens* is attached within a slide which can be moved longitudinally on rack and pinion gears by turning the *focusing screw*. Its purpose is to focus the image so that it is seen in the plane of the cross hairs.

The *reticle* is stationary and includes a ring and cross hairs. The cross hairs are made of spider web, fine wire or lines etched on glass. The ring that holds the cross hairs is held in position by capstan screws so that it can be adjusted vertically or horizontally within the tube but only in a plane perpendicular to the axis of the tube. It can also be rotated slightly so that the horizontal hair can be maintained truly horizontal

The *eyepiece* is a microscope containing four lenses close to the eye of the instrumentman. The purpose is to enlarge the image of the object and to invert it so that it appears right side up. The object image is at the cross hairs. The eyepiece is movable in a longitudinal direction so that it can be focused on the image to suit each individual eye.

The *line of sight* through the telescope is a line from the instrumentman's eye through the center of the cross hairs and through the optical center of the objective lens. This line must be horizontal when the level vial is horizontal. This is the reason the line of sight can be adjusted by moving the cross hairs. The level vial can be adjusted by moving one end of it up or down until the line of sight and the axis of the level vial are parallel.

Some telescopes focus the image in the plane of the cross hairs by sliding the objective lens in and out, and therefore have no focusing lens. They are called *external focusing* because the objective lens projects beyond the tube when focusing on nearby objects. External focusing instruments are not generally available now, but some may still be in use. The external focusing instruments are open to the atmosphere so that dust and moisture can enter the telescope tube and cause decreased visibility and abrasion of moving parts. The modern *internal focusing* telescope is sealed against dust and moisture.

The eyepieces of some telescopes do not reverse the image but show it upside down. These are called *inverting eye pieces* and provide a somewhat clearer image than the *erecting eyepieces*. This is because each lens absorbs some light which therefore does not get through to the eye, and because the inverting eyepiece has only two lenses instead of four.

The telescope is joined to a base plate by a *half ball joint* and rotated into level position about the half ball by four *leveling screws* arranged at 90° intervals around a circle and bearing on the *base plate*. Refer to Fig. 4-4 and note that because of the half ball connection the elevation of the telescope cannot be changed by adjusting the leveling screws. The telescope rotates about the center of the spherically shaped half ball and cannot go higher or lower without being out of level. The base plate is mounted on three long legs called a *tripod*. The legs include pointed steel shoes and are pivoted at the top. Their purpose is to provide a stable platform at eye height for the instrument.

The level position is indicated by the centering of an air bubble in a level vial containing alcohol or ether, attached to the telescope and parallel with the line of sight through the telescope. The curve of the vial is flatter and therefore more sensitive to a small change in direction than that of a hand level and thus it is more accurate. To facilitate aiming, the instrument includes a clamp to stop unwanted rotation and a tangent screw to rotate the line of sight to the position desired. A similar level of less accuracy used in simple construction work is called a *builder's level*.

The *self-leveling level* permits faster operation because it requires only approximate leveling to a stage where it levels itself and remains level even if moved slightly.

The *tilting level* permits faster and more accurate operation. It also needs to be leveled only approximately. While reading the rod, the instrumentman levels the instrument precisely with one screw. The level bubble is located so that it can be watched while one reads the rod to allow precise leveling.

The *level rod* is read through the level instrument to get backsights and foresights. The rod is calibrated to .01 ft in a bold, easy to read style, with zero at the bottom of the rod. A level rod is shown in Fig. 4-5. The rod is held vertically with the bottom on the bench mark or turning point so that the horizontal line of sight through the instrument intersects it at the height of instrument. The number read on the rod at this elevation is the backsight or foresight. In Fig. 4-1 the backsight (5.41 ft) and the foresight (3.28 ft) are read on a level rod.

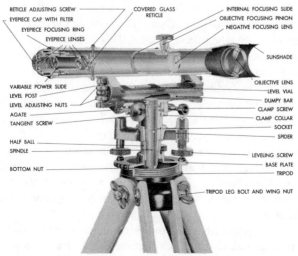

Figure 4-4 Inside of engineer's level

There are many styles of level rod. One of the most widely used, the 13 ft Philadelphia level rod, is described here and shown in Fig. 4-5. The Philadelphia rod consists of two sections, one behind the other. The rod can be extended by sliding the back section upward and clamping it in place. For ordinary accuracy, the rod is used at either of two settings — fully extended (high rod) or not extended at all (short rod). The front section is calibrated to 7 ft and the back section is calibrated so that when the rod is extended its full length it reads continuously from zero to 13 ft. A short part of the top of the front section reading 7 ft is attached to the back section, so that when the rod is extended the 7 ft mark is at the top where a 13 ft mark should be. Mistakes can be prevented by reading the number below the 7 before deciding whether it means 7 or 13.

Vernier and Its Use

Although the rod is calibrated to read to .01 ft, it can be read to .001 ft by the use of a vernier. The *vernier* is a device which allows more exact measurement with a measuring instrument than is possible with the scale of that instrument. It is a scale constructed with equal spaces of a size such that N spaces on the vernier equal $N - 1$ spaces on the instrument scale. A common type of vernier contains 10 spaces, with each vernier space equal to $\frac{9}{10}$ of the instrument space. Thus, 10 vernier spaces equal $10 - 1$ or 9 instrument spaces. This type of vernier will allow accurate readings of $\frac{1}{10}$ the size of the smallest instrument space. See Fig. 4-6 for an illustration of this vernier.

Visualize the index arrow on the vernier moving to the right until the 0.1 of the vernier lines up with the 1 of the instrument. Since the vernier space is $\frac{9}{10}$ the length of an instrument space, the index has moved $\frac{1}{10}$ the length of an instrument space when these line up. This could be estimated but not read accurately by noting the movement of the arrow. It can be read accurately by noting the position of the vernier line marked 0.1.

If the index moves farther until the 0.2 lines up with the 2 of the instrument, it will have moved $\frac{2}{10}$ of a space on the instrument scale. As the index moves to the right the vernier marks will line up with marks on the instrument one by one in succession, indicating the length of movement in tenths of an instrument space. The same vernier is shown in Fig. 4-7 with a measurement of 0.9 of an instrument space. The instrument is read by noting the position of the arrow for whole numbers and the vernier number that lines up with any scale number for the fraction or decimal parts to be added to the whole number.

The rod is equipped with a stationary vernier reading to .001 ft attached to a sleeve through which the back section slides. The reverse side of the back section is calibrated from 7 ft to 13 ft from top to bottom so that the

Figure 4-5 Level rod

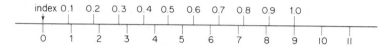

Figure 4-6 Vernier reading 0.0

Figure 4-7 Vernier reading 1.9

higher the rod is extended the higher the number at the vernier. The vernier reads 7.000 when the rod is closed and when the rod is extended it reads 7.000 plus the length of the extension.

Thus, if the rod is adjusted while at a point so that the line of sight intersects 7.00 on the front when the rod is extended, the rodman can read the B.S. or F.S. to the nearest .001 ft with the vernier on the reverse side of the rod. The instrumentman signals up or down to the rodman who adjusts the length of rod until the instrumentman reads 7.00 exactly. The rodman then clamps the extended section in place and reads it at the vernier. The rodman keeps notes or calls readings to the notekeeper.

A *target* with alternating red and white sectors arranged to define a horizontal line sharply can be fixed on 7.00 to improve the instrumentman's accuracy. The target is removable and can be used below 7 ft where the back vernier cannot be used. Here it is adjusted to the line of sight by the rodman, who can then read the rod to .001 ft using the vernier on the target.

4-4 DIFFERENTIAL LEVELING

Method

It is often necessary to establish the difference in elevation between two points such as the site of a water supply project and the source of water. This is usually done by converting the elevation of a bench mark, step by step, as shown in Fig. 4-1, to the elevation of a new bench mark installed at the new site. The new elevation should then be converted, step by step, to an elevation on the bench mark at the point of beginning. This process is called running a *level circuit*. The difference between the starting and ending elevations at the same B.M. is the error of closure. Accuracy is computed as described in Chap. 2.

Differential leveling is the process of determining the difference in elevation between two points. It is started from a bench mark of known elevation or one which is installed specifically for the project and assigned an arbitrary elevation such as 100.00. The level is set up and a backsight read on the rod on the bench mark. A foresight is then read on the rod on a convenient

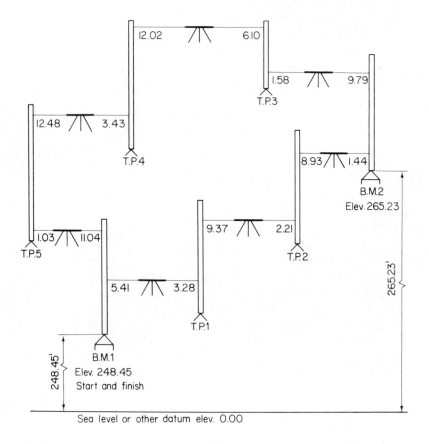

Sea level or other datum elev. 0.00

See Fig. 4—9 for field notes

Figure 4-8 Differential leveling showing elevations, but not true horizontal relationships

turning point. The turning point may be a natural object or a stake driven solidly enough to be used for the foresight and a subsequent backsight without any movement. It should have a definite, small, high point which will not break off when used.

Once the foresight is recorded, the elevation of the turning point is established. The level is moved to a new location and a backsight read on the same turning point to establish a new height of instrument. The process is repeated until the elevation is established for the desired point. Often the desired point is a new bench mark. See Fig. 4-8 for an illustration of differential leveling.

Notekeeping

A level circuit begins with a known elevation at a bench mark and succeeding elevations are computed as follows:

Elevation of B.M. 1		248.45
	plus B.S.	+5.41
Elevation of H.I. (line of sight)		253.86
	minus F.S.	−3.28
Elevation of T.P.1		250.58
	plus B.S.	+9.37
	H.I.	259.95

Sample differential leveling notes are shown in standard form in Fig. 4-9. Note that each backsight and foresight is on the same line as the bench mark or turning point on which that sight is taken. If they are not, notes are being improperly kept. The closing elevation on B.M. 1 is not the same as the starting elevation. The difference is the error of closure and is equal to + 0.01 ft. This is caused by accidental errors and therefore cannot be avoided.

In this case the elevation of B.M. 2 is accepted as 265.23 since it is not known where the error is. If the error of closure had been + 0.02 it could be assumed that the error is + 0.01 going out from B.M. 1 to B.M. 2 and + 0.01 returning from B.M. 2 to B.M. 1. B.M. 2 could then be adjusted by adding a correction equal and opposite in sign to the error from B.M. 1 to B.M. 2 (265. 23 − 0.01 = 265.22).

Note that if the total of all the backsights (positive sign) is equal to the total of all the foresights (negative sign), the final elevation will be the same as the starting elevation. Any difference in the closing elevation is due to a difference between the total backsights and the total foresights unless a mistake is made in adding or subtracting. The closing elevation should be

Sta.	B.S.(+)	H.I.	F.S.(–)	Elev.
B.M.1	5.41	253.86		248.45
T.P.1	9.37	259.95	3.28	250.58
T.P.2	8.93	266.67	2.21	257.74
B.M.2	9.79	275.02	1.44	265.23
T.P.3	6.10	279.54	1.58	273.44
T.P.4	3.43	270.95	12.02	267.52
T.P.5	1.03	259.50	12.48	258.47
B.M.1			11.04	248.46
+44.06			**–44.05**	

Total B.S. + 44.06   Closing elev. 248.46
Total F.S –44.05   Starting elev. 248.45
Error =   +0.01   Error =   +0.01

└─── Arithmetic check ───┘
equal in quantity
and sign.

Figure 4-9 Differential leveling field notes

higher (in a positive direction) than the starting elevation if the sum of backsights is greater than the sum of foresights and vice versa.

In computing the elevations as the work progresses, there is a chance for an arithmetic mistake. The difference between the sum of backsights and the sum of foresights will equal the difference between starting and closing elevations (error of closure) unless a mistake is made. A convenient check is to compare the difference between total backsights and total foresights with the error of closure and the notes are set up to facilitate this checking. See Fig. 4-9 for the arithmetic check which should be performed before leaving the field.

4–5 PROFILE LEVELING

For design of highways, pipelines and other long, narrow projects it is necessary to plot a continuous representation of the ground surface called a *profile*. The profile is a section view of the surface along the centerline of work. The information needed to plot the profile is obtained in the field by the process of profile leveling. Profile leveling consists of differential leveling with additional elevations being obtained at locations needed to plot the profile. The locations are often at 50 ft or 100 ft intervals along the project centerline and are designated by station. Rod readings are taken at the desired points from a known H.I. The rod is read only to the nearest tenth of a ft when the rod is placed on the ground. The readings are called *rod shots* to differentiate them from foresights which are part of the level circuit and must be used in calculating turning point elevations around the circuit. Rod shots are not part of the circuit and are not used in the arithmetic check.

Figures 4-10, 4-11 and 4-12 show a plan view of a profile leveling circuit, field notes, and a plot of the profile from the field notes. Notice that B.M. and T.P.s are not part of the profile. There is no reason for them to be located on the line of the profile. Instead, each T.P. should be located so that the maximum number of rod shots can be taken with each instrument setup.

The sequence is important. All rod shots from any one instrument position should be read and recorded before a foresight is read to prevent possible confusion of numbers. When working on soft ground or other surface the instrument might sink slightly and therefore change its elevation between the time of reading the B.S. and the time of reading the F.S. In this case a different procedure may be required. This is discussed in the section on systematic errors.

4-6 CROSS SECTION LEVELING

It is often desirable for the designer to have a representation of the surface on both sides of the centerline of work. This is usually shown by plotting short profiles at right angles to the line of work. These are called *cross sections* and are usually plotted at regular intervals and designated by stationing. The information needed is obtained in the field by the process of *cross section leveling*. Everything written in the preceding section about

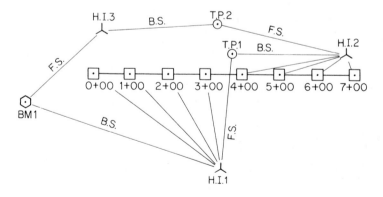

See Fig. 4-11 for field notes
See Fig. 4-12 for plot of profile

Figure 4-10 Plan view of profile leveling along a straight route

Sta.	B.S.(+)	H.I.	F.S. (−)	Rod(−)	Elev.
B.M.1	11.82	111.82			100.00
0+00				5.3	106.5
1+00				5.2	106.6
2+00				4.1	107.7
3+00				3.0	108.8
T.P.1	5.32	115.18	1.96		109.86
4+00				7.9	107.3
5+00				6.7	108.5
6+00				5.6	109.6
7+00				4.5	110.7
T.P.2	2.11	109.80	7.49		107.69
B.M.1			9.81		99.99
	+19.25		−19.26		
	−19.26		100.00	*Arithmetic Check*	
	+19.25		−0.01		
	−0.01		99.99		

Figure 4-11 Profile leveling field notes

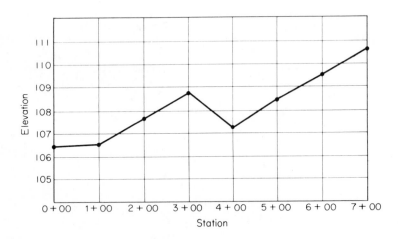

Figure 4-12 Plot of profile

profile leveling applies to cross section leveling. In addition, other rod shots are taken adjacent to each rod shot taken in profile leveling. The shots are taken at prescribed lateral distances from the centerline and at breaks in the ground slope on a line perpendicular to the survey line at the location of the profile shot. See Figs. 4-13, 4-14 and 4-15 for a plan of the field locations, notes, and plot of cross sections.

4-7 INVERTING THE ROD

Conventional leveling requires that the level instrument be higher than any point on which the rod is placed. It is sometimes necessary to obtain the elevation of an object higher than the instrument. A reading, whether B.S. or F.S., can be obtained as illustrated in Fig. 4-16. Notekeeping is standard except that a B.S. is minus and an F.S. is plus. A note should be put on the right hand side of the page to explain the reversal of signs.

4-8 SIGNALS

When the members of a survey party cannot hear each other because of distance or noisy working conditions, they can use hand signals. The following signals are in general use.

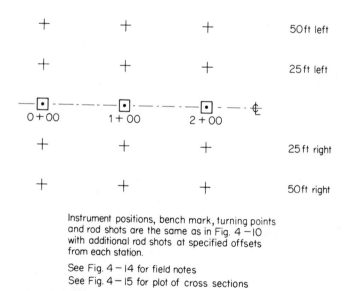

Instrument positions, bench mark, turning points and rod shots are the same as in Fig. 4 – 10 with additional rod shots at specified offsets from each station.

See Fig. 4 – 14 for field notes
See Fig. 4 – 15 for plot of cross sections

Figure 4-13 Plan view of cross section leveling showing only rod shot locations

The instrumentman signals the rodman to establish a T.P. by holding his index finger in the air and rotating it in a horizontal circle. This signal is used to prevent the rodman from going so far up or down a hill that the level line of sight falls below or above the level rod; it is also used to notify the

Round Hill Rd. Storm Drain Cross Sections.   p.14

Sta.	B.S.(+)	H.I.	F.S.(−)	Elev.	Left		℄	Right	
B.M.1	11.82	111.82		100.00					
0+00					105.7 6.1 50'	106.0 5.8 25'	106.5 5.3	106.8 5.0 25'	107.3 4.5 50'
1+00					105.3 6.5 50'	106.2 5.6 25'	106.6 5.2	106.8 5.0 10'	107.3 4.5 50'
2+00					105.8 6.0 50'	106.6 5.2 16'	107.7 4.1	107.4 4.4 8'	108.2 3.6 50'
3+00					106.0 5.8 50'	106.8 5.0 22'	108.8 3.0	107.8 4.0 20'	107.6 4.2 50'
T.P.1	5.32	115.18	1.96	109.86					
4+00					106.4 8.8 50'	106.7 8.5 32'	107.3 7.9	108.0 7.2 19'	107.4 7.8 50'
5+00					107.2 8.0 50'	107.4 7.8 18'	108.5 6.7	108.2 7.0 31'	107.4 7.8 50'
6+00					108.8 6.4 50'	109.2 6.0 25'	109.6 5.6	109.8 5.4 38'	109.6 5.6 50'
7+00					109.2 6.0 50'	108.7 6.5 25'	109.7 5.5	108.2 7.0 25'	107.7 7.5 50'
T.P.2 B.M.1	2.11 +19.25 −19.26 +19.25 −0.01	109.80 100.00 −0.01 99.99	7.49 9.81 −19.26	107.69 99.99	B.M.1 − E. side of Round Hill Rd. 500' N. of Mill Creek. Spike in N.side of 24" oak in S.fence line.			Date Level # 3128 Rod #3 Warm, hazy C.B. ⊼ R.M ▭ W.H. ⚹	

Arithmetic check

Note: Some rod shots are at a change in ground slope instead of a 25 ft. offset. No shots are needed beyond 50 ft. offset.

Figure 4-14 Cross section leveling field notes

instrumentman and notekeeper that the rod is on a turning point and not in a position for a rod shot. The instrumentman must know this because he reads the rod more accurately for a T.P. than for a rod shot, and the notekeeper must know in order to keep notes properly.

The party chief signals the instrumentman to move the instrument to the next location by extending both hands downward and outward and then

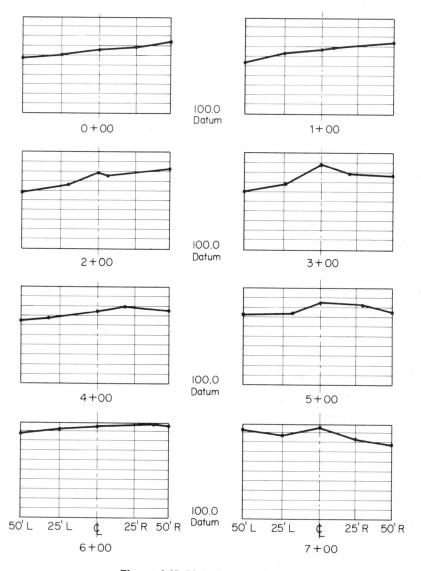

Figure 4-15 Plot of cross sections

raising them in a motion as if lifting the legs of an instrument. This signal is used to indicate that all readings needed from this instrument position have been obtained and the instrument should be moved to the next position. The instrumentman should not move the instrument until told to do so by the party chief who is responsible for obtaining complete field information.

The signal that an operation is completed is given by raising both hands above the head, then waving them outward and back to the original position. This signal, given by the instrumentman or party chief, tells the rodman that a rod reading is completed and that he should move into position for the next shot. This signal does not mean that the instrument can be moved.

If the instrumentman can see that the rod is not plumb, he should call "plumb the rod" or signal by extending his arm vertically and moving it in the direction in which the top of the rod should move.

The instrumentman cannot tell if the rod is leaning out of plumb toward or away from him; but, if he suspects it, he may require the rodman to wave the rod slowly toward and away from the instrument. As the rod leans farther toward the instrument, the reading becomes higher. As the rod starts back, the reading becomes lower until the rod is plumb and then becomes higher as the rod leans farther away from plumb. The instrumentman should therefore take the lowest reading. The instrumentman signals for this by holding his arm over his head and waving it slowly toward and away from the rodman.

If there is a small obstruction that prevents reading the rod, it may be possible to read it with sufficient accuracy if the rod is moved clear of the obstruction by waving it back and forth in a direction perpendicular to the line of sight. The instrumentman signals this by holding his arm above his head and waving it slowly from side to side.

Sometimes, when the rod is close to the instrument, the small section of rod that is visible does not include a whole foot number. In this case the rodman should raise the rod slowly in a vertical line until the instrumentman can read the whole foot. To notify the rodman to do this, the instrumentman calls "raise for red" or signals by holding his hand out palm up and raising it a short distance. He signals that the rod has been raised high enough and should

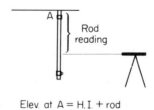

Elev. at A = H.I. + rod

Figure 4-16 Sighting rod above instrument

be returned by signalling that the operation is completed. The rodman returns the rod to the original point so that the instrumentman can verify his reading of tenths and hundredths.

4-9 STEP BY STEP OPERATION — INSTRUMENTMAN

Steadiness of the instrument depends on proper adjustment of the hinge thumbscrews at the top of the legs. If they are too loose, the entire instrument will be unsteady. If they are too tight, they might bind and allow slight distortion when the legs are moved into position. The distortion may relieve itself suddenly and put the instrument out of level or change the elevation. The legs of a properly adjusted tripod fall slowly of their own weight from a horizontal position toward the vertical.

Tripod legs should be set rigidly in place so that the footplate appears level by eye. Rigidity is obtained by driving the shoes into the earth or if the legs rest on a hard surface by tightening the hinge thumbscrews after the legs are in place. The footplate is leveled by moving legs in or out relative to the center under the instrument. On a hillside the uphill leg or legs must be farther away from the center than the downhill legs. The telescope should be at such a height that the instrumentman can use it comfortably.

The telescope is leveled by adjusting the leveling screws until the level bubble remains centered no matter which way the telescope is pointed. This is done by aligning the scope over one pair of leveling screws and centering the bubble by turning the two screws in opposite directions, then aligning the scope over the other pair of leveling screws and centering the bubble by turning those screws. The operation is repeated until the instrument is leveled satisfactorily. The level bubble will move in the direction the left thumb moves while turning the screw.

The cross hairs are then brought into focus by adjusting the focusing ring on the eye piece while looking at the cross hairs. The cross hairs will vary from extremely thin to thick and fuzzy within the adjustment range. They are in focus when they appear thick with a sharp outline. It will help the eye to concentrate on the cross hairs if the background is of a solid light color like the sky or a concrete wall. It may be necessary to make this adjustment occasionally. The condition of the cross hairs can easily be observed each time the telescope is used and an adjustment made when needed.

The rod is sighted and its image is brought into focus by adjusting the focusing screw until the image is in the same plane as the cross hairs. This adjustment must be made for each change in distance to the rod. The test for proper focusing is to move the eye up and down slightly. When the image and cross hairs are in the same plane there will be no movement between the cross hairs and the rod image. If they are not in the same plane, movement called parallax will be noticed. *Parallax* is the apparent movement

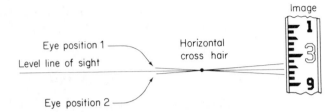

With the eye at position 1, the horizontal cross hair
    intersects the image at 2.93.

With the eye at position 2, the horizontal cross hair
    intersects the image at 2.97.

Although only the eye has moved, it appears the
    cross hair has moved across the image.

The closer the image is to the cross hairs, the
    smaller the possible error. When the image
    coincides with the cross hairs there can be no
    parallax.

Figure 4-17 Parallax in surveyor's telescope

between two objects at different distances caused by movement of the eye of the observer. Parallax is illustrated in Fig. 4-17.

After focusing, the telescope level vial is checked just before reading the rod and an adjustment is made if necessary. The rod is then read without touching the instrument. The rod should be read at the point of intersection of the horizontal and vertical cross hairs. If the horizontal hair is not exactly horizontal, this intersection is the only point on it that lies in a level line of sight. The rod may be read to .01 ft or estimated to .001 ft. Always check numbers above and below the reading to assure that the rod is read correctly. If the instrument is used with both eyes open, the eye being used will not tire so soon. The natural tendency is to close one eye and practice is required to learn to read the rod with both eyes open.

If the rod is not plumb by comparison to the vertical cross hair, if the rod cannot be read because of obstructions such as leaves or branches, or if no red, whole number can be seen, the appropriate signal or instruction is given to the rodman until a satisfactory reading is obtained. The rodman is then sent to the next location with a signal and the reading is recorded immediately.

4-10 CARE OF THE INSTRUMENT

The instrument should be kept in its carrying case until the work site is reached and even then should be carried in the case if it must be transported a long distance or over rough terrain before it will be used. Note how the manufacturer has placed the instrument in the case, or read the manufacturer's instructions on how to store the instrument, so that you can return it properly to the case. Precautions should be taken to prevent jarring the instrument even while in the case.

Most level instruments should be lifted from the case by gripping the telescope. The tripod should be set up solidly before the instrument is taken from the case. The telescope should be held firmly until the instrument is attached to the tripod. The sunshade should be placed on the telescope. This improves visibility whether the sun is out or not. Once the instrument is in place on the tripod it should not be left unattended.

The instrument is normally carried with the tripod on the shoulder and the instrument in back when moving from setup to setup; but it should be carried with the tripod held under one arm and the instrument in front supported by the other hand when there is danger of the instrument bumping something, such as when inside a building or in high brush. The motion should be clamped lightly before the instrument is picked up on the tripod.

A level instrument can be used in rain or snow. After using, it should be allowed to dry off in the most dustfree place available.

Storing in the carrying case with the cover ajar will provide protection while drying. Modern instruments are built to prevent dust from entering and generally are not harmed by use in a dusty atmosphere. When working in rain or dust the instrument should still be kept covered when it is not actually in use.

If either the objective lens or the eyepiece lens becomes so dirty that vision is impaired it can be cleaned with a camel hair brush or lens paper, but nothing rougher than these.

4-11 DUTIES OF RODMAN

The duties of the rodman appear simple compared to those of the instrument-man. However, the rodman must understand the leveling process and must employ proper procedures if the work is to be completed without mistakes. It should be realized that work of unacceptably low accuracy is most often caused by the poor performance of the rodman, not the instrumentman.

The rodman is responsible for placing the rod at the proper point for all shots, selecting turning points, and holding the rod vertical. He may locate points for shots with a tape and the help of another man by measuring with the level rod laid flat on the ground, or by pacing. He should watch the instrumentman or party chief for signals and comply promptly.

The rodman should stand on the opposite side of the rod facing the instrument and should balance the rod lightly with the fingertips of both hands. In this way, he can see that the rod is plumb while watching the instrumentman for signals, and his fingers cannot block the instrumentman's view of the rod. He can also keep the rod plumb by balancing it so that it doesn't lean against the fingertips of either hand. If a wind is blowing, the rod will be in balance while leaning into the wind. The rodman should learn to compensate for this and keep the rod vertical. Several kinds of devices called *rod levels* are available for indicating when the rod is vertical by the location of a level bubble.

4-12 DUTIES OF NOTEKEEPER

Level surveys are often made by a two-man party. If there are three men in the party, the third one is the notekeeper. He must record the correct elevation for the starting B.M. and describe it completely. He records each rod reading immediately and repeats it as he writes it to verify it with the originator. He must be sure of each station and record it correctly. He computes the elevation as the work progresses and checks the arithmetic at the end of the project and at the end of each day.

4-13 MISTAKES

1. The rod may be read incorrectly. When the next higher foot mark can be seen through the telescope, it is sometimes read accidentally, causing a one foot mistake. To prevent this, the instrumentman should read the foot numbers above and below the cross hair and should also count the hundredth place from the tenths numbers above and below the cross hair so that he doesn't read the wrong tenth.

2. Notes may be entered incorrectly. To prevent this, the notekeeper must understand the leveling process and visualize the operation for which he makes each entry. He should remember that the backsights and foresights are entered on the same line as the station being sighted.

3. The rod must be extended for shots with a large difference in elevation. Unless the numbers on the upper section of the rod are an accurate continuation of the numbers on the lower section, the reading will be incorrect. The rodman should extend the rod fully, hearing or feeling the click as the proper position is reached, and should look at the joint just before each shot to see that the numbers appear to be in correct alignment.

4. By mistake, the rod may be placed on different points for the foresight and backsight of a turning point. To prevent this, the rodman should mark the T.P. with crayon or paint before he uses it the first time and be

careful to use the same spot both times. If all rod shots are taken before the F.S. on the T.P., there will be little delay between F.S. and B.S. and little chance of losing the T.P. location before the B.S. is read.

The nature of these mistakes cannot ordinarily be determined without repeating the level circuit, or at least part of it. The exception is that note-keeping mistakes can sometimes be discovered and corrected in the office.

4–14 ERRORS AND CORRECTIONS

Systematic

1. If the telescope level vial and the line of sight are not perfectly parallel, the line of sight points up or down when the level bubble is centered. The result is an error consistently either plus or minus with magnitude in proportion to the distance between instrument and rod. Therefore, all B.S. and F.S. will be larger or all will be smaller than the correct value. Since a positive B.S. and a negative F.S. are entered in the notes for each instrument location (H.I.) the errors will partially cancel each other and will exactly cancel each other if the distances from rod to instrument and instrument to rod are equal for each instrument setup. Then the elevation of each T.P. or B.M. will have no error from this source.

    It is good practice to equalize the B.S. and F.S. distances from each instrument location by measuring, pacing, or estimating, depending on the accuracy needed. In ordinary work, the distances are paced where convenient and estimated where pacing is inconvenient. See Fig. 4-18.

    When an elevation is to be carried from one B.M. to another, with no intermediate elevations to be determined, it is not necessary that B.S. and F.S. distances be equal for each instrument setup.

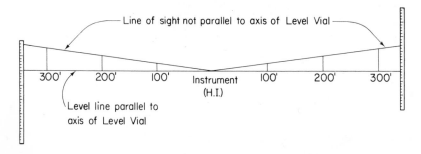

Error increases as distance from instrument increases.
B.S. error equals F.S. error if distances from instrument
are equal and therefore one cancels the other.

Figure 4-18 Error due to line of sight being out of level

Because error is directly proportional to distance, if the total of all B.S. distances in the survey equals the total of all F.S. distances, then total plus error will equal total minus error and the result will be no error from this source.

2. If the rod has an accurately calibrated scale, but the zero mark is not exactly at the bottom of the rod, there will be an error, the same in direction and magnitude, for every reading regardless of distance. This situation occurs if the bottom of the rod is worn excessively or if the scale, which may be printed on a plastic tape and attached to the wood rod, is not attached correctly. This error cancels itself in the same way as the previous error but is unaffected by distances to B.S. and F.S.

3. The instrument sinks downward over a period of time when resting on a surface, such as swampy ground, frozen ground, ice, or bituminous paving, which allows settlement under the weight of the instrument. The F.S. is then always read from a lower point than the B.S. The F.S. is less than it should be, giving a plus error to the new T.P. The total error increases with each setup on a yielding surface.

The effect can be minimized by providing a foundation of flat stones or blocks of wood for the tripod and by taking the F.S. as soon as possible after the B.S. The error can be made compensating by taking the F.S. before the B.S. on alternate instrument setups.

Accidental

1. The accuracy of a rod reading depends on many factors. Among these are the ability of the instrumentman and rodman, distance to rod, clearness of the atmosphere, heat waves rising from the ground, and wind which may shake the instrument. The required accuracy can generally be obtained by shortening the distance between instrument and rod to suit the weather conditions and the capabilities of the party members. Conditions may sometimes be such that leveling work should not be done. A distance of 300 ft is about the longest permissible for level readings. Accuracy may be increased by estimating readings to the third decimal place, even though no vernier is used. The end result will not be accurate to the third decimal place, but accuracy will be improved.

2. If the rod is not held plumb, the reading will be too high. The error from this source is always in the same direction and of unknown size. Since some errors will apply to B.S. ($+$) and some to F.S. ($-$), they tend to cancel one another. The correct reading can be determined by waving the rod toward and away from the instrumentman while he reads it. The reading will be lowest when the rod is plumb.

4–15 LONG SIGHTS

Very long sights are sometimes required because no intermediate points are accessible. This condition could be caused by a river. Three factors cause difficulty when an extremely long sight must be made.

1. It is difficult to read a level rod accurately at distances greater than about 300 ft.

2. A misalignment between the line of sight and the level vial results in a large error, since the error is proportional to the distance. Equalizing B.S. distance with F.S. distance to eliminate this error may not be possible and when it is possible there must be two very long sights with the accompanying loss of accuracy.

3. The line of sight is the level line only at the point where it is perpendicular to a plumb line. It deviates from level because it is theoretically straight while a level line curves to remain perpendicular to plumb lines at all points. The line of sight is actually bent due to refraction and is not truly straight. The relationships of the theoretically straight line of sight, the slightly curved actual line of sight, and the level line following the curve of the earth are shown in Fig. 4-19.

The deviation of the actual line of sight from a truly level line is insignificant in ordinary surveying for any one shot at distances up to 400 ft. If readings are taken to .001 ft the deviation is significant at about 200 ft. However, if B.S. and F.S. can be equalized, the errors caused by this deviation will cancel each other.

The method for accurately determining a difference in elevation between two widely separated points is shown in Fig. 4-20 for two consecutive turning points, T.P. 1 and T.P. 2. The difference is found by reading a B.S. and F.S. between them from each side of the river. The long sights must be of equal length. The error in the long sight causes the F.S. to be too high by an unknown amount from H.I. 1 (a minus error), and the B.S. to be too high by the same amount from H.I. 2 (a plus error). The errors cancel each other if an average is taken and an accurate elevation can be determined for T.P. 2 as shown in the field notes in Fig. 4-21.

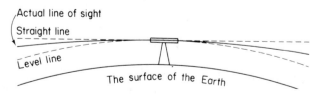

Figure 4-19 Diagram of actual line of sight

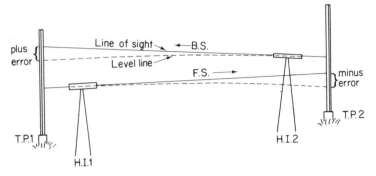

Figure 4-20 Method for accurate leveling over a great distance

Sta.	B.S.(+)	H.I.	F.S.(−)	Elev.	
B.M.1	5.22	342.64		337.42	
T.P. 1	5.72*	344.05	4.31	338.33	
T.P.2			2.10*	341.95	minus error in F.S
T.P. 1	6.30**	344.63			plus error in B.S.
T.P.2			2.62**	342.01	
T.P.2	5.17	347.15		341.98	Average elevation
T.P.3			4.98	342.17	

* sighted from H.I. 1
** sighted from H.I.2

Figure 4-21 Field notes for leveling method of Figure 4-20

This eliminates systematic error due to misalignment in the instrument and curvature of the earth. The short sights generally have no significant error. If they are considered long enough to introduce error, they should be made of equal length and their errors will also cancel each other.

In order to eliminate accidental errors as much as possible on long sights, a target should be used and the average of several readings taken.

PROBLEMS

1/ Prepare acceptable field notes, including an arithmetic check, from the following field data. Can you visualize that both circuits run up hill and back down?

	Sta.	B.S.	F.S.	Known Elevation
a.	B.M. 7	6.42		147.36
	T.P. 1	8.43	1.77	
	T.P. 2	12.49	2.08	
	T.B.M. 7–1	0.27	3.48	
	T.P. 3	2.76	11.86	
	T.P. 4	3.92	7.98	
	B.M. 7		7.10	147.36
b.	B.M. 16	11.75		347.62
	T.P. 1	10.96	1.16	
	T.P. 2	11.43	3.61	
	T.P. 3	5.22	10.84	
	T.B.M. 1	2.17	11.79	
	T.P. 4	1.05	9.91	
	B.M. 17		1.13	351.77

2/ Prepare field notes and plot a profile for the level circuit and rod shots shown here schematically.

a

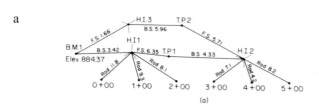

(a)

b.

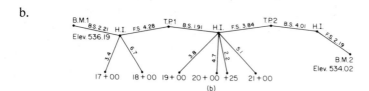

(b)

3/ Finish the following field notes and plot cross sections from them. Often the first one or two digits of elevations can be omitted to save time and space if no confusion will result.

(a)

Sta.	B.S.+	H.I.	F.S.-	Elev.	Left		℄	Right	
B.M. 8	11.19	358.41		347.22					
9+00					3.2/50	1.0/25	1.2	3.4/25	4.5/42
9+50					5.6/50	1.2/25	2.2	3.6/25	5.0/50
10+00					3.6/50	1.4/16	3.0	3.9/25	5.8/50
10+50					4.2/50	2.3/25	3.4	4.4/30	6.0/50
11+00					4.8/50	2.0/25	3.8	4.6/12 2.4/20	4.9/46
T.P.1	9.87		6.71						
11+50					2.2/50	2.4/25	3.0	4.2/25	5.6/50
T.P.2	6.45		10.11						
B.M. 8			10.69						

(b)

Sta.	B.S.+	H.I.	F.S.-	Elev.	50' Left	25'	℄	25'	Right	50'
B.M. 31	3.02	1137.24		1134.22						
0+00					9.9	8.8	7.9	6.3	7.8	6.0
0+50					10.8	9.6	8.8/6.3	7.2	9.4	6.0
1+00					10.6	9.0	8.0/7.2	8.0	8.0/40	6.2
T.P.1	1.08		2.92				20			
1+50					9.9	8.6	6.6/8.0	7.2		5.5
2+00					10.2	8.9	7.8/20	7.8		4.5
2+50					10.3	9.0	9.0	6.4		4.3
T.P.2	2.23		8.91							
T.B.M. 31			7.66							

Elev. T.B.M. 31−1 = 1121.05

4/ The elevation of the bottom of a beam is needed. The H.I. is determined by reading 4.63 on the rod in the normal way with the rod on a B.M. of 137.62 elevation. The rod is then held upside down against the bottom of the beam and 11.37 is read. What is the elevation of the bottom of the beam?

5/ In a mine a B.M. on the ceiling has an elevation of 118.92. A rod is held upside down against the B.M. and a H.I. determined by reading 9.76. A turning point on the floor is used with the rod in normal position and a F.S. of 4.92 and B.S. of 4.76 are read to establish a new H.I. A new B.M. is set on the ceiling and a F.S. of 9.02 is read on it. What is the elevation of the new B.M.?

INSTRUCTIONAL OBJECTIVES OF CHAPTER 5

1/ *Given a transit of a type decided on by the instructor and a point the size of a nail head, the student should be able to set up the transit over the point.*

2/ *Given a transit already set up over a point and two additional points, the student should be able to:*
   a. Turn an angle between the two points to the left or right or in deflection as directed.
   b. Double the angle between the two points and read it on the vernier.

3/ *Given a transit already set up over a point and one additional point, the student should be able to:*
   a. Determine the vertical angle to the point from a horizontal line.
   b. Extend a line by double centering.

4/ *Given a field notebook and horizontal and vertical angle data, the student should be able to enter satisfactory notes, including a sketch.*

5/ *Given a transit, with a compass, already set up over a point and one additional point, the student should be able to determine the magnetic bearing to the other point.*

chapter five

Measuring Angles

Distance alone is not sufficient to establish relationships between points. Direction is also needed. A review of Chap.1 shows that this is true whether relationship is shown by direction and distance, by coordinates, or by stationing and offset. Once a reference direction, such as north, is established, other directions are determined by angles from the reference direction — by bearings or azimuths, for example. Angular measuring is covered in this chapter.

5–1 KINDS OF ANGLES

An *angle* is formed by two lines drawn from one common point called the vertex. The size or measurement of the angle is the amount of divergence between the two lines. It is helpful to think of the angle as being formed by a stationary line and a revolving line which starts at the stationary line and swings about the vertex a certain distance in either direction to define the angle.

Angles used in surveying are either vertical or horizontal; that is, the revolving line either rotates in a vertical plane or it rotates in a horizontal plane. For horizontal angles, the stationary line is the *backsight* and the revolving line is the *foresight*.

Horizontal angles are turned to the right or left starting at the backsight or to the right or left looking forward 180° from the backsight. The second type is called a *deflection angle*. Figure 5-1 shows the four ways in which a horizontal angle may be turned.

The same angle is shown at *A* and *B*. The only difference is that it is turned in opposite directions. Any particular angle can be turned by any of the four methods. Often one way is most convenient. For example, it is convenient to turn a small deflection angle rather than a large angle right or left. From Fig. 5-1 it can be seen that a deflection angle is equal to 180° minus what the angle would be if turned the closest way.

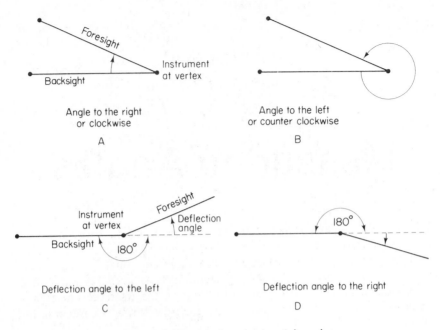

Figure 5-1 Ways to turn horizontal angles

Instead of "right" or "left", the terms "clockwise" and "counterclockwise" are sometimes used. In the field, it is easier to visualize right and left while turning angles than it is to visualize clockwise and counterclockwise motion.

Vertical angles are measured up or down from a horizontal line. If the vertical angle is turned upward, it is a *plus angle*, and if downward, it is a *minus angle*. An angle measured downward from a vertical line is called a *zenith angle*. These angles are measured from the major surveying reference directions (horizontal or vertical) and not between two points as horizontal angles are measured. See Fig. 5-2 for illustrations.

5-2 THE ENGINEER'S TRANSIT

Horizontal and vertical angles are measured with a transit. The transit is designed so that horizontal and vertical angles have their vertex at a common center. This *instrument center* is the intersection of three lines; one vertical, one horizontal, and one variable. The vertical line is the centerline of two vertical concentric, tapered cylinders called *spindles*, on which all the measuring devices of the transit are mounted. The horizontal line is the centerline of the *horizontal axle* and the variable line is the line of sight through the telescope. The instrument center is the vertex for any angle turned with the transit.

Geometric Relationships

The vertical line can be moved, while remaining vertical, so that it is coincident with a vertical line through a point to be used as the vertex of a horizontal angle. The horizontal line can be rotated in a complete circle about the vertical line while remaining horizontal. Thus, an angle turned in the plane of rotation of the horizontal line is a horizontal angle. The variable line of sight can be rotated in a vertical plane, but always passes through the instrument center and always is perpendicular to the horizontal line. The line of sight can thus turn a vertical angle or a horizontal angle. See Fig. 5-3 for illustration.

The line of sight can be rotated to point in any direction, but its rotation

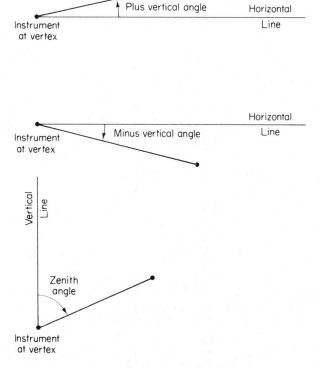

Figure 5-2 Vertical angles

always consists of horizontal and vertical components. Therefore, any change in direction consists of a horizontal angle only, a vertical angle only, or a horizontal angle plus a vertical angle.

The transit shown in Fig. 5-4 is of the kind known as *American type transits*. There are other transits differing greatly in details and appearance, but the basic principles of operation and methods of use are similar. The American type is discussed in this chapter.

The transit telescope is the same as the telescope of the level instrument described in Chap. 4. A level vial is attached parallel to the telescope, as on the level instrument, to indicate whether or not the line of sight is horizontal. This is the *telescope level*.

The transit telescope is mounted on trunnions, much like an old fashioned cannon, and is rotated on the trunnions, in a vertical plane. The trunnions, called the horizontal axle in this book, are supported by two frames called *standards*, one at each end of the axle.

The purpose of the standards is to hold the horizontal axle level so that a

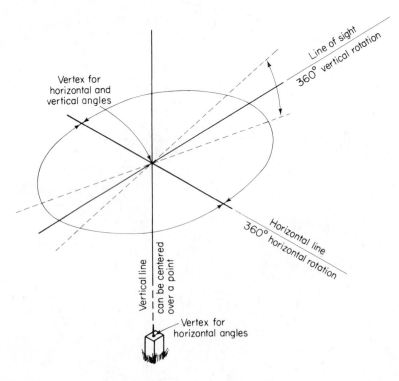

Figure 5-3 Basic relationships of the transit

Figure 5-4 Transit

vertical angle can be turned in a vertical plane and so that a horizontal angle can be turned accurately, regardless of a difference in elevation between backsight and foresight.

Measurement

A vertical circle calibrated in degrees and minutes is attached to the telescope and rotates with it. Note in Fig. 5-4 how the telescope and vertical circle rotate about the horizontal axle. The vertical angle up or down is indicated by the rotation of the vertical circle past a stationary index mark. The index is supplemented by a vernier on each side of it and the index and verniers together are called the *vertical vernier*. Any vertical angle turned on the instrument has its vertex at the instrument center.

Vertical motion is stopped approximately at the proper position with the *vertical motion clamp* and the cross hairs are trained exactly on the object with the *vertical tangent screw*.

The transit may be used for leveling since it has a level vial parallel to the

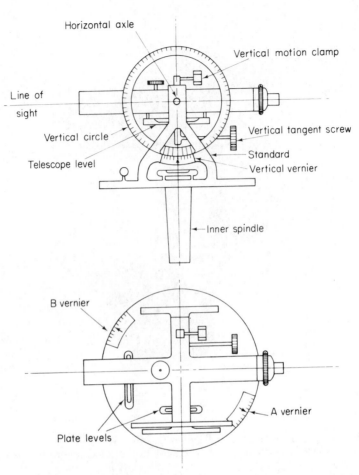

Figure 5-5 Transit upper plate

line of sight. It is more cumbersome to use than an engineer's level and is generally not as accurate. See Fig. 5-5 for the relationship of the devices used in turning vertical angles and leveling.

The telescope along with the base on which it is mounted is called the *upper plate* or *alidade*. This entire assembly rotates horizontally as a unit on the *inner spindle*. The assembly includes two additional level vials called *plate levels*, which indicate when the plate is level. One is parallel to the telescope and one is perpendicular to it. Both are perpendicular to the axis of the spindle. Therefore, the axis of the spindle is made vertical by leveling the upper plate.

Also included are two index marks 180° apart which indicate how far the upper plate is turned. Each mark has a vernier on either side of it for a more precise indication. Each mark including its verniers is called simply a *vernier*. One vernier is located below the eyepiece where it is easily used by the instrumentman and is called the *A vernier*. The opposite vernier is called the *B vernier*. The entire upper plate rotates within a calibrated horizontal circle so that the angle turned can be read with a vernier on the circle. See Fig. 5-5 for details of the upper plate.

The rotary motion of the upper plate is stopped at approximately the proper position with a clamp and the cross hairs are trained exactly on the object with a tangent screw. These are called the *upper motion clamp* and the *upper tangent screw*. The upper plate is often called the *upper motion*.

Below the upper plate is a horizontal circular plate divided around its circumference into 360° and subdivided into smaller parts, generally half degrees, one-third degrees, or quarter degrees. This plate, called the *lower plate*, can remain stationary or rotate, independently of the upper plate. Its level position is controlled by the upper plate because it is attached to a vertical *outer spindle* which is hollow and encloses the inner spindle of the upper plate. Both spindles are tapered and have a common axis. As they wear with use, they settle slightly lower but because of the tapered bearing surfaces neither one can become loose. They therefore continue to rotate truly about their common center. The rotary motion of the lower plate is stopped with a clamp and moved to exact position with a tangent screw. These are called the *lower motion clamp* and the *lower tangent screw*. The lower plate is often called the *lower motion*. See Fig. 5-6 for details of the lower plate.

With the lower plate clamped, the upper plate can be rotated and the *A* vernier made to mark any desired angle. Generally, the *A* vernier is set approximately on zero, clamped and then set precisely on zero with the upper tangent screw. The lower plate is then loosened and turned so that the line of sight is on the stationary line of the angle to be measured. It is clamped with the lower clamp and aimed precisely on line with the lower tangent screw. While the lower plate is turned the upper plate remains firmly clamped with the vernier marking zero. Thus, the vernier reads zero at the stationary side of the angle.

Next, the upper plate is loosened and the telescope (with the entire upper plate) is rotated until the line of sight is on the point at the other side of the angle. Here the upper plate is clamped and then adjusted with the upper tangent screw. The upper plate has now turned from one side of the angle to the other and the *A* vernier has moved from zero to the angle turned, which is read and recorded.

Transit Orientation

Some device is needed to align the upper and lower plates in a horizontal plane or, put in another way, to position the concentric spindles in a vertical

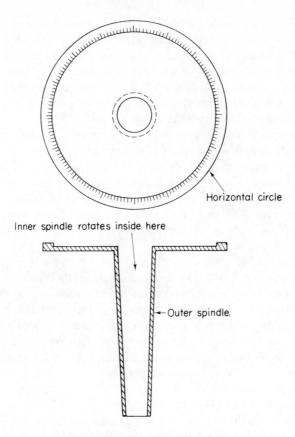

Figure 5-6 Transit lower plate

line. The device which serves this purpose is called the *leveling head.* It contains a vertical *socket* in which the outer spindle fits. The socket is attached through a *half ball joint* to the *shifting plate* which is free to move horizontally within the *footplate* which is fixed in position. The socket and thus the entire upper and lower plate assembly can be rotated in any direction about the half ball joint. Thus, these plates can be made precisely level even though the footplate is not quite level. The leveling head is mounted on a three legged stand called a *tripod.*

Leveling is accomplished by means of four vertical screws called *leveling screws* arranged 90° apart on a circle around the spindle socket. Sometimes there are three leveling screws 120° apart. The screws, encased in *shoes,* press against the foot plate. By lengthening one of a pair of opposite screws and shortening the other, the instrument can be rotated about the ball joint until it is level, at which position the axis of the spindles will be vertical.

Once the spindle axis is vertical, the upper plate and lower plate will remain level when they are rotated on their spindles.

At the bottom of the leveling head, on the spindle axis is a hook from which a plumb bob is hung. When the transit is level its centerline is a continuation of the vertical line of the plumb bob string, which means the instrument center is in the vertical line through the plumb bob point.

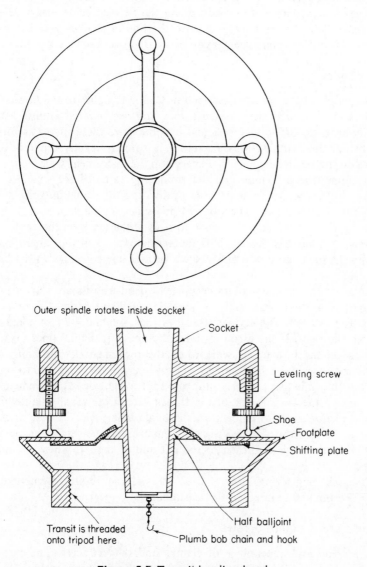

Figure 5-7 Transit leveling head

It is necessary for the instrument to be level and centered vertically over a point. This is accomplished by proper manipulation of the shifting plate and the leveling screws. When the instrument is thus located, the point below the instrument is the vertex of any horizontal angle turned by the instrument. See Fig. 5-7 for details of the leveling head and plumb bob attachment.

Some instruments are equipped with an optical centering device in which the line of sight passes downward along the vertical centerline of the two spindles. When the instrument is level, the line of sight is vertical, and by means of it the instrument center can be located over the vertex point.

The Vernier

The principle of the vernier described in Chap. 4 applies to the three transit verniers even though they measure min and sec of arc. Transit verniers usually have 15, 20, or 30 spaces and in some cases these spaces are divided into two or three subdivisions. Therefore, it is not so readily apparent that N spaces on the vernier equal $N - 1$ spaces on the instrument scale.

To apply the principle, first determine the value of the smallest space on the circle. The vernier is capable of dividing this value into the number of spaces on the vernier. The value of one space on the vernier is called the *least count* of the vernier. The angle to read is the mark on the circle which the vernier index has passed, plus the vernier spaces in the same direction beyond the index up to a point where a vernier line coincides with a line on the scale.

Some of the verniers commonly provided on transits are shown in Fig. 5-8. Note that these are double verniers, designed so that angles can be read to the right or left. The vernier shown in Figs. 4-6 and 4-7 is marked to be read to the right. If the arrow is moved to the left, the 0.9 lines up with a division on the instrument scale when the movement is one tenth of an instrument division. Thus, the vernier divisions are the same size to right or left, but they must be properly numbered for a right or left movement. The numbers on the correct side of the transit vernier are usually slanted in the same direction as the numbers on the angle being read in that direction. Look at the transit in Fig. 5-3 to help visualize that the vernier moves to the right when the angle is turned to the left and to the left when the angle is turned to the right.

A small magnifying glass is used to read the vernier. Sometimes the angle is estimated to one half the least count of the vernier.

Clamps and Tangent Screws

The position and appearance of clamps and tangent screws indicate their functions. This is deliberate, since the instrumentman cannot look at them

GRADUATED 30 MINUTES READING TO ONE MINUTE
DOUBLE DIRECT VERNIER

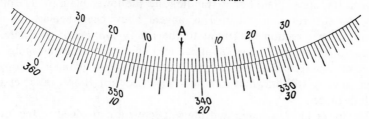

GRADUATED 20 MINUTES READING TO 30 SECONDS
DOUBLE DIRECT VERNIER

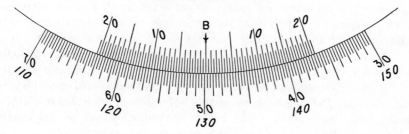

GRADUATED TO 15 MINUTES READING TO 20 SECONDS
DOUBLE DIRECT VERNIER

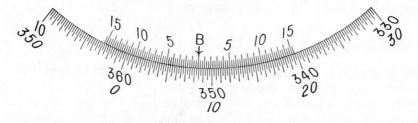

Figure 5-8 Three verniers

while using them. The clamp and tangent screw for the lower plate are below those for the upper plate and those for the vertical motion are near the horizontal axle. The clamp screws turn inward toward the center of the part they stop and the tangent screws turn in a direction tangent to the motion they control. Clamps are sometimes equipped with hexagonal heads and tangent screws with round ones, denoting smoother or finer adjustment.

The upper motion clamp and tangent screw are attached to the upper plate and rotate with it. This clamp is a screw which turns inward to tighten a collar around the outer spindle of the lower plate, thus stopping motion between the upper plate (inner spindle) and the lower plate (outer spindle). They can still rotate together. The tangent screw bears against the clamp housing in a direction tangential to the rotary motion of the plates and causes rotary motion between upper and lower plates by pushing when turned clockwise, and allows motion forced by a spring acting in the opposite direction when withdrawn by a counterclockwise turn. It operates over a very small distance.

The lower motion clamp and tangent screw are attached to the leveling head and do not rotate. This clamp also tightens a collar around the outer spindle and thus stops the motion between the lower plate (outer spindle) and leveling head. The upper plate (inner spindle) can still rotate within the outer spindle unless the upper motion is tightened. The lower tangent screw operates the same way as the upper one, but it is housed separately from the clamp and bears against an extension of the clamp housing.

The vertical motion clamp and vertical tangent screw operate the same way, but connect the axle to a standard to stop and adjust the axle motion.

The clamps should not be forced. They are designed to hold fast with very little pressure. The tangent screws should not be forced when they reach their limits. Since the tangent screws push when turned clockwise and merely release and allow a spring to push when turned counterclockwise, it is possible for some looseness to occur when the screw is released slightly against a weakened spring. A good habit to develop is that of finishing each fine adjustment with a clockwise turn. If you turn past the mark, return and come up to it again with a clockwise turn.

The Leveling Head and Plumb Bob

The leveling head is designed to permit the instrument to be leveled and centered on a vertical line over a point.

The transit is leveled with the upper plate aligned so that each of the two plate levels is parallel with a pair of leveling screws. The two screws 180° apart are considered as a pair since they operate together to rotate the entire instrument in an arc about the center of the half ball joint. The screws are always operated in pairs and always turned in opposite directions. They rotate the transit in a plane that passes through both screws and through the axis of the spindles so that a plate level parallel to the two screws indicates only the rotation caused by those two screws.

They indicate it perfectly only if the plane of rotation is vertical. Since this plane is vertical only when the other plate level is leveled, a small component of the rotational movement will usually exist perpendicular to the major movement through the two screws being used, and will cause the other plate level bubble to move also.

The bubble in the parallel level is approximately centered with the two screws and they are left slightly loose. Before these can be operated, the other pair of screws usually must be loosened. After one bubble is nearly centered, the other bubble is nearly centered with the opposite pair of screws. This process is continued, each time leveling more accurately and each time leaving the screws a little tighter until the instrument is leveled.

An experienced instrumentman adjusts each bubble two or three times in making a setup. A handy rule to remember when leveling the transit is that the bubble moves in the direction the left thumb moves when turning the screws.

The rotational movements may cause the plumb bob to move off the point and the leveling operation must be interrupted to reposition the transit over the point by moving the shifting plate without moving the footplate or tripod. The shoes on the leveling screws readily slide across the footplate when they are slightly loose, thus allowing the transit to move in any direction.

An experienced instrumentman sets up the instrument with one or two such movements. The student can expect to make half a dozen such movements on his first few attempts. The leveling and shifting must be coordinated so that the transit is both level and centered at the end of the operation.

Figure 5-9 shows the relationship between the half ball joint on which the upper and lower plates rotate and the plumb bob chain attachment. In the figure the centerline of the plumb bob chain and string always passes through the center of the half ball because this is also the center of the *half ring* the chain hangs on; and it is always vertical because it is directed by gravity. The transit vertical centerline always passes through the center of the half ball and is vertical only when the plates are leveled. Therefore, a continuous vertical line is formed from the instrument center to the tip of the plumb bob when the transit is level.

This construction is ideal and not all transits are constructed this way. The center of plumb bob rotation may be vertically above or below the half ball center a slight amount, but it cannot be to one side. If the centers are displaced vertically, any rotation of the half ball (by turning leveling screws) causes horizontal movement of the plumb bob because the half ring center rotates about the same center with the half ball. Setting up the instrument is more difficult in this case because the shifting head must be moved more to compensate for horizontal movement caused by leveling. If the centers are displaced horizontally (through being damaged, since they are not manufactured this way), the instrument center cannot be aligned vertically over the plumb bob.

When an optical plumb line is used, the sight line is fixed as an extension of the vertical centerline and therefore it moves more during leveling than a plumb bob hanging on a vertical string does. It is important that the instru-

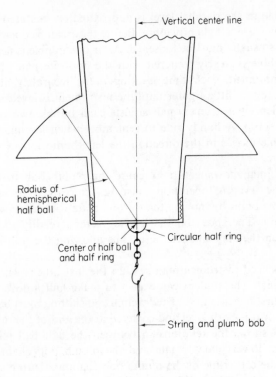

Figure 5-9 Detail of half ball and plumb bob attachment

ment be nearly level the first time it is centered over a point. A *shifting head tripod* is available with a shifting plate in the head of the tripod to allow greater movement in centering over a point.

Optical centering is usually faster than centering with a plumb bob because fastening the plumb bob and stopping its swinging take time. The optical method is more accurate, especially in wind. However, with the optical plumb line the beginner has difficulty getting the point within the field of vision and often a plumb bob is used for approximate centering and the optical line for final centering.

Tripod

The tripod serves as a base to prevent movement of the instrument after it is set up, and to facilitate making a setup. The tripod is equipped with pointed *shoes* which are forced into the ground by pressing with the foot. They should be pressed in deeply enough so the tripod will not settle while standing. Usually a *spur* is provided on each shoe to facilitate pushing the point in.

On hard surfaces the shoes must rest on the surface. In either case, the legs should be spread wide enough to provide a stable platform for the instrument. If a shoe becomes loose, it must be tightened before the tripod can be used with accuracy.

The tripod legs are hinged at the top. If the hinges are loose, the instrument will move while being used. However, they must be loose enough to adjust readily while the shoes are being set into the ground. If they are bolted too tight, they may bind instead of adjusting when the tripod is set up and later spring free while in use, thereby moving the instrument. Each hinge should be snug enough so that the leg will almost stand out horizontally with no support. Many tripods have legs which are adjustable in length. These are easier to set up than tripods with fixed-length legs. An experienced instrumentman can very nearly center and level an instrument with tripod leg adjustments. This leaves little adjusting with the leveling screws and the shifting plate.

Compass

A transit is usually equipped with a compass which is used to establish *magnetic north* as a reference direction. See Chap. 1 and Chap. 6 for discussions of directions referred to north.

A compass consists of a magnetized steel needle mounted in such a way that it is free to align itself with the earth's magnetic field. When so aligned, it is said to point toward magnetic north. The magnetic north pole is located in the Hudson Bay area of Canada roughly 1000 miles from the true north pole.

However, the compass needle does not necessarily point directly to the magnetic north pole, but usually approximately toward it. The needle's direction is different at different places on the earth and is constantly changing slowly at any one location.

The earth's magnetic field pulls the compass needle downward as well as horizontally. The downward direction of the needle is called *dip*. It is balanced by a weight (coil of wire) on the south end of the needle. The weight may sometimes have to be adjusted to balance the needle and allow free movement.

The needle must move freely to give accurate readings. It is fitted with a cup shaped jewel bearing which rests on a finely pointed steel pivot. It is equipped with a lever to lift the bearing off the pivot and a screw to hold it in place against the glass cover of the compass. The bearing should rest on the pivot only when being used in order to avoid wear or damage to the jewel bearing.

The difference between compass, or magnetic, north and true north is called *declination*. Declination is said to be east or west according to whether the compass points east or west of true north.

Charts showing the declinations throughout the United States and the predicted variations in the declinations are prepared by the National Geodetic Survey. True north can be determined by the use of one of these charts called *isogonic charts* in conjunction with the observed magnetic north as demonstrated in Fig. 5-10.

True north can be determined more accurately by observation of the sun or north star using the transit. True north and magnetic north may be established with the transit from the same point and the observed declination used to determine true direction of other lines in the area from their magnetic direction. See Fig. 5-10 for illustration.

The bearing system of designating directions is easy to use with a compass. The north and south lines are provided by the compass and the direction of any point can be read as a bearing. Bearings are discussed in Chaps. 1 and 6. Compasses are usually calibrated from 0° to 90° to east and west of the north arrow and to east and west of the south arrow. See Fig. 5-11 for a typical compass face.

The compass is used in the following way. With the instrument set up over a point, the compass needle is released and the telescope is aimed at a point. A mark on the edge of the compass circle, at the north point, is under the line of sight and therefore points at whatever object the cross hairs are fixed on.

Note that east and west are reversed on the compass. This is so that the

Prob. 1   Given : Magnetic bearing of line 1 – 2 38° E
                     Declination   7° East

           Find : True bearing of line 1 – 2

Prob. 2   Given: Magnetic North 38° left of line 1 – 2
                     True North   45° left of line 1 – 2

           Find : Declination

                     See diagram for solutions

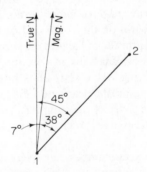

Figure 5-10 Relationships, true and magnetic bearings

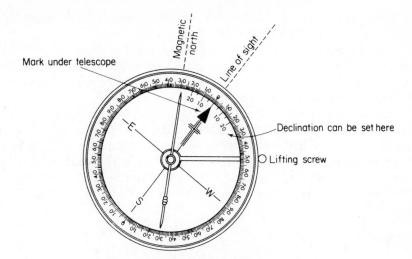

Figure 5-11 Compass face

bearing direction can be read at the north or south needle. In Fig. 5-11 the needle points to magnetic north (remember the needle doesn't move, the compass circle moves with the telescope) and the zero is toward the point sighted. The compass needle indicates the magnetic bearing to the point sighted.

The magnetic declination can be set into the compass with a set screw so that the compass needle reads the true bearing. This is done by setting zero on the compass circle to the left of the mark for west declination and to the right of the mark for east declination. The setting is made before the needle is released. This operation can be visualized with the help of Fig. 5-11.

The compass needle must settle down before a bearing can be read. Even then the accuracy is probably no better than one degree although the compass is commonly read to the nearest quarter of a degree. Iron, steel or electric current nearby cause a variation in the expected declination. Cars passing, power lines overhead, or a steel tape or pocket knife near the instrument can be the source of what is called *local attraction* which deflects the needle from magnetic north.

5–3 PURPOSE OF TURNING AN ANGLE

The operation of turning an angle is performed either to *measure an angle* or to *lay off an angle*.

To determine the location of an existing point, an angle must be measured.

A backsight is taken on a known line, an angle is turned to the new point, and the angle is read on the vernier.

To set a new point, an angle must be laid off. The angle is known first and the point is established at that angle from a given line. A backsight is taken on the known line, the angle is set on the vernier, and the new point is placed at that angle from the B.S.

The instrumentman must *take line* on a known point to measure an angle or lay one off. If he cannot see the point, another man *gives line* by holding an object in a vertical line over the point for the instrumentman to sight. If an angle is being measured, the instrumentman takes line again on another known point to complete the angle. If a point is being set, the instrumentman gives line in a known direction to another man who takes line in order to set the point.

5–4 STEP BY STEP OPERATION

The processes of measuring and laying off angles are covered here. These are the most common operations performed with the transit. They consist of setting up the transit over a point, backsighting a point, and turning an angle to a foresight on another point. A point may be marked by a pipe or steel reinforcing rod stuck in the ground, a tack in a wooden stake, an X chiselled in a concrete walk or pavement, or in many other ways.

Before starting a setup, the leveling screws should be adjusted to the same length so that the upper and lower plates are parallel to the footplate, and the shifting plate should be centered in the footplate. The tripod legs should be adjusted to equal length. The plumb bob should be attached. In this way, each setup is begun with standard conditions.

1. Set the legs firmly in place with the footplate level by eye and the plumb bob over the point as nearly as your skill permits. If the instrument is being set up on sloping ground, plant two legs the same distance downhill from the point and the same distance outward from the point. Raise the third leg and pass it uphill directly over the point so that the plumb bob follows it and swings up to the point. Plant the third leg in the position where it stops the plumb bob over the point. Adjust the legs as desired to keep the footplate level and bring the plumb bob more accurately over the point. The eyepiece should be at such height that it can be used comfortably. Always use the sunshade. Attach and remove it with a clockwise motion to avoid loosening the objective.

2. With leveling screws and shifting plate bring the instrument level and over the point.

3. Clamp lower plate.
    Set vernier to zero with upper motion clamp and tangent screw.
    Release lower motion clamp.
    Turn to B.S. and focus telescope on it.
    Set cross hairs on B.S. with lower motion clamp and tangent screw.

The transit now reads zero at the stationary line of the angle (B.S). It is ready to measure or lay off an angle. Measuring an angle to right or left involves these additional steps.

4. Release upper motion clamp.
    Turn to F.S. and focus telescope on it.
    Set cross hairs on F.S. with upper motion clamp and tangent screw.
    Instrument now reads the angle turned.

5. Read the vernier and record the angle.

6. Center the shifting plate and adjust the leveling screws so the same length of each screw shows. Turn the telescope up and clamp it lightly. This makes the telescope less likely to be hooked on something while being carried. Pick up the transit and carry it to the next point.

Laying off an angle to right or left involves these additional steps after step 3.

4. Release upper motion clamp.
    Turn in appropriate direction until you read the angle with the vernier.
    Set this angle with upper motion clamp and tangent screw.

5. The telescope cross hairs now point to the opposite side of the angle which has been laid off.

A point, such as a nail, set on the new line is in the correct direction.

When the point is set, the transit should be adjusted as in the previous step 6 before moving it.

A deflection angle is measured or laid off by the process of *plunging the telescope* and then turning the angle. Plunging consists of turning the telescope about the horizontal axle from the normal or direct position to the inverted or reversed position so that it is still aligned on the same line, but with the ends reversed. It is thus pointed forward 180° horizontally from the B.S. The upper and lower plates remain clamped during the plunging operation. The upper plate is then released and the deflection angle turned.

Once the transit is set up, it should not be touched any more than absolutely necessary to operate it. When reading the vernier with a magnifying glass, brace the hand by placing the little finger against the transit.

If the instrument or a tripod leg is brushed even by clothing such as a hat brim or shirt tail, the instrument must be releveled and resighted. Do not walk near the instrument any more than necessary, especially on soft ground. Accomplish the work as rapidly as can be done with the required accuracy because the tripod feet often settle unevenly while the instrument is standing.

5-5 SIGHTING POINTS

The instrumentman should sight the actual point whenever he can, but often he is unable to see the point and must be given a vertical line directly above it to sight. A pencil may be held vertically on the point. The instrumentman should sight as close to the bottom of the pencil as he can to eliminate error due to the pencil being out of plumb. A plumb bob point may be held on the point or a plumb bob suspended by a string over the point. The string should be kept as short as possible for greater accuracy.

If swinging of the plumb bob cannot be prevented, every effort should be made to equalize the swinging to both sides of the point and the instrumentman should read the average. The man holding the plumb bob: should position himself so that he is comfortable; should be able to see the point of the plumb bob; should steady his hands on a firm support (using both hands) whenever possible; and should call "good" or "mark" when the plumb bob crosses the point if the swinging cannot be stopped.

A range pole may be held on the point and balanced in a vertical position in the same way a level rod is balanced. On long sights a range pole may be needed if a string cannot be seen. No accuracy is lost on long sights by the thickness of the pole. Some transits have two parallel vertical cross hairs which are positioned one on each edge of the range pole for greater accuracy.

When a point that can't be seen is going to be needed again, a semi-permanent mark may be established above the point or on line with it. Examples are a range pole left stuck into the ground on line directly behind a point; a nail projecting next to a flat tack and bent so that the head is directly over the tack; and a plumb bob or metal rod suspended over the point from a tripod.

5-6 CARE OF TRANSITS

Transits should be cared for much as engineer's levels, whose care is discussed in Chap. 4. Transits should be lifted by the standards from the carrying case to the tripod. Generally, carrying cases are designed to hold the instrument firmly in one position so that it need not be clamped. Clamping any part of the instrument puts a strain on the instrument if it then has to be forced to fit the case. The dustcap should be put on the objective before the transit is stored in the case.

All motions should be clamped lightly before picking the instrument up on the tripod. Thus, there will be no loose motion and yet the clamp will give if the instrument hits an object. Do not carry the instrument while crossing a fence or similar obstruction. When the instrument is set down the legs should be well spread so that it is stable even if it is to be left only momentarily. Do not leave the instrument set up with no one watching it. Graduated circles and verniers should not be touched with fingers.

5-7 COMMON MISTAKES

The mistakes usually made are:

1. Confusing clamps or tangent screws and turning the wrong one.
2. Reading the horizontal circle in the wrong direction.
3. Reading the wrong side of the vernier.
4. Forgetting part of the angle from the circle while reading the vernier. For example, the 20″ vernier of Fig. 5-8 could mistakenly be read 351°06′00″ instead of 351°36′00″ if the instrumentman is not careful.

After practice is acquired in reading horizontal angles it may be doubly difficult to read a vertical angle correctly. The vertical vernier is outside the vertical circle while the A and B verniers are inside the horizontal circle. This reverses the appearance and causes confusion if the instrumentman does not think about what he is doing. In addition, the same mistakes which can be made in setting and reading horizontal angles must also be guarded against in setting and reading vertical angles.

The instrumentman must visualize fully what he is doing and constantly check his work. The ability to visualize in space what he is doing with the instrument comes only with practice.

5-8 SOURCES OF ERROR AND COMPENSATION

All the possible sources of error, instrumental, human, and natural, should be understood. Those errors which are carried from one point to another as small offsets with no increase in size from one point to another are not as dangerous as angular misalignments which cause small errors at short distances and large errors at greater distances. The difference should be understood so that precautions which are justified by the size of the potential error can be taken. See Fig. 5-12 for illustration.

Angles turned with longer sights will be more accurate than those with shorter sights. This applies until extreme range reduces visibility because of

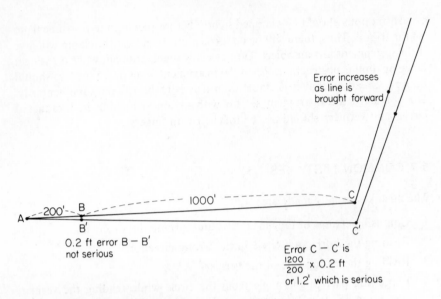

Figure 5-12 Demonstration of seriousness of small angular error

limitations of the telescope or the instrumentman's eyes. At longer distances the object appears smaller compared to the thickness of the vertical cross hair and therefore the hair is more accurately centered. In addition, the same linear inaccuracy (caused, for example, by swinging of the plumb bob being sighted) results in greater angular error at short distances, as illustrated in Fig. 5-13.

For the same reason, when an angle is being laid off, it is important to take a long backsight. If there is a choice, a long B.S. and short F.S. are preferable to a short B.S. and long F.S. Figure 5-14 illustrates why.

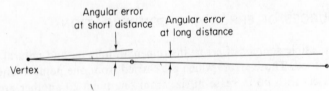

Sighting errors of equal size result in a smaller angular error at the longer distance.

The error in measuring an angle is equal to the algebraic sum of the errors at both sides of the angle.

Figure 5-13 Long sights improve accuracy in measuring an angle

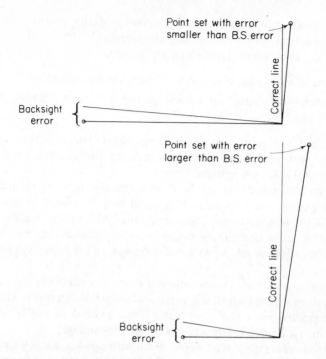

Size of error in laying off an angle is illustrated. It is assumed there is an error in the B.S. and no error in turning the angle. With equal B.S. errors, the angular error is smaller with a long B.S. The angular error of the B.S. is carried forward. The longer the F.S. is the farther the new point is from the correct line.

Figure 5-14 A long backsight improves accuracy in laying off an angle

Instrumental Errors

The transit is the most complex instrument covered in this book. Its operation depends on precise relationships among all its parts. It is, therefore, manufactured with great precision.

The design and use of the transit require the following relationships.

1. The telescope centerline must be perpendicular to the horizontal axle.
2. The horizontal axle must be perpendicular to the vertical centerline of the spindles.
3. The centerlines of all three must pass through a common point within the telescope (the instrument center).
4. The upper and lower plates must be perpendicular to the spindle axis.

These relationships assure that the parts of the transit constitute a vertical-horizontal framework among themselves. If the transit is to be of practical use, two other relationships are needed.

1. The line of sight must coincide with the telescope centerline.

2. The plumb bob string or optical plumb line must coincide with the spindle axis.

These last two must also be precisely aligned because they bring the transit, the instrumentman, and the area being surveyed into one vertical and horizontal reference system.

Adjustable connections are built into transits because manufacturing cannot be perfect and because misalignment may be caused by handling or transporting a transit. If the parts were attached together rigidly with no allowances for adjustment there would be no way to eliminate built-in errors and a factory repair would be required to realign a transit that was jarred into misalignment.

Transits as now built can be adjusted to greater precision than could be built into them without adjustable parts; and some misalignments which occur can be corrected by a skilled instrumentman instead of requiring factory repairs which are more costly and more time consuming.

Adjustments are made with screws fitted with capstan heads which require special small steel pins to turn them. They are located at strategic points for positioning one part with respect to another to achieve the relationships described in this section. Not all movable parts are provided with adjustments.

1. The reticle holding the cross hairs is equipped with adjustment screws so the cross hairs can be centered at the centerline of the telescope, thus assuring that the line of sight passes through the instrument center. The vertical hair can be made perpendicular to the horizontal axle with these screws.

2. The telescope can be rotated about the horizontal axle and thus it is perpendicular to the vertical centerline of the spindles at only one position. That position must be where the vernier marks zero. The vertical vernier is equipped with an adjustment screw to position it.

3. There is no adjustment to align the telescope with the horizontal axle. Construction is such that misalignment can be caused only by a severe blow, and when this happens factory repair is required.

4. The horizontal axle is adjusted perpendicular to the vertical centerline of the spindles by an adjustment screw in one of the standards to raise or lower one end of the axle until it is properly aligned.

5. There is no screw to adjust the plates relative to the spindles. Misalignment can be caused only by a severe blow and factory repairs are then required.

6. All level vials are equipped with adjustment screws to align them parallel to the appropriate part of the transit — the plate levels to the upper and lower plates and the telescope level to the telescope centerline.

The entire transit is oriented for use by leveling the plate levels. If all parts of the transit are in adjustment, the plates are then horizontal, the spindle axis is vertical, the horizontal axle is horizontal, and the telescope is horizontal with the telescope level bubble centered and the vertical vernier marking zero. The instrument is then in agreement with the basic surveying references — vertical and horizontal directions.

Transit adjustments should be made in certain ways and in a particular sequence so that an adjustment does not disturb any previous adjustment. Procedures are explained in detail in more advanced surveying books.

Just as instruments cannot be manufactured perfectly, neither can they be adjusted perfectly. The adjustments provide sufficient accuracy for almost all surveying. For higher order work, special methods are used which can completely eliminate errors due to manufacturing imperfections or imperfect adjustments. Some of these methods will even compensate for the instrument being out of adjustment and will produce results free from instrumental error. Ways in which a transit may be out of adjustment are discussed here with surveying methods of eliminating the resulting errors.

Note that very little can be done to obtain accurate vertical angles if the instrument is out of adjustment; but, in nearly all situations, accurate horizontal angles can be obtained by turning the angle twice, once with the scope direct and once with the scope reversed. The error is in the opposite direction when the scope is reversed and therefore the error is eliminated by averaging the two angles. This operation is called "doubling an angle" and it is described in more detail in this chapter under the section entitled "Important Operations."

If the vertical vernier does not mark zero when the telescope line of sight is horizontal the vernier can be adjusted to read zero. Vertical angle accuracy does not depend on vernier alignment, however, and angles can be turned accurately with the vernier misaligned. They can be read accurately if the vernier is read when the line of sight is level and after the angle is turned. The vertical angle turned is the difference between the readings, taking into account the direction (plus or minus) of each reading.

The line of sight may not be perpendicular to the horizontal axle either because the telescope has been knocked out of alignment by a blow or because the cross hairs are not correctly aligned. The first case requires factory repair and the second requires that the cross hairs be adjusted to the centerline of the telescope.

The transit can be used while the line of sight is out of alignment. If the line of sight still passes through the instrument center, the misalignment causes error only when extending a straight line by plunging the scope. If the line of sight passes to left or right of the instrument center, which is likely, an error is introduced into horizontal angles also. Error can be eliminated in either case by doubling the operation. Doubling an angle and extending a straight line by double centering are both discussed in this chapter.

There will be no error from this source in turning vertical angles unless the line of sight passes above or below the instrument center. However, this is also likely.

Doubling the vertical angle or, when feasible, taking the average of a plus vertical angle between two points from one of the points and a minus vertical angle from the other point without reversing the scope improves accuracy, but error is not eliminated.

The horizontal axle may not be level when the plate levels are. This can be caused by one of several misalignments. If the horizontal axle is not perpendicular to the standards, the axle can be adjusted. If the plate levels are not parallel to the plates, the level vials can be adjusted. If the standards are not perpendicular to the plates, the upper plate is not perpendicular to the spindles, the inner spindle does not fit accurately within the outer spindle, or the outer spindle does not fit accurately within its socket, factory repair is necessary.

When the horizontal axle is out of level, error is introduced into all operations performed with the transit. See Figs. 5-15 and 5-16 for illustration. Error in turning horizontal angles or extending a straight line by plunging the

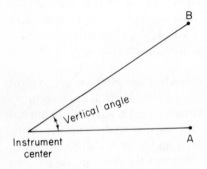

Side view showing angle
between points A and B

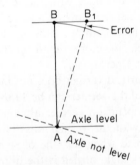

End view showing longer arc (and greater angle) traveled by telescope when axle not level. The line of sight is turned horizontally to left to sight B; but, A – B₁ represents arc that is measured always with a plus error.

Figure 5-15 Error in vertical angle when horizontal axle not level

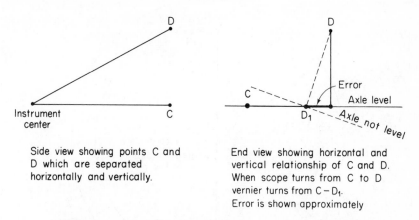

Side view showing points C and
D which are separated
horizontally and vertically.

End view showing horizontal and
vertical relationship of C and D.
When scope turns from C to D
vernier turns from C – D₁.
Error is shown approximately

Figure 5-16 Error in horizontal angle when horizontal axle
not level

scope can be eliminated in all cases by doubling the operation unless the
source of error is the wearing of a part so much that looseness results.

The error cannot be eliminated from vertical angles by doubling because
the angle turned is always too large.

If the plumb bob does not hang from a point on the vertical centerline
or the optical plumb line does not coincide with the vertical centerline, error
results when horizontal angles are turned or a line is extended by plunging
the scope. The error cannot be eliminated by field methods and factory repair
is required if the error is significant.

The graduated circle is manufactured with division marks cut at equal
spacing radially from its center. This center is not precisely at its center of
rotation which is on the centerline of the spindles. Thus, an eccentricity exists
which causes slightly different readings at different locations on the circle
when an angle is turned. If the angle is read at opposite sides of the circle,
the average angle is the true angle turned. See Fig. 5-17 for further explanation.

An angle generates a longer arc when the radius is longer. The longer arc
includes more scale divisions. Of all points around the circle in Fig. 5-17,
the longest radius about the center of rotation is at point *A* and the shortest
is at point *B*. During any movement between the circle and the upper plate
more division marks pass point *A* than any other point and fewer pass point *B*
than any other point. At points *C* and *D*, nearly perpendicular to a line from
A to *B*, the correct number of scale divisions pass because at these two points
the radius of the circle as manufactured equals the radius of rotation of
the circle about the vertical centerline of the transit.

Vernier readings for an angle depend on where the verniers are in relation
to the two centers. The readings vary around the circle from readings with

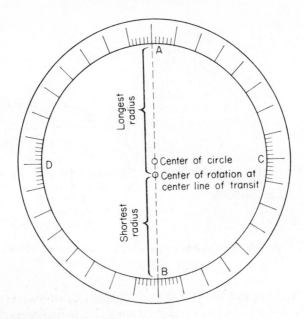

Scale divisions are inscribed in factory from center of circle.
Horizontal circle rotates in use about centerline of transit.

Figure 5-17 Eccentricity in horizontal circle

maximum plus error at *A* to maximum minus error at *B* with zero error at *C* and *D*. As long as the verniers are 180° apart, the true angle turned is the average of their readings regardless of what part of the circle they are on. The error is accidental and is so small that it is ignored in ordinary work and only the *A* vernier is read.

When the *B* vernier is used it must be read at B.S. and F.S. When the *A* vernier is zeroed for the B.S. the *B* vernier will not read zero at some settings. Notes must be carefully kept. Sample notes are shown in Fig. 5-18.

Degrees are the same at *A* and *B* vernier with few exceptions. Seconds and, sometimes, minutes differ. In the notes of Fig. 5-18, the *A* and *B* vernier readings are recorded and averaged in separate columns. The first two angles are doubled. The averages of *A* and *B* vernier readings are computed first and used to determine the total angle turned. Then the average angle is computed.

The notes also include an angle turned six times. The vernier may go past 360° several times in this process. Each time 60° (360° divided by 6) is allocated to the average angle. The final angles indicated by the verniers are recorded and the average is divided by six to compute the total average angle. In turning this angle the vernier turned two complete circles plus the angle noted.

It is not necessary to record all repetitions nor to record the number of times the vernier turns a full 360°. The number of times to add 60° can be determined by the size of the angle turned once since the average angle will approximately equal it. The notation indicates how many times the angle is repeated and whether direct or reversed.

Human Errors

The main source of human error is in the eyesight of the instrumentman. Steadiness of the instrumentman's hands and the eyesight and steadiness of the man marking backsights and foresights are also important. All the human errors are accidental.

1. If the instrument is not centered over the point which should be the vertex of an angle, the angle will be turned from another vertex — the instrument center. This condition is the same as that resulting from the plumb line not coinciding with the vertical axis. The size and direction of error are completely random in this case, which they are not in the case of a plumb line out of alignment. This is an accidental error and the previous one is not. Refer to Fig. 5-19 for illustration of the maximum probable error in one sight. The setup error shown is in a direction to

Sta.	Degrees	A	B	Avg.	
1,2,3	0	00–00	00–20	00–10	∡ R
1 D	65	27–20	27–20		
2 R	130	55–00	54–40	54–50	
Avg.	65°–27'–20"				
2,3,4	0	00–00	59–40	59–50	∡ L
1 D	113	42–20	41–40		
2 R	227	24–20	23–40	24–00	
Avg.	113°–42'–05"				
3,4,5	0	00–00	00–40	00–20	∡ R
1 D	146	03–20	03–20		
3D,3R	156	19–20	19–40	19–30	
Avg.	146°–03'–11.7"				

Figure 5-18 Field notes when B vernier used, angles doubled and turned six times

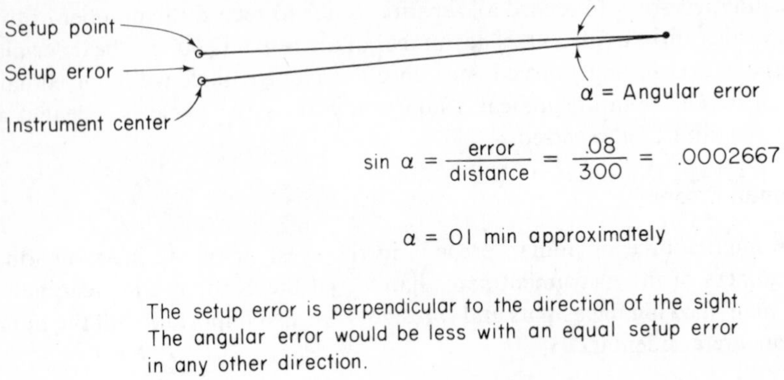

Setup point

Setup error

Instrument center

α = Angular error

$$\sin \alpha = \frac{error}{distance} = \frac{.08}{300} = .0002667$$

α = 01 min approximately

The setup error is perpendicular to the direction of the sight.
The angular error would be less with an equal setup error
in any other direction.

Figure 5-19 Maximum error in sighting a point caused by inaccurate
transit

cause maximum angular error. A setup of one in. (.08 ft) and a distance
of 300 ft result in a maximum angular error of approximately one min.
The same setup error in any other direction results in less angular error.
Decreasing the error in the setup decreases the angular error and decreasing the distance increases the angular error. The fact that one in. at 300 ft
results in one min. angular error is worth remembering. Other relationships are roughly proportional up to five min. Thus, $\frac{1}{4}$ in. at 300 ft results
in $\frac{1}{4}$ min angular error, while $\frac{1}{4}$ in. at 150 ft results in $\frac{1}{2}$ min angular error,
conforming to the principle that longer sights result in greater accuracy.
All these figures are approximate.

a. The error in turning an angle is not the same as the error in one sight.
    The error in turning an angle caused by inaccurate location of the
    instrument may vary from zero to twice the maximum angular error in
    one sight, depending on the direction of setup error compared to the
    two sides of the angle. See Fig. 5-20 for examples.

b. The linear error in setting a point by laying off an angle may vary
    from zero to many times the setup error. The amount depends on the
    relationship between the direction of the setup error and the directions
    of the sides of the angle. The probable error in laying off an angle will
    be less if B.S. is longer than F.S. and more if B.S. is shorter than F.S.
    In measuring an angle between two points the error is the same from
    either direction. See Fig. 5-21 for illustration.

2. Some error is introduced each time the vernier is set and each time the
   vernier is read. Generally, the maximum probable error is one half the
   least count of the vernier. When the vernier count is small, the difficulty of
   reading may result in a maximum probable error greater than one half the

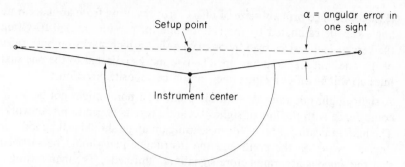

The error in the angle measured is twice as large as α.
The error increases as the angle increases.
An angle of approximately 90° would have an error equal to α.

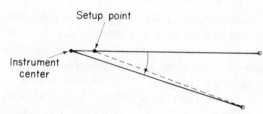

The error in the angle measured is almost zero.
An angle of 180° would have no error.
An angle of approximately 90° would have the largest error.

Figure 5-20 Probable error in measuring an angle caused by inaccurate transit setup

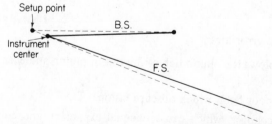

Error in B.S. is inversely proportional to distance to B.S.
Therefore longer B.S. means less error.
Error in F.S. is proportional to F.S. distance
Therefore longer F.S. means more error.

Figure 5-21 Error in laying off an angle caused by inaccurate centering of the instrument

least count. The probable size of offset error resulting from an inaccurate angle can be estimated by the rule of one in. per min at 300 ft. Often the vernier can best be read by observing the vernier marks on both sides of the one that seems to line up. The two marks adjacent to the one that lines up will be offset by the same amount in opposite directions.

3. A sight might not coincide with the point or a point might not be set in coincidence with the line of sight. Accurate results depend on teamwork. The man indicating a point for measuring an angle should call "good" or "mark" while on the point and the instrumentman should be satisfied that the angle is accurate before signalling "finished". The man setting a point should call for as many repetitions as needed to satisfy himself that he has set the point as accurately as required before he signals "finished."

4. Parallax is a source of error and should be eliminated as described in Chap. 4 for the level telescope.

5. Inaccurate leveling of the instrument causes error in turning vertical angles and horizontal angles and in extending lines by plunging. This condition is the same as that caused by the horizontal axle being out of adjustment. This error is an accidental one, and that caused by the horizontal axis being out of adjustment is not. The quantity of error depends on the direction of the operation relative to the direction of the leveling error.

All the human errors are accidental and must be controlled by care and proper methods. Some people have a tendency to favor one side when sighting a point or reading a vernier. Such practice must be avoided because it causes systematic error.

Natural Errors

Natural sources of error are:

1. Wind, which blows the plumb bob string out of plumb and even vibrates the transit.
2. Dust, fog, or poor light, which obscure vision.
3. Temperature changes, which cause unequal expansion and contraction of the parts of the transit.
4. Heat waves, which bend the line of sight.
5. Soft ground, which allows the transit to move by settlement.

Poor weather conditions such as wet brush, very low temperature, and heat with high humidity cause surveyors such discomfort that a high level of accuracy is not possible.

5-9 IMPORTANT OPERATIONS

In surveying work, some operations are required frequently. Procedures have been devised for these operations which are accepted practice in the surveying field and they should be understood and used when appropriate.

Repeating an Angle

An angle turned with a transit can be read with confidence to the least count of the vernier. It may be estimated to one half that value. In addition, there is a way in which any desired accuracy can be achieved. When an angle is turned and read there is usually some small difference between the actual angle and the vernier reading which cannot be separated with the human eye. Nevertheless it is there, on the ground, and recorded in the horizontal circle of the instrument. If the lower motion clamp is released and the telescope returned to the backsight while the original angle is still marked by the vernier, the lower motion can be clamped and the angle turned again and the vernier will read twice the angle. The small difference which could not be picked out by the human eye will now be twice as large and may be large enough to be read on the vernier. If it is not yet large enough to be significant on the vernier, repetitions of the operation will increase it until its effect is noticeable on the vernier.

For example, if 20°00′07″ is read with a 20 second vernier, it will be read as 20°00′00″. This reading is correct to the nearest 20″ or the least count of the vernier. If the angle is accumulated two times on the vernier as described here it will be 40°00′14″ and will read 40°00′20″. Dividing by two gives 20°00′10″ which is correct to the nearest 10″ or one half the least count of the vernier. The accuracy is doubled.

If the angle is accumulated four times, it will be 80°00′28″ and will read 80°00′20″. Dividing by four gives 20°00′05″, which is correct to the nearest 5″ or one fourth the least count of the vernier. The accuracy is quadrupled.

It is theoretically possible to accumulate the angle enough times to achieve one second accuracy or even more with the 20″ instrument referred to in the example. However, inaccuracies in the manufacturing of the transit and in the operation preclude such accuracy. In practice, angles are seldom turned more than six times.

After several repetitions, further increases in accuracy can be prevented by very small errors in the transit or in setting up. It is customary to turn half the angles with the telescope normal and half with the telescope inverted to eliminate error from these sources.

Doubling an Angle

Doubling an angle eliminates many instrumental errors as explained in this chapter under "Instrumental Errors" and also eliminates any error due to the horizontal axle being set up out of level. The procedure also serves to prevent mistakes in reading the angle and is probably used more often for this purpose. Using this procedure, the instrumentman reads two different angles, and if he misreads the first angle he is not likely to make a comparable mistake reading the second. A mistake in reading either angle causes a discrepancy in the notes and so is immediately apparent. The same angle could be read twice as a check. However, people have a tendency to make the same mistake again when faced with the same situation.

Doubling an angle is an important procedure and should be understood. The steps are as follows:

1. Turn the angle from B.S. to F.S. in the normal way.

2. Plunge the telescope.

3. Loosen the lower plate.

4. Sight the B.S. with the first angle held in the instrument.

5. Turn the angle from B.S. to F.S. with the telescope reversed.

6. Read the doubled angle on the *A* vernier where it was originally read (since the telescope was reversed for the second turning the *A* vernier will be at the opposite side).

Notes are kept as shown in Fig. 5-22 and the final angle is compared with the original angle before the transit is moved. Reversing the telescope is a refinement which may not be necessary when the instrument is in proper adjustment and the purpose of doubling is solely to catch a possible mistake in reading the angle the first time.

Extending a Line

It is often necessary to establish a long straight line where it is impossible to see both ends from any one point. With the instrument at one end, a new point

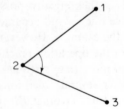

1	1D	67° – 12' – 20"
2	2R	134° – 25' – 00"
3	Avg.	67° – 12' – 30"

Point 1 = B.S.
Point 2 = Transit location
Point 3 = F.S.
  1D   = Once, scope direct
  2R   = Twice, scope reversed

Figure 5-22 Field notes, angle doubled for increased accuracy

Figure 5-23 Double centering

is established on the line. The instrument is set up on the new point and the line extended from the end point through the instrument to another new point. The instrument must then be set up on the second new point and the line extended through the instrument again to a third new point. This is repeated as many times as necessary to reach the opposite end.

A line can be extended more accurately by plunging the telescope than by turning a 180° angle. Upper and lower plates must be clamped when the scope is plunged. Plunging the scope eliminates the errors which occur when setting and reading the vernier. Error due to telescope misalignment or to the horizontal axle not being level can be eliminated by a procedure called *double centering*. After one point is set by plunging the scope, the inverted telescope is turned through a horizontal angle, aligned on the B.S., and plunged again. It is then upright. The two sights will have equal and opposite errors. Therefore, another point is set on line and the corrected line passes through a point midway between the two points. See Fig. 5-23 for illustration.

It is not necessary to go through the double centering procedure to extend a line unless a high degree of accuracy is needed or the transit is out of adjustment. However, it should be appreciated that an instrumental error in plunging the scope is usually systematic. It is greater with longer foresights and the angular deflection of the line approximately doubles with each setup. In a long line or one with many setups the errors may be significant even in a survey of third order accuracy.

Extending a Line Beyond an Obstruction

METHOD 1
PARALLEL LINE

A transit may be taken around an obstruction and brought back on line by the method shown in Fig. 5-24. The instrument is set up at each point and a 90° angle turned. This method is satisfactory for surveys below third order accuracy.

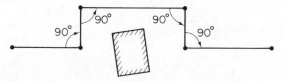

Figure 5-24 Extending a line beyond an obstruction with a low degree of accuracy

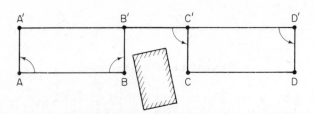

Figure 5-25 Extending a line beyond an obstruction with higher degree of accuracy

More accuracy is obtained by taking longer sights as follows: Set points *A* and *B* on line. Set offset points *A'* and *B'* at right angles at the same distance from *A* and *B*. This establishes a parallel line through *A'* and *B'*. This line is extended to *C'* and *D'*. To return to the original line the offsets *C* and *D* are established. If *C' D'* is as long as *A' B'* no accuracy will be lost in establishing the second parallel line. The procedure is illustrated in Fig. 5-25.

METHOD 2
RANDOM ANGLE

An obstruction can be bypassed and line continued by the method shown in Fig. 5-26. Deflection angles of a convenient size are used and a convenient distance *L* is chosen. The distance *BD* is twice the length of a leg of a right triangle having a hypotenuse *L* and an adjacent angle α. Distance *BD* equals $2\,L \cos \alpha$. The transit is set up at each point shown in Fig. 5-26 and the next point is set at the appropriate angle and distance.

Bucking In

It is sometimes necessary, between two points which are not visible from each other, to establish a line which can be seen from a point between them. The instrument is set up as close to the line as the instrumentman can align

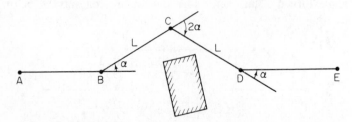

Figure 5-26 Extending a line beyond an obstruction by random angle

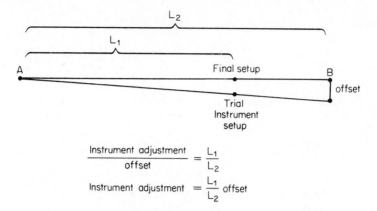

Figure 5-27 Bucking in

himself by eye. The farther point is sighted and the telescope plunged. The line of sight will then be offset from the nearer point. The instrument must be moved a fraction of the offset distance to be on line. The offset distance may be measured and called to the instrumentman or the instrumentman may estimate it. The transit is then moved toward the line by an amount estimated to be the correct fraction. The process is repeated until the instrument is on line. The final adjustment can be made by double centering if the greatest possible accuracy is desired. See Fig. 5-27.

Establishing a Point of Intersection

It is sometimes necessary to establish the point of intersection of two lines when the directions of the lines are known but the distances to the intersection point are not known. One line is extended as already described, by double centering if necessary. Points are set on line in the vicinity of the intersection. Judgment is required to do this efficiently. The points can be spaced according to the required accuracy, but not more than a few feet apart. There should be at least one point on each side of the intersection. Two points may be enough to accomplish this.

The other line is then extended and two points are set on line, one on each side of the first line. A string is stretched between points on each line so that the strings intersect at the point of intersection of the lines. See Fig. 5-28 for illustration. This is a practical application of locating a point by directions from two other points as covered in Chap. 2. It is subject to the inaccuracies depicted in Fig. 2-1, Method 2. A right angle intersection will result in the least probable error. If the intersecting angle is too sharp this method should be avoided.

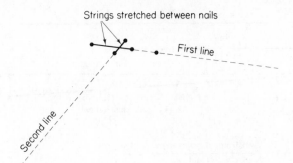

Figure 5-28 Establishing point of intersection of two lines

Sta.	Angle	Type	
1,2,3	88°–32'–20"	∡ L	
2,3,4	11°–06'–00"	defl. R	
3	46°–13'–00"		
4	92°–26'–20"		
5	46°–13'–10"	∡ R	
4	224°–09'–40"		
5	088°–19'–20"		
6	244°–09'–40"	∡ R	

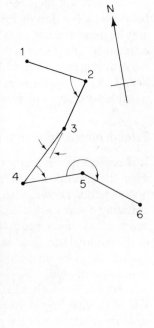

Angles 1,2,3 and 2,3,4 are turned once.
Angles 3,4,5 and 4,5,6 are doubled without plunging scope.

Figure 5-29 Angle notes

5–10 SIGNALS

Commonly used signals are as follows:

"Right" or "left" when setting a point or giving line. Extend the arm in the direction of desired movement making a long slow motion for a large distance and a short quick motion for a small distance. A handkerchief may be held in the hand for better visibility over long distances.

"Foresight" when the instrumentman wants a foresight or another member wants the instrumentman to take or give a foresight. Extend one arm vertically over the head as if holding a plumb bob string high over a point.

5–11 NOTEKEEPING

Notes must show the following:

1. Location of the angle (vertex and two sides).
2. Type and direction of angle (angle right, angle left, deflection angle right, deflection angle left).
3. Method used (single, double direct, double direct and reversed).
4. Size of angle.

All this information is needed if another person is to understand what was done in the field. A sketch is helpful for this purpose and also for keeping the notekeeper himself orientated in the field. Notekeeping examples are shown in Fig. 5-29 to illustrate the method.

5–12 THE THEODOLITE

A *theodolite* is an instrument designed for the same purposes as a transit — to measure vertical and horizontal angles and to extend straight lines. The appearance of a theodolite distinguishes it from a transit. Theodolites are smaller, with short telescopes and no exposed verniers, compasses, clamps, or tangent screws. There is only one horizontal motion so that angles cannot be repeated. These are called *pointing instruments* and the American style transit is a *repeating instrument*. Optical devices allow angles to be read as accurately with a single turning as they can be read by repetition with a transit; and, with some models, they can be read more accurately. Some instruments with the characteristics of theodolites have upper and lower plates so that angles can be repeated. These are called theodolites by some manufacturers and transits by others. Thus, the term theodolite is not fully agreed upon.

Characteristics of theodolites vary so much that they are not covered in detail here. Manufacturer's literature is available for each type. The transit described in this chapter has its parts exposed so that functions of the parts can be visualized and understood while the transit is being used. This is not true of theodolites. If the student learns the fundamentals of surveying using an American style transit, he will understand principles more completely and should have little difficulty using any theodolite later.

PROBLEMS

1/ Read the angles of Fig. 5–8 to right and to left.

GRADUATED 30 MINUTES READING TO ONE MINUTE
DOUBLE DIRECT VERNIER

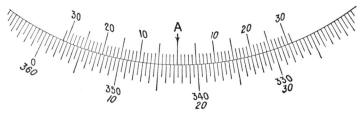

GRADUATED 20 MINUTES READING TO 30 SECONDS
DOUBLE DIRECT VERNIER

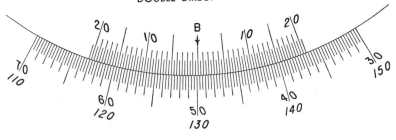

GRADUATED TO 15 MINUTES READING TO 20 SECONDS
DOUBLE DIRECT VERNIER

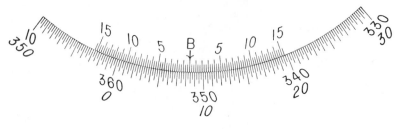

2/ Using the following field data, prepare field notes including sketches.

Inst. @	B.S.	F.S.	Angle	No. of Times Turned
a. 2	1	3	96°–30′ ⋏ R	1
17	16	18	17°–19′ defl. ⋏ L	1
C	B	D	9°–11′ defl. ⋏ R	1
3	2	4	136°–35′ ⋏ L	1
b. 2	1	3	7°–14′–30″ / 14°–29′–15″ ⋏ R	2
2	1	2A	72°–15′–15″ / 144°–30′–15″ ⋏ L	2
D	C	E	21°–36′–20″ / 43°–12′–20° defl. ⋏ R	2
D	C	D1	6°–13′–40″ / 12°–27′–00″ defl. ⋏ L	2

3/ A bearing turned from magnetic north is N 37°–30′ E. What is the true bearing if the declination is 1°–15′ E?

4/ A bearing turned from magnetic north is S 46°–45′ E. What is the true bearing if the declination is 2°–30′ W?

INSTRUCTIONAL OBJECTIVES OF CHAPTER 6

1/ Given angles and distances verbally as they would be read in the field the student should be able to record complete traverse notes including a sketch.

2/ Given complete field notes for a traverse, the student should be able to:

   a. Plot the traverse to scale.

   b. Determine angular error and adjust the angles.

   c. Determine bearings of all courses based on the bearing of one course in the notes.

   d. Determine differences in latitudes and departures for each course.

   e. Determine accuracy of the survey.

   f. Determine corrections for each station.

   g. Adjust the traverse.

3/ Given coordinates in latitude and departure of two stations the student should be able to determine bearing and distance of one from the other by inversing.

4/ Given coordinates of the corners of a polygon the student should be able to determine the area enclosed within the polygon by double meridian distances.

chapter six

The Traverse

In both preliminary surveys and construction surveys an accurate framework is needed that allows the surveyor to locate objects from convenient points on the framework and relate them to each other quickly, without mistakes and without accumulating errors. Not all objects that must eventually be located can be located at the time of the first survey. Many will be needed later with short notice.

Therefore, semi-permanent control points are established throughout the area of the survey as a first step in all but very minor surveying projects. As new points must be located, they are located in relation to the control points.

6-1 THE TRAVERSE AS A MEANS OF HORIZONTAL CONTROL

A *control survey* consists of points established with high accuracy so that other objects can be located by reference to these points. The control survey must always be of higher accuracy than the secondary points it controls. This is necessarily so because the secondary points are established with some error in addition to the error of the control points and are thus less accurate. Only horizontal control is considered in this chapter.

The *traverse* consists of a series of accurately positioned points called *stations* each of which is located by direction and distance from adjacent stations. Stations are connected by lines called *courses*. Each station is marked by a *hub*, which is a wood stake with a nail in the top, or by some other semi-permanent marker.

A *loop traverse* closes on, or returns to, the first station thus forming a polygon. A *connecting traverse* begins at a station of known location and closes on, or ends at, another station of known location. Either of these is a *closed traverse*. A closed traverse can be checked for accuracy and can be mathematically adjusted. A traverse which does not close is called an *open*

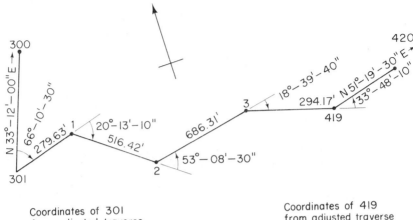

Coordinates of 301
from adjusted traverse
    N 3470.13
    E 8062.45

Coordinates of 419
from adjusted traverse
    N 3468.43
    E 9709.91

Figure 6-1 Traverse as established in field—connecting traverse

traverse. An open traverse cannot be checked for mistakes or excessive error, nor can it be adjusted. It is never used on important work.

Once a traverse is established, positions of existing objects can be determined by direction and distance from a traverse station or key points for proposed construction can be set by direction and distance from a traverse station. Figure 6-1 shows a connecting traverse as established in the field and Fig. 6-13 shows a loop traverse.

6–2 FIELD WORK

For a connecting traverse such as shown in Fig. 6-1, two points and two directions are already established. The first transit position is at one of the established points and the first backsight is in the direction of the adjacent course. The transit must always be set up on a point of known location. The first B.S. can be on another station or on magnetic or true north instead of a station. In Fig. 6-1, the transit is first set up on sta 301 and a B.S. taken on sta 300. Field notes are in Fig. 6-2.

While the instrumentman and others are setting up the transit and taking line for a B.S., the head tapeman drives a stake into the ground and drives a nail or tack into the top for the forward station. He gives line on the station and the first angle is measured. The angles of Fig. 6-2 are doubled to increase accuracy, so the telescope is reversed for the second measurement.

The two tapemen then measure the distance ahead to the forward station (sta 1) while the instrumentman keeps them on line. They need not be on line with great accuracy as explained in Chap. 3. The distance is normally measured forward from the transit to the next station and this need not be specified in the notes. It is understood unless noted otherwise.

When intermediate points are needed to measure a course, the head tapeman may put a nail into the ground on line and measure to it, or he may set a nail on line every 100 ft. The field notes in Fig. 6-2 show that taping is done in 100 ft increments. Field notes in Fig. 6-12 show that the other method is used for the loop traverse.

After the distance is measured and recorded the instrumentman sets up on the forward station while the head tapeman moves ahead to establish the next station. Experience is required to lay out a traverse so that the stations are in convenient locations for their purpose and so that there is not an excessive number of them. The head tapeman is the key man, controlling

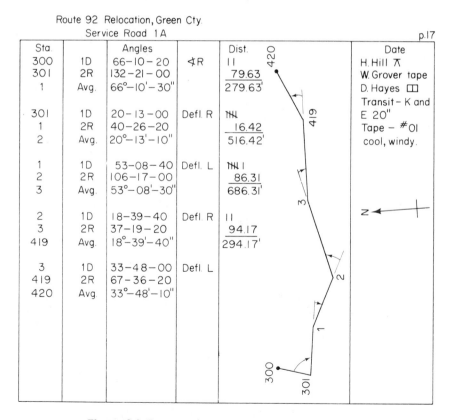

Figure 6-2 Traverse field notes—connecting traverse

the location of stations and the speed of the operation. The party chief usually is the head tapeman or notekeeper in a four man party. In a three man party he is usually the head tapeman and notekeeper.

The head tapeman continues to move ahead, establishing new stations, while the instrumentman continues to set up the instrument one station behind, and another member clears the courses of any brush or other obstacles to the line of sight or tape. The party proceeds until the traverse is closed by measuring distance 3-419 and measuring angle 3, 419, 420.

Often the instrumentman cannot sight the adjacent hubs. With a four man party, one man is assigned to give line for backsights and the head tapeman gives line for foresights. With fewer men it is not efficient for a man to stay behind for the B.S. The instrumentman, after measuring the angle, gives line to the rear tapeman who sets a nail on the F.S. line near the transit where it can be seen and used as a B.S. when the transit is moved to the next station. This nail is accurately set because it is set with a short F.S. from a long B.S. This is called *setting a backsight*. Another method is to use tall stakes with projecting nails which can be seen by the instrumentman.

For a loop traverse three stations must be established before the first angle can be measured. See the first angle of the field notes in Fig. 6-12. The party chief designates the position for the first transit setup and a stake is driven there and a nail is driven into the stake, While the instrumentman is setting up the transit over the nail the party chief designates locations for a back station and a forward station. The rear tapeman puts in a hub for the back station and gives line on it. The head tapeman puts in a hub for the forward station and gives line. The angle is measured and recorded. The angles of Fig. 6-12 are doubled and the telescope is not reversed for the second measurement. As discussed in Chap. 5, the scope is sometimes not reversed when the angle is doubled only as a precaution against mistakes.

6–3 TAPING SLOPE DISTANCES

Distances are often taped on a slope while running a traverse. The party chief decides whether to break tape several times on a long slope or to measure a slope distance in one operation and convert it to a level distance.

Methods of converting a slope distance to a horizontal distance are discussed in Chap. 3. Ways of measuring a slope distance in the field are discussed here.

METHOD 1

The transit telescope is set at a vertical angle so that the line of sight passes over the station ahead. The tape is held over the back station at the center of the horizontal axle of the transit. Thus it is at the elevation of the line of sight, but offset several inches. The slight offset causes no inaccuracy. The tape is held over the forward station at a height on the line of sight as directed by the instrumentman. The instrumentman directs the head tapeman up or down until he sees the tape in the head tapeman's hand at the cross-hairs. The head tapeman adjusts his plumb bob string as needed. If the distance is long, it can be measured in steps provided both ends of the tape can be kept on the line of sight by the instrumentmen. Taped distances and vertical angles are noted in the field book. Conversion to horizontal distances is made using a table such as Table IV in the back of this book or by multiplying the slope distance by the cos of the vertical angle. See Fig. 6-3 for illustration of the field method and Fig. 6-4 for field notes.

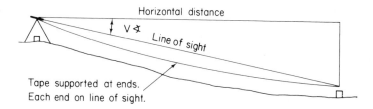

Method 1 Distance measured along line of sight

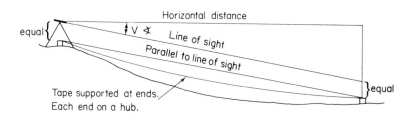

Method 2 Distance measured parallel to line of sight

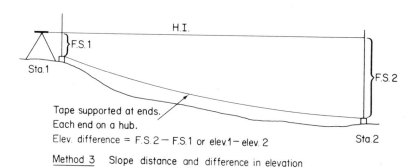

Method 3 Slope distance and difference in elevation

Figure 6-3 Methods of taping slope distances

Method 1 and 2

Sta.		H ∡		V ∡	Dist.	Corr. Dist.
4	1	63°-27'-30"	∡R	4°-12'	134.86'	-0.36'
5	2	126°-54'-30"				134.50'
6	Avg.	63°-27'-15"				

Fm. Table **IV**

Method 3

Sta.		H ∡		Dist.	Corr.	Corr. dist.
5	1	174°-18'-30"		192.32'	-0.06'	192.26'
6	2	348°-37'-30"				
7	Avg.	174°-18'-45"				

Sta.	B.S.(+)	H.I.	F.S.(-)	Rod (-)	Elev.
B.M.	4.96	104.96			100.00
6				4.34	100.62
7				8.92	96.04
B.M.			4.96		100.00

$$C = \frac{d^2}{2L} = \frac{(100.62 - 96.04)^2}{2 \times 192.32} = 0.06$$

Figure 6-4 Field notes for slope distances

METHOD 2

The height from the top of hub to center of transit horizontal axle is measured with a level rod. The level rod is then held on the forward hub and the transit cross hairs trained on the same height. The line of sight is thus parallel to a line from the top of one hub to the top of the other hub, making a vertical angle in the transit the same as that from one hub top to the other.

The vertical angle is recorded. The distance is measured from hub to hub, holding the tape on the hub tops. It is thus measured at the slope of the recorded vertical angle. The entire length must be measured in one step. Conversion to horizontal distance is the same as for method 1. See Figs. 6-3 and 6-4.

METHOD 3

Each distance is measured with the tape held on hub tops at both ends. The tape may be held at a predetermined distance above the hub tops so that it measures a line parallel to a line from hub top to hub top. The difference in elevation between hub tops is determined from a level circuit including all necessary hub tops. Hub elevations may be obtained from rod shots. The horizontal distance is determined by use of the Pythagorean identities or by subtracting the correction $C_s - d^2/2L$ (described in Chap. 3). See Figs. 6-3 and 6-4.

6-4 ERROR OF CLOSURE

Figures 6-1 and 6-13 show traverses as established in the field. Since all measurements include some error, angles and distances are not exactly as measured. Even though the traverses are closed on points of known location in the field, if an accurate determination is made using angles and distances from the field, the last course will not end exactly on the closing station. In other words, the traverse does not close. It closes physically in the field, but because of measuring errors does not close mathematically. This discrepancy is the *error of closure*. It can be determined mathematically.

The student should review error and accuracy from Chap. 2 and also bearings and coordinates from Chap. 1.

For the sake of consistency, the probable error due to angular inaccuracies should be about the same as the probable error due to linear inaccuracies. Taping with ordinary care should produce an accuracy of 1:5000. The use of a new tape with a spring tension handle and temperature corrections at frequent intervals should produce an accuracy of 1:10,000. To correspond approximately to this accuracy, a transit should read to 1' and 30" respectively. Many instruments read to 30" or 20" and it is customary to double angles as a check for error even if the additional accuracy is not needed. Therefore, the angular accuracy usually exceeds the linear accuracy with no additional effort.

6-5 ADJUSTING A TRAVERSE

The procedure for computing error of closure and distributing the correction is demonstrated for the traverses shown in Figs. 6-1 and 6-13. The procedure is called *adjusting a traverse*.

Traverse adjustment is a classic example of the engineering approach to problem solving. The form is standardized and is so well designed that it could be studied for its format. It removes the chance for undetected mistakes and reduces a complex problem to simple operations.

The work is tabulated so that calculations are in a logical form, easy to compute with calculator and easy to check for mistakes. Built-in checks are provided at various points and if the end result does not equal a predetermined quantity a mistake has been made. The mistake must be found and corrected. Its correction requires a minimum of revised calculations.

Some problems cannot be solved as neatly with as many check points along the way. However, the principles of tabulation and checking by alternative solutions can and should be applied to most problems.

The example in Fig. 6-1 is a connecting traverse beginning at a station in a previously adjusted traverse and ending at another station in a previously adjusted traverse. It represents an auxiliary traverse to control design of a short road between sections of highway each controlled by its own traverse. The two bearings shown are from a map of the original traverses after adjustment.

The original traverses are established with accuracy the same as or greater than the auxiliary traverse and they control the auxiliary. Therefore, the auxiliary traverse can be adjusted mathematically to conform to the originals, but no part of the original ones should be adjusted to conform to the auxiliary.

Field work must include angles joining the new traverse to two courses of the controlling traverses; if not, there will be no way to adjust angles. Distances within the original traverses are not needed. Step by step adjustment of the traverse of Fig. 6-1 follows:

1. Plot the traverse to scale. This is necessary in order to visualize computations and to check for any obvious mistake which must be corrected before proceeding with calculations. Figure 6-1 shows the traverse plotted from field notes of Fig. 6-2.

   A traverse can be plotted using a protractor, straight edge, and scale. A line is drawn to scale to represent the first course of the traverse. A protractor is placed with its center on the vertex of the first angle and zero toward the B.S., or 180° from the B.S. if it is a deflection angle. Then the angle from the field notes is laid off on the protractor in the same direction it was turned in the field. A mark is made on the plotting sheet. Using the straight edge, a line is drawn from the vertex through the mark and scaled to the right length. The end of this line is the vertex of the next angle.

   Angles can be plotted with an accuracy to the nearest one half degree. The accuracy of plotting distances depends on the scale used. The procedure is a duplication in miniature of field measurements. The angle is laid off and marked. Then the distance is measured. The plotter must visualize himself at the vertex turning the angle the way it was turned in the field. See Fig. 6-5 for plotting method.

2. Adjust field angles to make them mathematically correct. The bearings of the two original traverses are held and the new angles are adjusted to make them conform. The angular error is found by holding the bearing from one original traverse and computing the closing bearing for the other from field angles.

   The difference between the closing bearing and the correct bearing is the total error, and an equal and opposite correction is distributed among the traverse angles as demonstrated in Fig. 6-6. Each angle is adjusted the same amount whether it is a large angle or a small one, since there is equal chance for error in each of them.

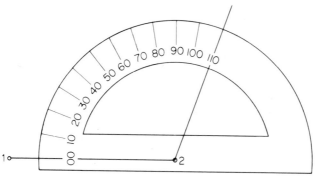

Plotting an angle to the right of 110°

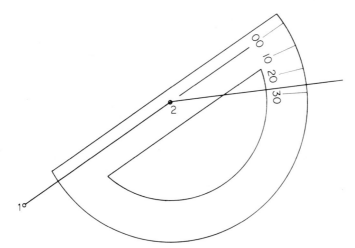

Plotting a deflection angle to the right of 27°

Figure 6-5 Plotting a traverse

Angles are usually adjusted to the nearest second with excess seconds being distributed one at a time without overcorrecting any one part of the traverse and, when possible, favoring larger angles. For example, three seconds would be distributed one to every other angle of a six sided traverse, and either one to every fourth angle of a 12 sided traverse, or one to each of the three largest angles as long as they aren't too close together.

The result of this distribution is an apparent accuracy to the nearest second. In order to indicate the true accuracy, the correction can be distributed in increments equal to the accuracy with which the angles were read. This is the least count of the vernier, or less if the angles are

Computation and distribution of angular corrections
Hold 301−300 N 33°−12'−00" E

	Defl. R (+)		Defl. L (−)
301 − 1	66°−10'−30"		
1 − 2	20°−13'−10"	2 − 3	53°−08'−30"
3 − 319	18°−39'−40"	419 − 420	33°−48'−10"
	105°−03'−20"		86°−56'−40"

Bearing of 419−420 by field survey

$$
\begin{array}{ll}
& \text{N } 33-12-00 \text{ E} \\
+ & 105-03-20 \quad \text{to right} \\
- & 86-56-40 \quad \text{to left} \\
\end{array}
$$

Answer: N 51°−18'−40" E
Correct bearing   N 51°−19'−30" E

Difference is error   −50"
Correction   +50"
Correction per angle $\dfrac{50"}{5} = +10"$

Field angles	Adjusted angles
+ 66°−10'−30"	+ 66°−10'−40"
+ 20°−13'−10"	+ 20°−13'−20"
− 53°−08'−30"	− 53°−08'−20"
+ 18°−39'−40"	+ 18°−39'−50"
− 33°−48'−10"	− 33°−48'−00"
	+ 105°−03'−50"
	− 86°−56'−20"

+ N 33°− 12'−00" E   Bearing of 301−300

N 51°− 19'−30" E   Correct bearing of
                 419−420

Bearing of 301−300 plus algebraic sum of adjusted
angles equals correct bearing of 419−420.
Therefore angles are correctly adjusted.

Figure 6-6 Adjustment of traverse field angles—connecting traverse

repeated. Adjustment is the same as for one second increments. An example follows:

No. of angles	=12
Total correction	=+80″
Increment	=10″

Eight corrections are to be distributed to 12 angles. Therefore, two-thirds of the angles are corrected. Every third angle has no correction. Arrange the corrections so that larger angles receive the corrections as much as possible without disturbing the pattern. If the number of angles is 13, the results are the same except that there is one instance of two successive angles with no correction. These should be small angles if feasible.

In a particular case, the surveyor might assign the entire correction to one or two angles measured under such adverse field conditions that error is to be expected there.

3. Determine the bearings for all courses. Starting with course 301-1 the bearing is determined for each course in succession by applying the adjusted angle to the preceding bearing until course 419-420 is reached. If the work is correct, the correct bearing will be obtained for the final course. The method is shown in Fig. 6-7. Bearings are more readily determined from deflection angles than from right or left angles and deflection angles may be preferred for this reason.

4. Determine differences in latitudes and departures from the beginning to the end of the traverse. The bearing and distance of each course are used to determine the difference in coordinates from one station to the next. The algebraic sum of the latitude differences and departure differences added algebraically to the latitude and departure of station 301 should, if there is no error, equal the latitude and departure of station 419.

The difference between what it does equal and what it should equal is the error of closure. The process of adding latitude and departure differences algebraically is shown graphically in Fig. 6-8 with the error of closure shown in detail.

Calculations necessary to compute differences in latitudes and departures are shown on the left side of the computation sheet in Fig. 6-9. The error in departure is greater than the error in latitude, which is expected because differences in departures depend primarily on taped distances which are less accurate than the angles which primarily control latitude differences.

Inspection of Fig. 6-1 shows that excessive error in latitude must be caused by a mistake in angular measurement and excessive error in departure must be caused by a mistake in distance measurement. The bearings of courses in Fig. 6-9 verify this. They all run roughly east-west. When excessive error is found in a traverse, inspection sometimes indicates its source and, thereby, the field work that must be redone to correct it.

5. Compute the accuracy of the survey from the results of the differences in latitudes and departures. If the accuracy is unacceptable, there is no use continuing the calculations until the reason is determined and the error rectified. Usually this requires checking work in the field. The method of computing accuracy is shown in Fig. 6-9.

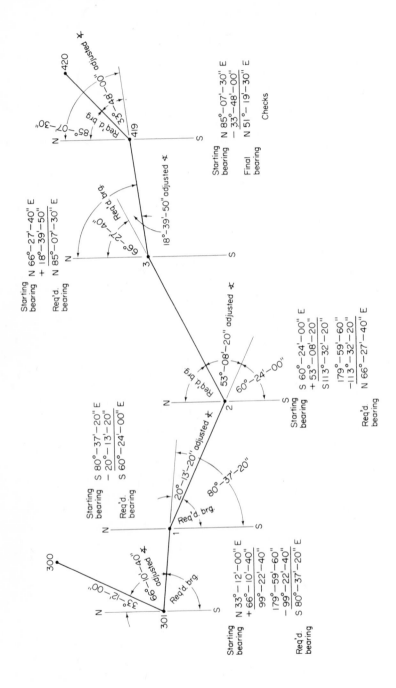

Figure 6-7 Determining bearings from deflection angles—connecting traverse

The figure contains the following annotations:

Near point 420 and 419:
adjusted ⋆
33°–48'–00"
Req'd. brg
85°–07'–30"

Starting bearing N 85°–07'–30" E
– 33°–48'–00"
Final bearing N 51°–19'–30" E
Checks

Near point 3:
Req'd. brg
66°–27'–40"
18°–39'–50" adjusted ⋆

Starting bearing N 66°–27'–40" E
+ 18°–39'–50"
Req'd. bearing N 85°–07'–30" E

Near point 2:
Req'd. brg
53°–08'–20" adjusted ⋆
60°–24'–00"

Starting bearing S 60°–24'–00" E
+ 53°–08'–20"
S113°–32'–20"
179°–59'–60"
–113°–32'–20"
Req'd. bearing N 66°–27'–40" E

Near point 1:
20°–13'–20" adjusted ⋆
80°–37'–20"
Req'd. brg.

Starting bearing S 80°–37'–20" E
– 20°–13'–20"
Req'd. bearing S 60°–24'–00" E

Near point 301 and 300:
66°–10'–40" adjusted ⋆
33°–12'–00"
Req'd. brg

Starting bearing N 33°–12'–00" E
+ 66°–10'–40"
99°–22'–40"
179°–59'–60"
–99°–22'–40"
Req'd. bearing S 80°–37'–20" E

132

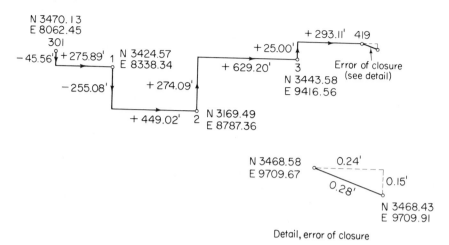

Figure 6-8 Differences in latitudes and departures for each course—connecting traverse

6. Compute corrections using a mathematical process which distributes the corrections according to some reasonable plan. The total correction must be equal to the error of closure with opposite sign.

   a. The *compass rule* assigns corrections to the coordinate position of each station in proportion to the length of the course leading from the previous station to that station. In a connecting traverse, each station is mathematically moved except the starting and closing stations.

   The first station is moved in latitude and departure in amounts determined by multiplying the total corrections for latitude and departure by the length of the first course divided by the total length of traverse. The rest of the traverse moves with it so that all following stations are adjusted the same amount.

   The second station is then moved an additional amount in the two coordinate directions according to the length of the second course. All succeeding stations move the same amount.

   This process continues, each succeeding station moving farther from its original position than the previous one until the end of the final course moves the length of the total correction and coincides with the final station which does not move.

   b. The *transit rule* assigns corrections to the coordinate position of each station in proportion to the length of difference in latitudes and difference in departures of the course leading from the previous station to that station. The procedure is similar to the procedure using the

	Length	Brg	cos	sin	Difference in Lats	Difference in Deps	Correction Lat	Correction Dep	Lat	Dep
301									3470.13	8062.45
	279.63	S80°-37'-20"E	.1629433	.9866354	−45.56	+275.89	−0.02	+0.04	−45.58	+275.93
1									3424.55	8338.38
	516.42	S60°-24'-00"E	.4939419	.8694949	−255.08	+449.02	−0.04	+0.07	−255.12	+449.09
2									3169.43	8787.47
	686.31	N66°-27'-40"E	.3993714	.9167892	+274.09	+629.20	−0.06	+0.09	+274.03	+629.29
3									3443.46	9416.76
	294.17	N85°-07'-30"E	.0849822	.9963825	+25.00	+293.11	−0.03	+0.04	+24.97	+293.15
419									3468.43	9709.91
							−0.15	+0.24		

Total 1776.53

Total of field differences*   − 1.55   +1647.22
Theoretical differences**   − 1.70   +1647.46
Errors   +0.15   − 0.24
Corrections   − 0.15   +0.24

Error of closure:

$$\sqrt{.15^2 + .24^2} = 0.28 \text{ ft}$$

Accuracy

$$\frac{0.28}{1776.53} = \frac{1}{6340}$$

*Algebraic sums of diff in lats. and diff in deps.
**Theoretical differences from sta. 301 to sta. 419

	Lat		Dep
301	3470.13	419	9709.91
419	3468.43	301	8062.45
	−1.70		1647.46

Figure 6-9 Calculation of accuracy and traverse adjustment—connecting traverse

compass rule, but the latitude corrections depend on length of difference in latitudes for the preceding course, and departure corrections depend on length of difference in departures for the preceding course, instead of both depending on length of preceding course.

Corrections for the traverse are worked out by both methods in Fig. 6-10. Graphic application of the corrections is shown in Fig. 6-11.

The lengths used in Fig. 6-10 to compute corrections need not be carried out to decimal places. It is done here so that the student can easily see

Corrections by compass rule

Course	Lat. calcs.	Corr.
301-1	$\frac{279.63}{1776.53} \times 0.15 = .024$	0.02
1-2	$\frac{516.42}{1776.53} \times 0.15 = .044$	0.04
2-3	$\frac{686.31}{1776.53} \times 0.15 = .058$	0.06
3-419	$\frac{294.17}{1776.53} \times 0.15 = .025$	0.03
Total		0.15

Course	Dep. calcs.	Corr.
301-1	$\frac{279.63}{1776.53} \times 0.24 = .038$	0.04
1-2	$\frac{516.42}{1776.53} \times 0.24 = .070$	0.07
2-3	$\frac{686.31}{1776.53} \times 0.24 = .093$	0.09
3-419	$\frac{294.17}{1776.53} \times 0.24 = .040$	0.04
Total		0.24

Denominator is total distance along traverse for lat. and dep. corrections.

Corrections by transit rule

Course	Lat. calcs.	Corr.
301-1	$\frac{45.56}{599.73} \times 0.15 = .011$	0.01
1-2	$\frac{255.08}{599.73} \times 0.15 = .064$	0.06
2-3	$\frac{274.09}{599.73} \times 0.15 = .069$	0.07
3-419	$\frac{25.00}{599.73} \times 0.15 = .006$	0.01
Total		0.15

Course	Dep. calcs.	Corr.
301-1	$\frac{275.89}{1647.22} \times 0.24 = .040$	0.04
1-2	$\frac{449.02}{1647.22} \times 0.24 = .065$	0.07
2-3	$\frac{629.20}{1647.22} \times 0.24 = .092$	0.09
3-419	$\frac{293.11}{1647.22} \times 0.24 = .043$	0.04
Total		0.24

Denominator is sum of lat. differences disregarding signs

45.56
255.08
274.09
25.00
599.73

Denominator is sum of dep. differences disregarding signs

275.89
449.02
629.20
293.11
1647.22

Figure 6-10 Computation of corrections—connecting traverse

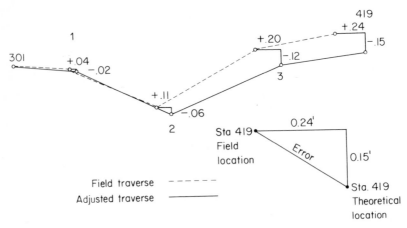

Figure 6-11 Applying corrections to traverse—connecting traverse

where each number comes from. Calculations can be performed on a slide rule since corrections are carried only to two significant places. It is advisable to carry each one to three decimal places as a preliminary step so that the final corrections can be distributed to the nearest hundredth to equal the total correction.

Corrections shown in Fig. 6-9 are the ones computed by the compass rule. This method is more commonly used and is mathematically more correct. The transit rule theoretically changes lengths with little effect on angles. This is logical because angles are more accurate than distances in a transit and tape survey. However, some angles are changed excessively under certain conditions. Results depend on the orientation of the traverse with the north line and are not consistent.

Corrections are sometimes made to coordinates of each station solely on the basis of the difficulty of the measuring conditions for the course preceding that station. This method is as valid as any other when performed carefully by an experienced surveyor. The *method of least squares* is a mathematically exact method which is so laborious to compute that it is not practical without a computer. When a computer is used, it is no more difficult than other methods and is the most satisfactory mathematically.

The *Crandall method* is a method suitable for use where the method of linear measurements is much less accurate than the method of angular measurements. It is more reliable than the transit method, but the computations are time consuming and are not usually performed except by computer.

7. Adjust the traverse by adding the corrections to the coordinates of each station. In practice the corrections are added at the same time as the difference in latitudes and difference in departures. See Fig. 6-9 for the procedure.

The adjustment of the loop traverse of Fig. 6-13 is also shown. The work is similar and some steps are repetitious. They are included so that each example — the connecting traverse and the loop traverse — will stand by itself.

Field work must include every angle and course of the loop traverse. This is obvious when looking at the plot, but is an oversight easily made in the field when the last station is sometimes forgotten because it has already been used for a B.S. Field notes and the traverse as established in the field are shown in Figs. 6-12 and 6-13.

Step by step adjustment of the loop traverse follows:

1. Plot the traverse to scale. This is necessary in order to visualize computations and to check for any obvious mistake which must be corrected before proceeding with calculations.

McNamara Property, Williamstown
Prelim. Survey Traverse

Sta.		Angle	Dist.		Date
1	1	79 −10−30			
2	2	158 −21 −00			E. McC. 𝜋
3	Avg.	79°−10'−30"	163.29'		K.S. head tape
					J.C. rear tape
2	1	187 −20−30	79.02		F.C. notes
3	2	14 −41 −00	102.77		Gurley 30" transit
4	Avg.	187°−20'−30"	181.79'		Tape #14
3	1	80 −38−30	143.15	N	Hot, humid
4	2	161 −17−30	102.18		All ⦞s to right
5	Avg.	80°−38'−45"	245.33'		
4	1	88 −56−00	151.36		
5	2	177 −52−00	144.24		
1	Avg.	88°−56'−00"	295.60'		
5	1	103 −54−00	197.62		
1	2	207 −47−30	12.11		
2	Avg.	103°−53'−45"	209.73'		
1−2	1	N 10°−15' E			
Mag.	2	N 9°−45' E			
brg.	Avg.	N 10° E			

Figure 6-12 Traverse field notes—loop traverse

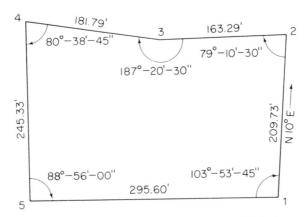

Figure 6-13 Traverse as established in field—loop traverse

2. Adjust field angles to make them mathematically correct. The sum of the interior angles of a closed traverse equals $(N-2)$ 180° where N is the number of angles. The algebraic total of deflection angles left and right around a closed traverse is zero. Either rule can be used to determine the total angular error. The total correction (equal to the total error and opposite in sign) is distributed as equally as can be among all the angles of the traverse since there is equal chance for error in each of them. See Fig. 6-14 for procedure.

   Often the angular error is computed in the field. It is an easy calculation and if a large error is discovered the source might be recalled while the work is still fresh in mind. If not, all angles must be checked until the excessive error is found. The checking can be started immediately rather than requiring a return trip to the field.

3. Determine the bearings for all courses. One bearing must be determined either by using the transit compass, sighting the sun or a star, using a map, or assuming a bearing. A magnetic bearing is shown for course 1-2 in the field notes of Fig. 6-12. Bearings of other courses are calculated in succession around the traverse starting from that bearing and applying the adjusted angles. If the work is correct, the final bearing will be the same as it was upon starting. The method is shown in Fig. 6-15.

4. Determine differences in latitudes and departures from the beginning to the end of the traverse. The bearing and distance of each course are used to determine the difference in coordinates from one station to the next. The algebraic sums of these differences added to the starting coordinates should equal the ending coordinates if there are no errors. A loop traverse ends where it starts, so the total difference in latitudes and departures

should be zero. The algebraic sums of latitude and departure differences around the traverse therefore represent the error of closure.

Station 1 of the traverse of Fig. 6-13 is assigned coordinates of N1000.00, E1000.00 so that we may determine coordinates of all stations and return to station 1 without being outside the first quadrant, which would involve negative numbers. The process of adding latitude and departure differences algebraically is shown graphically in Fig. 6-16 with the error of closure shown in detail. The calculations necessary to compute differences in latitudes and departures are shown on the left side of the computation sheet in Fig. 6-17.

5. Compute the accuracy of the survey from the results of the differences in latitudes and departures. If the accuracy is unacceptable, there is no use continuing the calculations until the reason is determined and the error rectified. The method of computing accuracy is shown in Fig. 6-17.

6. Compute corrections using an acceptable method. In a loop traverse each station is moved except the first station which is also the final station. The procedure is the same as for a connecting traverse except that the

<u>Computation and Distribution of Angular Corrections</u>

Unadjusted Interior Angles

79°10′30″
187°20′30″
80°38′45″
88°56′00″
103°53′45″

Total Unadjusted ⦡s = 539°59′30″
$(N-2)180 = 540°00′00″$

Angular Error	−30″
Angular Correction	+30″
No. of Angles	5

Correction per ⦡ $\dfrac{+30″}{5} = +6″$

Adjusted Interior Angles

79°10′36″
187°20′36″
80°38′51″
88°56′06″
103°53′51″

Total Adjusted ⦡s   540°00′00″

Total shows angles are correctly adjusted.

Figure 6-14 Adjustment of Traverse Field Angles—Loop Traverse

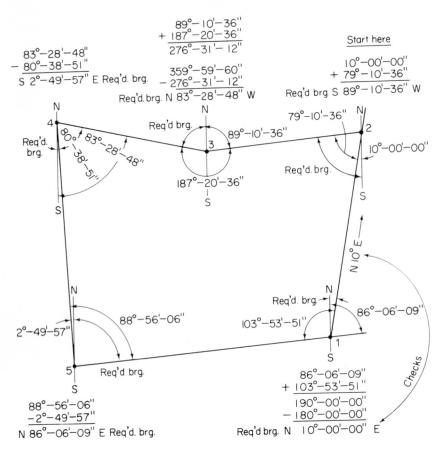

Figure 6-15 Determining bearings from interior angles—loop traverse

courses are adjusted to close on the starting point. Corrections shown in Fig. 6-17 are computed by the compass rule. Corrections are worked out by transit rule and compass rule in Fig. 6-18.

7. Adjust latitudes and departures by adding or subtracting corrections, accumulating corrections as you proceed from station to station. This is done in the last two columns of Fig. 6-17 in which differences in latitudes and departures are combined with corrections and applied to each station in succession returning to station 1 as a check.

Two points should be remembered:

1. If systematic errors are made throughout a loop traverse, they will not cause an excessive error and therefore will not be discovered by computing

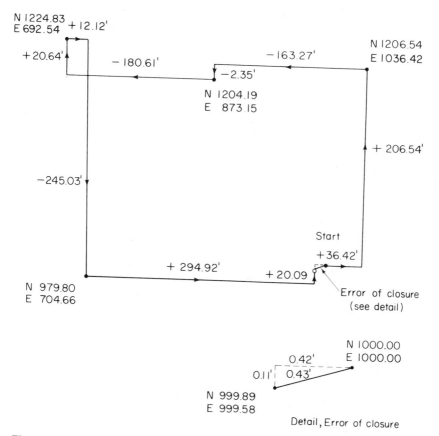

Figure 6-16 Differences in latitudes and departures for each course—loop traverse

error of closure. For example, if a tape is consistently pulled with too little tension, all readings will be too long in the same ratio for each measurement. The result will be a traverse that appears larger in the field notes than it actually is. However, north error from this source will equal south error and east error will equal west error, so that closure will be as accurate as without the systematic error. Thus there may be no way to expose an excessive systematic error.

2. Sometimes an accuracy is calculated which is much higher than expected from the field methods used. This is a false accuracy caused by lucky cancelling of some errors by others. The fact that the final station determined mathematically is close to the final station in the field does not mean that all other stations are located that accurately.

Sta.	Length	Brg.	cos	sin	Difference in		Correction		Lat.	Dep.
					Lats.	Deps.	Lat.	Dep.		
1									1000.00*	1000.00*
	209.73	N 10°–00'–00"E	.9848078	.1736482	+206.54	+36.42	+0.02	+0.08	+206.56	+36.50
2									1206.56	1036.50
	163.29	S 89°–10'–36"W	.0127985	.9998965	–2.35	–163.27	+0.02	+0.06	–2.33	–163.21
3									1204.23	873.29
	181.79	N 83°–28'–48"W	.1135500	.9935323	+20.64	–180.61	+0.02	+0.07	+20.66	–180.54
4									1224.89	692.75
	245.33	S 2°–49'–57"E	.9987782	.0494163	–245.03	+12.12	+0.02	+0.10	–245.01	+12.22
5									979.88	704.97
	295.60	N 86°–06'–09"E	.0679718	.9976873	+20.09	+294.92	+0.03	+0.11	+20.12	+295.03
1									1000.00	1000.00

Total 1095.74

+ Total	247.27	343.46
– Total	247.38	343.88
Errors	–0.11	–0.42
Corrections	+0.11	+0.42

Error of closure

$$\sqrt{.11^2 + .42^2} = .43 \text{ ft}$$

Accuracy

$$\frac{.43}{1095.74} = \frac{1}{2550}$$

*Coordinates are assumed for sta.1

Figure 6-17 Calculation of accuracy and traverse adjustment—loop traverse

142

Corrections by compass rule

Course	Lat. calcs.	Corr.	Course	Dep. calcs.	Corr.
1-2	$\frac{209.73}{1095.74} \times 0.11 = .021$	0.02	1-2	$\frac{209.73}{1095.74} \times 0.42 = .080$	0.08
2-3	$\frac{163.29}{1095.74} \times 0.11 = .016$	0.02	2-3	$\frac{163.29}{1095.74} \times 0.42 = .062$	0.06
3-4	$\frac{181.79}{1095.74} \times 0.11 = .018$	0.02	3-4	$\frac{181.79}{1095.74} \times 0.42 = .069$	0.07
4-5	$\frac{245.33}{1095.74} \times 0.11 = .025$	0.02	4-5	$\frac{245.33}{1095.74} \times 0.42 = .093$	0.10
5-1	$\frac{295.60}{1095.74} \times 0.11 = .030$	0.03	5-1	$\frac{295.60}{1095.74} \times 0.42 = .113$	0.11
Total		0.11	Total		0.42

Denominator is total distance around traverse for lat. and dep. corrections

Corrections by transit rule

Course	Lat. calcs.	Corr.	Course	Dep. calcs.	Corr.
1-2	$\frac{206.54}{494.65} \times 0.11 = .046$	0.04	1-2	$\frac{36.42}{687.34} \times 0.42 = .022$	0.02
2-3	$\frac{2.35}{494.65} \times 0.11 = .000$	0.00	2-3	$\frac{163.27}{687.34} \times 0.42 = .100$	0.10
3-4	$\frac{20.64}{494.65} \times 0.11 = .005$	0.01	3-4	$\frac{180.61}{687.34} \times 0.42 = .110$	0.11
4-5	$\frac{245.03}{494.65} \times 0.11 = .054$	0.05	4-5	$\frac{12.12}{687.34} \times 0.42 = .007$	0.01
5-1	$\frac{20.09}{494.65} \times 0.11 = .004$	0.01	5-1	$\frac{294.92}{687.34} \times 0.42 = .181$	0.18
Total		0.11	Total		0.42

Denominator is sum of lat.	206.54	Denominator is sum of dep. 36.42
differences disregarding signs.	2.35	differences disregarding signs. 163.27
	20.64	180.61
	245.03	12.12
	20.09	294.92
	494.65	687.34

Figure 6-18 Computation of corrections—loop traverse

6–6 LOCATIONS OF POINTS NOT ON TRAVERSE

As explained at the beginning of this chapter the traverse is a framework to establish other locations. An example is shown in Fig. 6-19, in which the traverse of Fig. 6-1 is shown with six critical points of the many that are needed to design a connecting road between two highways. Two points are to establish the edge of pavement of each highway and two points are to locate the centerline of a railroad track. The points are all located by *sideshots*.

In Fig. 6-20 a set of field notes for the connecting traverse is shown including sideshots to points 11, 12, 21, 22, 31, and 32. The system used here to differentiate between traverse stations and other points is to assign two digit numbers to sideshots with the first digit being the number of the station from which the sideshot is taken. Some such system should be used for orderly notekeeping.

The locations of points 11, 12, 21, 22, 31, and 32 are more useful in coordinate form. Coordinates can be computed by applying the sideshot angles and distances from the field notes to the previously computed coordinates of the appropriate stations.

First, sideshot angles are converted to bearings using new traverse bearings determined from adjusted station coordinates. Then bearings and distances are converted to differences in latitudes and departures. Adding

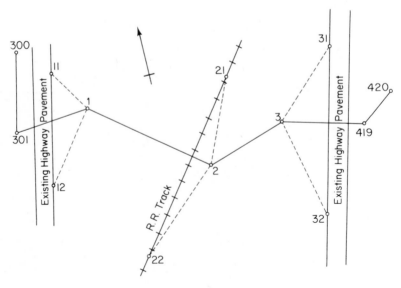

Figure 6-19 Connecting traverse used to locate design information

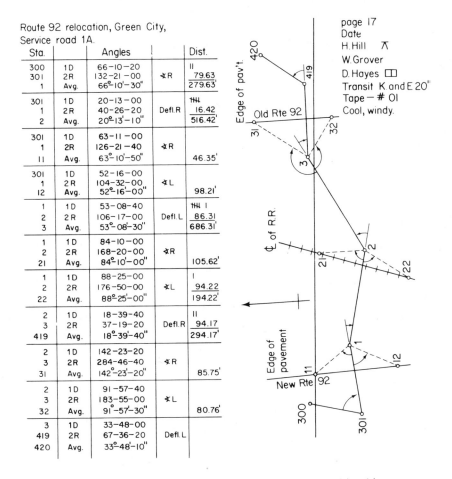

Route 92 relocation, Green City,
Service road 1A.

Sta.		Angles		Dist.
300	1 D	66–10–20		II
301	2 R	132–21–00	∡R	79.63'
1	Avg.	66°10'–30"		279.63'
301	1 D	20–13–00		⊞⊞
1	2 R	40–26–20	Defl.R	16.42
2	Avg.	20°13'–10"		516.42'
301	1 D	63–11–00		
1	2 R	126–21–40	∡R	
11	Avg.	63°10'–50"		46.35'
301	1 D	52–16–00		
1	2 R	104–32–00	∡L	
12	Avg.	52°16'–00"		98.21'
1	1 D	53–08–40		⊞⊞ I
2	2 R	106–17–00	Defl.L	86.31
3	Avg.	53°08'–30"		686.31'
1	1 D	84–10–00		
2	2 R	168–20–00	∡R	
21	Avg.	84°10'–00"		105.62'
1	1 D	88–25–00		I
2	2 R	176–50–00	∡L	94.22
22	Avg.	88°25'–00"		194.22'
2	1 D	18–39–40		II
3	2 R	37–19–20	Defl.R	94.17
419	Avg.	18°39'–40"		294.17'
2	1 D	142–23–20		
3	2 R	284–46–40	∡R	
31	Avg.	142°23'–20"		85.75'
2	1 D	91–57–40		
3	2 R	183–55–00	∡L	
32	Avg.	91°57'–30"		80.76'
3	1 D	33–48–00		
419	2 R	67–36–20	Defl.L	
420	Avg.	33°48'–10"		

page 17
Date
H. Hill 🗛
W. Grover
D. Hayes ⊞
Transit K and E 20"
Tape – # 01
Cool, windy.

Figure 6-20 Field notes—connecting traverse with side-shots

these algebraically to station coordinates gives the coordinates of the six points. The process involves the same steps we originally used to determine coordinates for our stations. There is no way to adjust these new points. Figure 6-21 illustrates the procedure for points 21 and 22.

The two points, 21 and 22, are now located in the coordinate system. It is necessary to find the direction of the track so that the angle for the road crossing can be decided. Whether the road crosses by bridge, by underpass, or at grade, this angle is critical for design. The direction of the road is determined by the crossing angle selected.

Figure 6-22 shows how to find bearing and length of the track between the two points. This process is called *inversing* because it is the opposite or

Compute bearing for course 2−1 using adjusted station coordinates. This is the back sight for side shots to 21 and 22.

Course	From fig 6−9		tan brg. ∡ Δ dep./Δ lat.	Adjusted bearing	
	Δ lat.	Δ dep.			
2 − 1	+255.12	−449.09	1.7603088	N 60°−24'−00" W	Bearing does not change

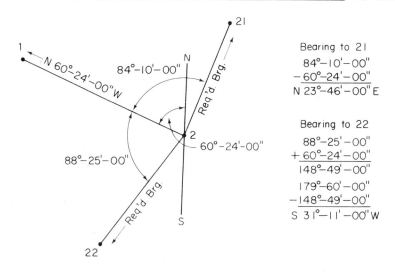

Bearing to 21

$$84°-10'-00''$$
$$-60°-24'-00''$$
$$\overline{N\ 23°-46'-00''\ E}$$

Bearing to 22

$$88°-25'-00''$$
$$+60°-24'-00''$$
$$\overline{148°-49'-00''}$$

$$179°-60'-00''$$
$$-148°-49'-00''$$
$$\overline{S\ 31°-11'-00''\ W}$$

	Length	Brg.	cos	sin	Difference in		Lat.	Dep.
					Lats.	Deps.		
2							3169.43	8787.47
	105.62'	N 23°−46'−00"E	.9151943	.4030129	+96.66	+42.57		
21							3266.09	8830.04
2							3169.43	8787.47
	194.22'	S 31°−11'−00" W	.8555149	.5177782	−166.16	−100.56		
22							3003.27	8686.91

Figure 6-21 Computing coordinates from sideshots

inverse of the process of determining coordinates. The process is described in Chap. 1 under "coordinates" although it is not called inversing there. Differences in latitudes and departures are designated Δ lat and Δ dep in this chapter.

The tan of the bearing angle is $\dfrac{\Delta\ \text{dep}}{\Delta\ \text{lat}}$.

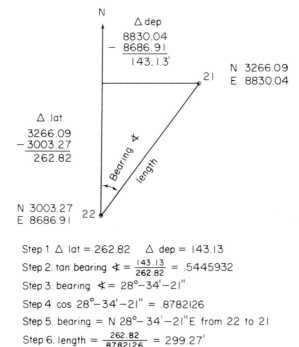

Step 1. Δ lat = 262.82   Δ dep = 143.13

Step 2. tan bearing $\sphericalangle = \frac{143.13}{262.82} = .5445932$

Step 3. bearing $\sphericalangle = 28°-34'-21''$

Step 4. cos $28°-34'-21'' = .8782126$

Step 5. bearing = N $28°-34'-21''$E from 22 to 21

Step 6. length $= \frac{262.82}{.8782126} = 299.27'$

Figure 6-22 Inversing to determine bearing and length of a line

The cos of the bearing angle is $\dfrac{\Delta \text{ lat}}{\text{length}}$ and the sin of the bearing angle is $\dfrac{\Delta \text{ dep}}{\text{length}}$. These three relationships are seen by studying Fig. 6-22.

The steps in inversing are as follows:

1. Calculate Δ lat and Δ dep.
2. Calculate tan of bearing angle.
3. Look up bearing angle in table of trig functions.
4. Look up sin or cos of bearing angle.
5. Determine bearing from the directions of Δ lat and Δ dep.
6. Determine length from the formula: cos bearing angle $= \dfrac{\Delta \text{ lat}}{\text{length}}$; or, sin bearing angle $= \dfrac{\Delta \text{ dep.}}{\text{length}}$

Traverses are frequently used to determine dimensions of property. In Fig. 6-23, the traverse of Fig. 6-13 is shown as used to locate property corners.

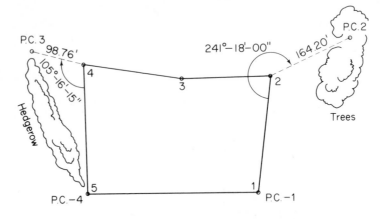

Figure 6-23 Loop traverse used to locate property corners

In this example, the property corners are marked by iron pipes and the owner wants to know the dimensions of his property and the area enclosed by its boundaries.

A station is located at each property corner if this is convenient. In the example, trees or bushes are in the way and excessive cutting would be required, so only two traverse stations are on property corners. Similarly, the points located for design in Fig. 6-19 would have been stations in the traverse if that had been convenient.

The traverse is already adjusted, which provides coordinates for P.C. 1 and P.C. 4. The coordinates for P.C. 2 and P.C. 3 are computed. Bearings and distances of the four sides of the property are obtained by inversing. The necessary calculations are performed in Fig. 6-24.

A property map may show sides of the boundary labeled with bearings and distances, or it may show lengths of sides and size of angles. The two methods are illustrated in Fig. 6-25.

6–7 AREA DETERMINATION

Any area enclosed by straight lines can be found by using *double meridian distances*. A north-south line is constructed through the westernmost corner of the area. Perpendiculars are constructed from the north-south line to the other corners of the area boundary. See Fig. 6-26.

The area boundary lines, together with the north-south line and its perpendiculars, form trapezoids and triangles. Two sides of the trapezoids and

Compute bearings for courses $2-1$ and $4-5$ using adjusted station coordinates. Both are back sights for side shots to property corners.

Course	From fig 6-17		tan brg ∠	Adjusted
	Δ lat.	Δ dep.	Δ dep./Δ lat.	bearing
2-1	− 206.56	− 36.50	.1767041	S10°−01'−14" W
4-5	− 245.01	+ 12.22	.049876	S 2°−51'−21" E

Coordinates

Sta.	Length	Brg.	cos	sin	Δ lat.	Δ dep.	Lat.	Dep.
2							1206.56	1036.50
	164.20	N 71°−19'−14" E	.3202732	.9473252	+52.59	+155.55	52.59	155.55
P.C.2							1259.15	1192.05
4							1224.89	692.75
	98.76	N 77°−35'−06" W	.2149910	.9766161	+21.23	−96.45	21.23	96.45
P.C.3							1246.12	596.30

Sta.	Δ lat.	Δ dep.	Δdep./Δlat. = tan brg. ∠	Brg.	cos or sin	Length*
P.C.1	1000.00	1000.00				
	+259.15	+192.05	(+192.05 / +259.15) .7410765	N 36°−32'−29" E	cos .8034270	322.56'
P.C.2	1259.15	1192.05				
	−13.03	−595.75	(−595.75 / −13.03) 45.721412	S 88°−44'−49" W	sin .9997608	595.89'
P.C.3	1246.12	596.30				
	−266.24	+108.67	(+108.67 / −266.24) .4081655	S 22°−12'−13" E	cos .9258468	287.57'
P.C.4	979.88	704.97				
	+20.12	+295.03	(+295.03 / +20.12) 14.663519	N 86°−05'−55" E	sin .9976827	295.72'
P.C.1	1000.00	1000.00				

Check

$$*\text{Length} = \frac{\Delta \text{ lat.}}{\cos \beta} \text{ or } \frac{\Delta \text{ dep.}}{\sin \beta}$$
Use the larger of Δ lat. or Δ dep.

Figure 6-24 Computing bearing and length of property boundary from sideshots

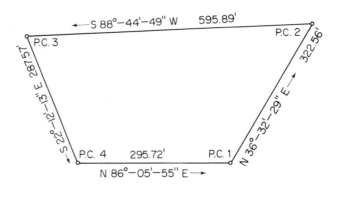

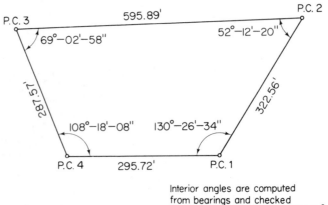

Interior angles are computed
from bearings and checked
to see that they equal $(N-2)\,180°$

Figure 6-25 Typical property maps

one side of the triangles are in an east-west direction, and the widths are in a north-south direction. Proper addition and subtraction of these geometric figures leaves the area enclosed by the boundary lines as a remainder.

Study of Fig. 6-26 shows how this is done with the area under discussion. Note that all departures are plus so that, if the difference in latitudes is north, the area is plus and, if the difference in latitudes is south, the area is minus. This results in adding large areas as we proceed up the right side of the figure and deducting parts of those areas as we proceed down the left side.

The area of a trapezoid is equal to the average length of the two parallel sides multiplied by the width or distance between them. The area of a triangle is equal to one half the length multiplied by the width. In Fig. 6-26 the lengths are in an east-west direction and the widths are in a north-south direction. The length of a side is equal to the difference between the departures of its ends and a width is equal to the difference between the latitudes of the two sides.

$$\text{Trapezoid Area} = \frac{\Delta \text{ dep side } 1 + \Delta \text{ dep side } 2 \times \Delta \text{ lat}}{2}$$

$$\text{Triangle Area} = \frac{\Delta \text{ dep}}{2} \times \Delta \text{ lat}$$

The various areas can be calculated using this approach and the desired total area determined by adding and subtracting properly.

The desired area is obtained with greater ease by using a tabular form as shown in Fig. 6-27. The method of determining area by double meridian distance (DMD) using the tabular form is as follows:

1. Begin with the course that has the most westerly departure at its starting point.

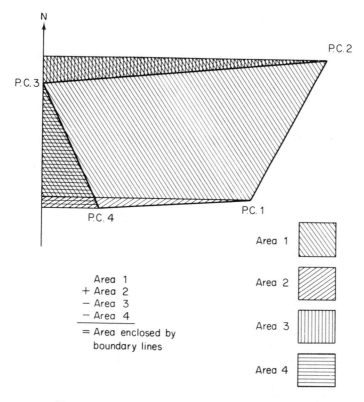

Figure 6-26 Area by double meridian distances

Course	Δ Lat.	Δ Dep.	DMD	Double areas
3 – 4	– 266.24	+ 108.67	+ 108.67	– 28,932.30
4 – 1	+ 20.12	+ 295.03	+ 108.67 + 108.67 + 295.03 <u>+ 512.37</u>	+ 10,308.88
1 – 2	+ 259.15	+ 192.05	+ 512.37 + 295.03 + 192.05 <u>+ 999.45</u>	+ 259,007.47
2 – 3	– 13.03	– 595.75	+ 999.45 + 192.05 – 595.75 <u>+ 595.75</u>	– 7,762.62 Check

$$\text{Total area} = \frac{232,621.43}{2} = 116,310.71 \text{ sq. ft. or } 2.668 \text{ acres}$$

Figure 6-27 Computing area by double meridian distances

2. Enter difference in latitudes and departures for each course consecutively. The difference is plus if the course goes north or east and minus if the course goes south or west.

3. Determine double meridian distances (DMD) using the following formulas:
   a. DMD of first course equals difference in departures of first course. Begin at most westerly point.
   b. DMD of other courses equals DMD of previous course plus difference in departures of previous course plus difference in departures of the course itself.

4. Determine double areas by multiplying each DMD by the difference in latitudes.

5. Total the double areas, deducting minus areas, and divide the total by 2 to obtain the total area.

As a check, the DMD of the last course should be numerically equal to its departure with opposite sign.

The process results in adding the distance from the north-south line of one end of each course to the distance from the north-south line of the other end of the course and multiplying the sum by the distance along the north-south line. The result is that the two parallel sides of each trapezoid and triangle are added and their sum multiplied by the width if a triangle is considered a trapezoid with one of the parallel sides equal to zero. This equals twice the area of each trapezoid and triangle since the sum of the parallel sides is not divided by two. The algebraic total is thus twice the area and must be divided by two.

PROBLEMS

1/ From the following loop traverse data prepare field notes, plot traverses to scale, adjust angles, determine bearings, determine accuracy and adjust the traverses by the compass rule. Assign a bearing of N10°–00′–00″ E to course 1—2 and coordinates of 1000.00, 1000.00 to station 1. Accurate final coordinates may vary slightly when rounded to two decimal places.

a.

1	104°–29′–40″ 208°–59′–20″	199.72′
2	77°–47′–40″ 155°–35′–20″	157.73′
3	188°–50′–20″ 17°–40′–20″	176.69′
4	79°–56′–40″ 159°–53′–20″	233.85′
5	88°–55′–00″ 177°–50′–20″	285.64′

b.

1	105°–52′–00″ 211°–44′–20″	179.03′
2	73°–54′–40″ 147°–49′–20″	146.97′
3	193°–28′–40″ 26°–57′–20″	166.87′
4	77°–46′–40″ 155°–33′–20″	209.85′
5	88°–57′–40″ 177°–55′–20″	264.30′

2/ Given the following coordinates determine bearings and distances from A to B. Distance is more accurate if the larger of the two differences (latitude or departure) is used.

	A	*B*
a.	N 900.00, E 1000.00	N 1000.00, E 918.20
b.	N 900.00, E 1081.80	N 1000.00, E 1000.00
c.	N 1000.00, E 1000.00	N 900.00, E 600.00
d.	N 339.97, E 308.89	N 200.01, E 1269.72
e.	N 121.34, E 237.56	N 790.07, E 715.35

3/ Use the unadjusted field data shown in the sketch.

   a. Adjust the traverse by the compass rule. Station A has coordinates of N 1000.00, E 1000.00 and the true bearing of B–C is S3°–11′–00″ E. If B–C is assigned a bearing of S 3°–11′–00″ E before adjustment the bearing will be slightly different after adjustment and must be changed to S 3°–11′–00″ E. To find the true bearing of any line whose location is determined from the adjusted traverse, the line must be rotated the same as B–C.

   b. Determine coordinates of manholes.

   c. Determine bearing and distance from MH–1 to MH–2 and from MH–2 to MH–3. Rotate the bearings to orient them to true north.

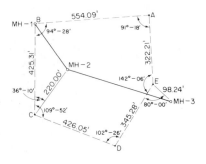

4/ Find the areas by double meridian distances within polygons whose corners have the following coordinates. Corners are listed in counterclockwise order.

a.
1) 1176.07, 1000.00
2) 1177.39, 831.35
3) 1199.10, 645.50
4) 941.93, 655.96
5) 959.53, 961.84

b.
1) 1000.00, 1000.00
2) 1200.97, 1153.56
3) 1189.77, 1070.87
4) 1220.42, 981.89
5) 971.86, 1097.44

c.
1) 1000.00, 1000.00
2) 1206.55, 1036.44
3) 1204.21, 873.19
4) 1224.85, 692.60
5) 979.88, 704.75

d.
1) 1000.00, 1000.00
2) 1176.29, 1031.08
3) 1160.68, 884.93
4) 1182.13, 719.44
5) 973.00, 737.10

INSTRUCTIONAL OBJECTIVES OF CHAPTER 7

1/ *Given a transit already set up over a traverse station, one additional traverse station, and the assistance of a rodman, the student should be able to obtain proper data to locate an object in plan and elevation relative to the traverse stations.*

2/ *Given stadia field data as they would be read in the field, the student should be able to set up field notes and enter the data correctly.*

3/ *Given stadia field data, the student should be able to reduce them to obtain horizontal distances and elevations.*

4/ *Given field data which have been reduced, the student should be able to plot a planimetric map or traverse.*

5/ *Given a map with key elevations plotted on it, the student should be able to prepare contour lines at a required contour interval.*

chapter seven

Stadia Surveying and Mapping

The stadia method may be used for measuring horizontal distances and determining elevations. It is not as accurate as taping distances or determining elevations with an engineer's level, but it is faster. The stadia method is sometimes used in traverse work and sometimes for leveling, but its chief use is to obtain field information for mapping.

7–1 STADIA PRINCIPLES

The distance between two lines diverging from a common point (vertex) increases in proportion to the distance from the common point. This principle is illustrated in Fig. 7-1 and it is demonstrated that the vertical distance between the two lines can be used to indicate the horizontal distance from the common point. Each vertical distance, if multiplied by a constant, equals the corresponding horizontal distance from the vertex. The constant is the ratio $\dfrac{H_1}{V_1}$.

In the transit telescope, two *stadia hairs* are aligned horizontally at equal distances above and below the horizontal cross hair. The *stadia intercept* or distance between stadia hairs is 1/100 of the horizontal distance between vertex and stadia hairs. When the instrumentman looks through the telescope he sees the stadia hairs imposed on the image. The greater the distance to the object sighted, the farther apart the stadia hairs will be on the image. If a level rod is vertical and the telescope is horizontal, the length of rod seen between stadia hairs is 1/100 of the distance to the rod from the vertex. Distance can thus be measured by multiplying the stadia intercept by 100. Figure 7-2 illustrates the relationship.

The simple diagram of Fig. 7-2 does not show the optical properties of the telescope. These are illustrated in Fig. 4-3. However, this simplification provides a means of visualizing the relationship between stadia intercept and

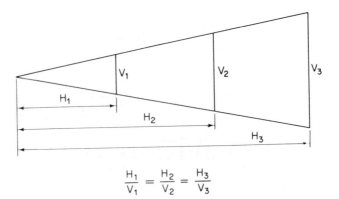

$$\frac{H_1}{V_1} = \frac{H_2}{V_2} = \frac{H_3}{V_3}$$

Any horizontal distance equals the corresponding vertical distance

multiplied by the ratio $\dfrac{H_1}{V_1}$

Figure 7-1 Stadia principle

horizontal distance. The actual relationship involves exactly the same principle. The vertex is located within an inch or two of the instrument center for internal focusing transits and approximately one ft from the instrument center toward the object for external focusing transits.

The discrepancy is ignored for internal focusing instruments and the

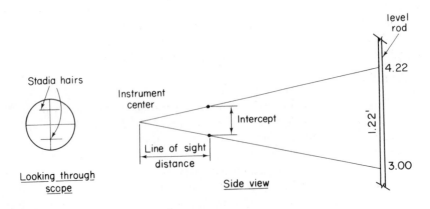

Intercept equals $\frac{1}{100}$ of line of sight distance within the transit and this ratio holds true for extensions beyond the transit. The rod is 122 ft from the instrument center.

Figure 7-2 Simplified relationship between transit and level rod

vertex assumed to be over the plumb bob. When using an external focusing instrument one foot should be added to the distance determined by proportion. External focusing transits can be recognized by movement in and out of the objective slide when the instrument is focused.

Horizontal Sights

The stadia intercept read on a level rod with a horizontal line of sight is 1/100 of the horizontal distance. Thus, the distance from the instrument to the rod can be calculated mentally from the stadia intercept. The direction to the rod can be determined by horizontal angle from a backsight of known direction. The elevation of the bottom of the rod can be determined by differential leveling procedures using the horizontal cross hair, not the stadia hairs.

Reduced to mathematical formulas, horizontal distance to rod and elevation at bottom of rod are:

$$H = 100 \, S$$

and

$$\text{Elev.} = \text{H.I.} - \text{F.S.}$$

Inclined Sights

The ratio illustrated in Fig. 7-1 applies when rod and line of sight are perpendicular to each other.

If the line of sight is inclined, the intercept on a vertical rod will be greater than 1/100 of the distance between vertex and rod. The intercept as read can be converted to the slope distance by reducing it to the value of a perpendicular intercept and multiplying by 100.

The intercept as read is reduced to the proper length by multiplying it by the cos of the vertical angle. See Fig. 7-3 for illustration. The use of the cos function does not provide a mathematically exact answer, but one which is accurate enough for stadia work.

The following formulas are illustrated in Fig. 7-3:

$$S = S' \cos \alpha$$
$$D = 100 \, S$$
$$\therefore D = 100 \, S' \cos \alpha$$

The slope distance can be converted to a horizontal distance from instrument center to rod and to a vertical distance from instrument center to the intersection of the line of sight with the rod. The horizontal and vertical components of the slope distance are illustrated in Fig. 7-4.

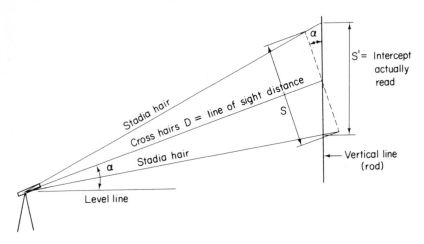

Figure 7-3 Inclined stadia sight

The two formulas illustrated in Fig. 7-4 are:

$$H = D \cos \alpha$$

and

$$V = D \sin \alpha$$

Substituting the value 100 S' cos α for D as illustrated in Fig. 7-3, the two formulas become:

$$H = 100\ S' \cos^2 \alpha$$
$$V = {}^-100\ S' \cos \alpha \sin \alpha$$

These formulas reduce field observations to horizontal and vertical components. Usually, tables such as Tables V and VI prepared from these formulas are used.

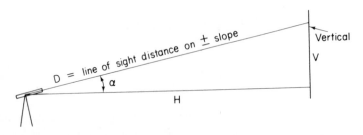

Figure 7-4 Horizontal and vertical components of inclined stadia distance

7-2 STADIA FIELD METHODS

A two or three man party usually performs stadia work. An instrumentman and rod man can perform the work with either one keeping notes. If the party has a third man he keeps notes. One instrumentman and one notekeeper can keep two rod men busy in some situations so that a four man party is sometimes economical. The party chief is usually rod man or notekeeper.

When an object is to be located by stadia in relation to the transit, the horizontal and vertical location of the instrument center must be determined. The transit is normally set up over a station of known horizontal and vertical location, such as a station hub for which elevation is determined by differential leveling. The H.I. (height of the instrument) is found by holding the level rod on the hub top and reading the height to the center of the transit horizontal axle. This height is called h.i. The elevation of the hub plus the h.i. equals the H.I. The instrument is thus located horizontally and vertically. Note that H.I. is an elevation and h.i. is a distance.

The location of an object is determined by horizontal angle from a backsight of known direction, by horizontal distance from transit to the object, and by difference in elevation above or below the instrument center. The B.S. can be a traverse station or other point having a known direction from the transit or it can be true or magnetic north. If the B.S. is a visible point, direction is indicated by recording an angle from it. If it is the north direction, a bearing or azimuth is recorded. Stadia intercept and vertical angle are recorded and horizontal and vertical distances from the instrument determined from them.

The elevation of an object can be determined by stadia from a known elevation as shown in Fig. 7-5. The method is shown for a level line of sight and for inclined lines of sight.

An inclined line of sight is often necessary to achieve the full potential of the stadia method. When obtaining information for preparation of a map, the more shots a party can obtain from one instrument setup, the more efficient the operation is. More shots are taken before moving the transit if the line of sight is raised for objects uphill and lowered for objects downhill than if all shots are kept level. However each inclined sight takes longer than a level sight because a vertical angle must be read.

If the situation justifies taking only level sights, the instrumentman levels the telescope before each sight. He reads the rod where marked by the cross hairs. He raises or lowers the line of sight with the vertical tangent screw until the lower stadia hair marks the nearest full foot. He can then determine the stadia intercept mentally by subtracting the full foot value from the reading at the upper stadia hair.

The slight angle caused by this adjustment does not cause a significant

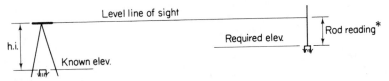

Required elev. = Known elev. + h.i. − rod

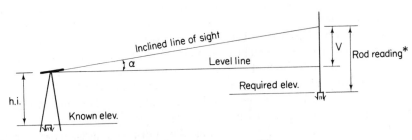

Required elev. = Known elev. + h.i. + V** − rod

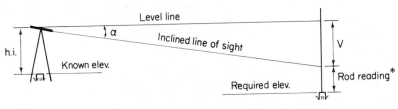

Required elev. = Known elev. + h.i. − V** − rod

  * Rod is read with cross hairs, not stadia hairs

** V = 100S′ cos α sin α (Fig. 7 − 4 and discussion following it)

Figure 7-5 Elevation by stadia

error. Speed is increased because of the simple mental arithmetic, and the chance of making a mistake is greatly decreased.

The rod reading at the cross hairs and the stadia intercept are recorded along with the horizontal angle which is read after the level rod. Figure 7-6 illustrates the procedure for reading the rod.

When sights may be either inclined or level, the instrumentman adjusts the line of sight while taking each shot so that the cross hairs intersect the

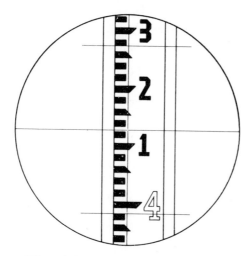

With vertical tangent screw raise telescope until
lower stadia hair is at 4.00. The upper stadia
hair will be at 4.29 and the stadia intercept
is still 0.29 but easier to determine.

Figure 7-6 Stadia sight on level rod

rod at the h.i. The scope might then be level, but it is usually inclined. This
makes the line of sight parallel to a line from the station hub below the instrument to the bottom of the level rod. This alignment simplifies calculations
as demonstrated in Fig. 7-7.

The instrumentman raises or lowers the line of sight until the lower
stadia hair marks the nearest full foot. He determines the stadia intercept
mentally by subtracting the full foot value from the reading at the upper
stadia hair. He then returns the cross hairs to the h.i. so that the vertical angle

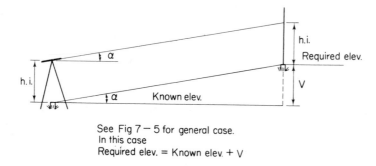

See Fig 7 – 5 for general case.
In this case
Required elev. = Known elev. + V

Figure 7-7 Stadia field method for determining elevation

is accurate. The stadia intercept is recorded and then horizontal and vertical angles are read and recorded. The rodman is waved to the next point as soon as rod readings are complete and goes there while angles are read.

7-3 STADIA TRAVERSE

If a traverse is to be established by stadia the transit is set up over a station and a horizontal angle measured between the back station and the forward station. The angles may be read to the accuracy of the transit or to a reduced accuracy more suitable to the stadia accuracy. The distance to the forward station is obtained by reading the stadia intercept on a level rod held on the hub and reading the vertical angle. Stations are usually marked by hubs with no nails because stadia accuracy does not justify centering the instrument over a nail head.

The transit is moved to the next station and the distance measured to the first station by stadia. The distance for each course is measured once from each end to check for mistakes and the two distances are averaged to improve accuracy. The angle to the next station and the distance to the next station are then obtained.

7-4 STADIA MAP SURVEY

To locate an object for mapping, it must be located in relation to a control traverse. The traverse is established by transit and tape or, for less accurate mapping, by stadia. The stadia traverse and side shots for map information may be run together. Horizontal angles are usually read only to the nearest degree or half degree for side shots. Maps of several acres or less are made from stadia field data. However, field data for most larger mapping projects are obtained by aerial photography.

7-5 NOTEKEEPING

The notes must first completely define the transit and line of sight location both horizontally and vertically. The following information is required:

1. Transit location, by station.
2. Backsight direction, by station, bearing, or azimuth.
3. Elevation of station, above appropriate datum.
4. Instrument height above station (h.i.) measured with a level rod.

The notes then locate each desired object relative to the transit and backsight. The following information is obtained in the field:

1. Stadia intercept.
2. Horizontal angle from B.S. to object.
3. Vertical angle,

    or

4. Rod reading, if all sights are level.

The following additional information is calculated in the field book:

1. Horizontal distance from transit.
2. Vertical distance above or below transit elevation.
3. Elevation of the object.

Examples of notekeeping are shown in Figs. 7-8 and 7-9. Figure 7-8 shows notes for the location of two objects, house and well, from the loop traverse previously established with transit and tape. All sights are level so no vertical angles are recorded. The elevation of station 1 is established from a B.S. on B.M.1. Note that the transit is moved before returning to B.M.1. This completes a differential leveling circuit and safeguards against mis-reading the same number twice on the rod. The elevation of station 1 is used to determine the elevation of station 2 by stadia. A check is made on station 1 after work is complete.

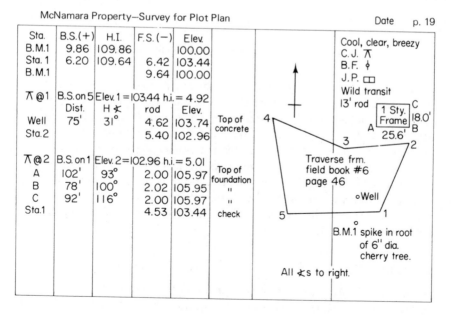

Figure 7-8 Stadia field notes with level sights

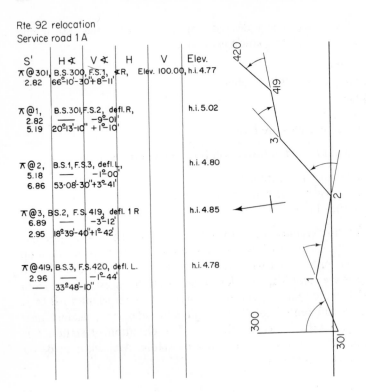

Rte. 92 relocation
Service road 1 A

Date   p. 21
F.H. ⵏ
C.H. rod, notes
Transit #7
Phila. rod
Cool,
high winds

S'	H ⵏ	V ⵏ	H	V	Elev.
ⵏ @ 301,	B.S. 300, F.S.1, ⵏR,		Elev. 100.00, h.i. 4.77		
2.82	66°-10-30'	+8°-11'			
ⵏ @ 1,	B.S. 301, F.S. 2, defl. R,		h.i. 5.02		
2.82	—	-9°-01'			
5.19	20°-13'-10"	+1°-10'			
ⵏ @ 2,	B.S.1, F.S.3, defl. L,		h.i. 4.80		
5.18	—	-1°-00'			
6.86	53-08-30"	+3°-41'			
ⵏ @ 3,	BS.2, F.S. 419, defl. 1 R		h.i. 4.85		
6.89	—	-3°-12'			
2.95	18°-39'-40"	+1°-42'			
ⵏ @ 419,	B.S.3, F.S. 420, defl. L.		h.i. 4.78		
2.96	—	-1°-44'			
—	33°-48'-10"				

Figure 7-9 Stadia field notes with inclined sights

The method of locating a building is shown. The sides of the building are measured with a cloth tape or steel tape. Stadia intercepts are not recorded but are multiplied by 100 and recorded as distances. Because this traverse is already complete no traverse courses are measured by stadia.

Figure 7-9 shows stadia notes for the connecting traverse of Fig. 6-2. Inclined sights are used. Stadia readings are taken from both ends of each course and the average distance used. Elevations are determined for each station starting with an assumed elevation at 301. They are not shown in the field notes because they are normally computed from V in the office after field work is finished.

7-6 MAPPING

A *map* is a drawing of part of the earth's surface. Natural and man-made features may be shown. Because the map must be much smaller than the actual surface it represents, it cannot show all the features that can be seen at the site and those features that are shown must be shown by use of *symbols*. Commonly used symbols are shown in Fig. 7-10. However, there is some variation in symbol usage.

The features to be shown will depend on the purpose of the map. Unnecessary features will clutter the map and make it difficult to see what should be seen. For example, a map prepared as a guide for new arrivals at a college campus would not require information on underground utilities. A property map must show property boundaries, but the slope of the ground is not necessary. A *plot plan* to be used to design a building must show property boundaries, ground slopes, and underground utilities so that the building can be designed intelligently.

Information to be shown on the map must be decided before the field party begins work. This saves time that might be spent obtaining unnecessary information and assures that necessary information is obtained. Stadia notes for mapping using a previously established traverse are shown in Fig. 7-8. Locations of a building and a well are obtained.

The scale of the map is selected to show all necessary information without

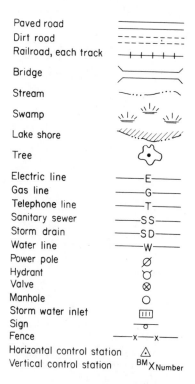

Figure 7-10 Map symbols

crowding. *Scale* means ratio between the length of a horizontal line on the map and the length of the same line on the ground. Scale is indicated by a *representative fraction* such as $\dfrac{1}{2400}$ or an *equivalent* such as 1 in. = 200 ft. This representative fraction means that any one unit of linear measurement on the map represents 2400 of the same units on the ground. In this case, one inch equals 2400 inches or 200 ft. The representative fraction $\dfrac{1}{2400}$ and the equivalent 1 in. = 200 ft indicate the same scale. Commonly used scales are 1 in. = 20, 40, 50, or 100 ft.

The map is begun by plotting the control traverse at the map scale. A protractor and engineer's scale may be used to reproduce the field angles and distances and plot stations by duplicating field procedures in miniature as shown in Fig. 6.5. When each station is plotted from the previous station, accidental plotting errors are accumulated. In addition, angles cannot be plotted accurately with a protractor. A traverse plot of many courses becomes too inaccurate when plotted this way and must be plotted by coordinates.

When plotting by coordinates each point is plotted from two baselines as shown in Fig. 7-11. The unavoidable plotting error at each station is not carried to any other station.

Next, locations from the field notes are plotted on the map with protractor and straight edge. Distances are laid off at the selected scale. There is no further accumulation of errors because each location is plotted in one opera-

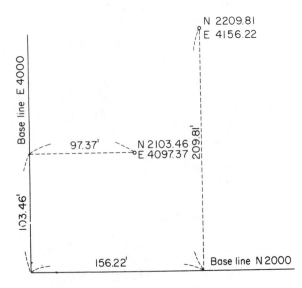

Figure 7-11 Plotting traverse by coordinates

tion. Except for very simple maps the plotting is done on a worksheet and the finished map traced from the worksheet. If the traverse is shown at all on the finished map, it is shown lightly because it is not of primary importance. It is a tool used in preparing the map and it may also be used later to control construction.

A map which does not indicate differences in elevation of the ground surface is called a *planimetric map*. This type is sufficient for many purposes, but in some cases the shape of the ground surface, or *topography*, must be shown. A map showing topography is called a *topographic map*.

Topography is indicated by contour lines. A *contour line* connects all points on the surface which are at the elevation of the contour line. The elevation is always a whole foot. Contour lines are spaced at a uniform elevation interval called the *contour interval*. Commonly used contour intervals are one, two, five, and ten ft. Usually every fifth or tenth line is a heavy line and is labeled with its elevation. The elevation is written uphill of the contour line, or the line is interrupted for it. A topographic map or *contour map* is shown in Fig. 7-12 with a profile to help in visualizing the land shape.

Some rules are given for plotting contours.

1. Each contour line forms a loop, closing on itself within the map or outside the map.

2. No single contour line can lie between two lower contour lines or between two higher ones. The highest contour line on a ridge has a lower contour line adjacent downhill and a contour line of equal elevation adjacent to it on the other side of the ridge. The lowest contour line in a valley has a higher contour line adjacent uphill and a contour line of equal elevation adjacent to it on the other side of the valley.

3. Contour lines cannot cross. Since they represent different elevations, two cannot occupy the same space even at only one point. (The case of a vertical cliff is an exception.)

Some rules for interpreting contours are given.

1. The horizontal distance between contour lines is inversely proportional to the slope. Closely spaced contour lines represent steep ground and widely spaced contour lines represent ground more nearly level.

2. Uniform spacing indicates uniform slope.

3. Contour lines are perpendicular to the steepest slope. Therefore, water flow is perpendicular to contour lines.

4. Straight contour lines parallel to each other represent man-made features.

5. Contour lines crossing a stream point upstream (see Fig. 7-12).

Topography is measured in the field by taking *ground shots* at key points

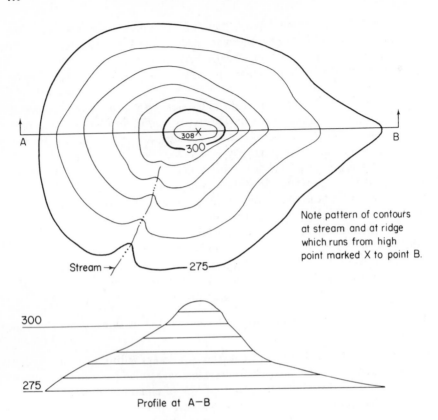

Note pattern of contours at stream and at ridge which runs from high point marked X to point B.

Profile at A—B

Figure 7-12 Contour map of hill with five foot contour interval

on the ground surface. The rod is held on the ground and the ground elevation is determined to the nearest 0.1 ft. These locations are plotted with the elevations written alongside. One method is to put the decimal point of the elevation at the plotted point.

Key points are selected in the field so that the ground slopes uniformly from each key point to all adjacent points. Then the horizontal map distance between points must be divided into equal parts to represent equal elevation differences. See Fig. 7-13 for illustration. The key points are high points, low points, and all points of slope change in any direction. Ridge lines and valleys must be defined by ground shots.

A method of plotting contour lines is shown in Fig. 7-14. A plot is shown in Fig. 7-15 with key points and the resulting contour lines. In some cases approximate plotting by eye is accurate enough.

Ground shots may be taken at regular intervals in a grid pattern and contour lines plotted from the results. The method is illustrated in Fig. 7-16. Preliminary work is time consuming because the grid system must be laid out and markers placed at the intersections. Measurements for the layout may be made with a cloth tape. Shots are taken at each grid location plus any other high or low points. Generally, more shots are read this way because some of the grid locations will not be key points.

The grid method assures that enough spot elevations will be obtained even with personnel not experienced at selecting the key points. On surface with very slight grades and no definite breaks in slope the grid system is the most practical method even for experienced personnel. The grid size must be selected to obtain enough shots, but not an excessive number. The work can often be done with an engineer's level which provides greater accuracy.

The rodman proceeds from point to point in a predetermined order for ease in notekeeping. If an extra sight is required, he lays off the distance to it in both grid directions by placing the rod to the ground and calling the distances to the notekeeper. Notes for the project shown in Fig. 7-16 are shown in Fig. 7-17. After elevations are plotted and labeled, contour lines are plotted in the usual way.

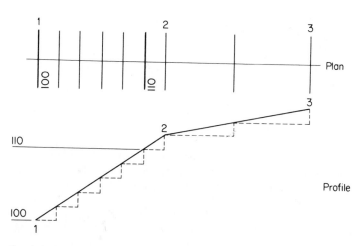

Equal vertical distances (two ft. contour interval) on a uniform slope result in equal horizontal spacing on a contour map.
Rod shots are needed at 1,2, and 3 to define the slope.

Figure 7-13 Plan and profile showing contour line spacing for a nonuniform slope

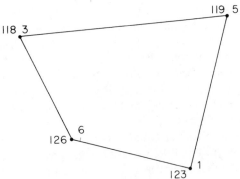

1. Plot points of known elevation and draw straight lines between them.

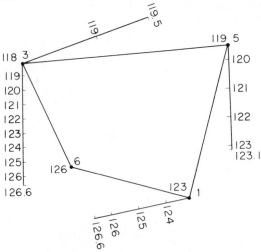

2. Construct auxiliary lines at any convenient angle and proportion them to any convenient scale to find whole foot locations. Because of the straight grades from point to point, spacing between contour lines is uniform, but the space from a plotted point to the nearest contour line is a fraction of a full space according to the elevation of the point compared to the elevation of the contour line. The purpose of the auxiliary lines is to locate points where contour lines cross the original lines.

Figure 7-14 Plotting contour lines

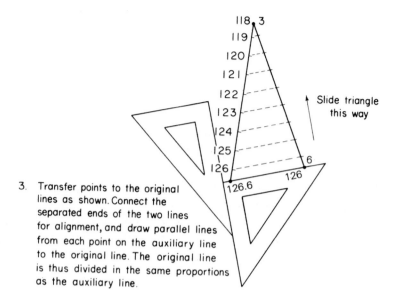

3. Transfer points to the original
   lines as shown. Connect the
   separated ends of the two lines
   for alignment, and draw parallel lines
   from each point on the auxiliary line
   to the original line. The original line
   is thus divided in the same proportions
   as the auxiliary line.

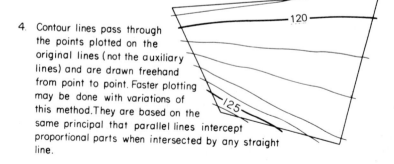

4. Contour lines pass through
   the points plotted on the
   original lines (not the auxiliary
   lines) and are drawn freehand
   from point to point. Faster plotting
   may be done with variations of
   this method. They are based on the
   same principal that parallel lines intercept
   proportional parts when intersected by any straight
   line.

Figure 7-14 (Continued)

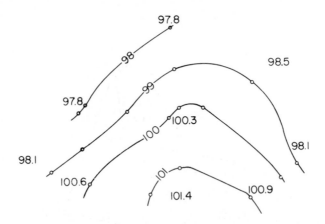

Figure 7-15 Contour lines drawn through points plotted between key points

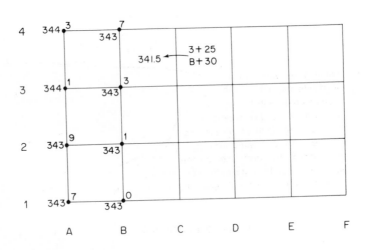

Figure 7-16 Grid layout with spot elevations partially finished

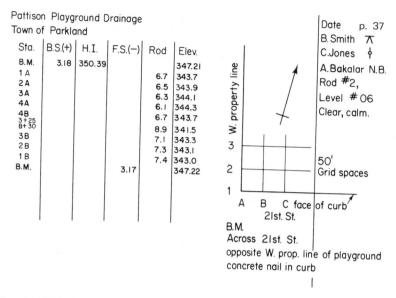

Pattison Playground Drainage
Town of Parkland

Sta.	B.S.(+)	H.I.	F.S.(−)	Rod	Elev.
B.M.	3.18	350.39			347.21
1 A				6.7	343.7
2 A				6.5	343.9
3 A				6.3	344.1
4 A				6.1	344.3
4 B				6.7	343.7
3+25				8.9	341.5
B+30					
3 B				7.1	343.3
2 B				7.3	343.1
1 B				7.4	343.0
B.M.			3.17		347.22

Date   p. 37
B. Smith ⊼
C. Jones ⌀
A. Bakalar N.B.
Rod #2,
Level # 06
Clear, calm.

W. property line

3
2
1
   A   B   C face of curb
        21st. St.
B.M.
Across 21st. St.
opposite W. prop. line of playground
concrete nail in curb

50'
Grid spaces

Figure 7-17 Field notes for contour leveling with engineer's level using grid method

PROBLEMS

1/ Set up field notes and reduce them for the following situations:

a. A connecting traverse of three stations is run starting with the instrument set up at station 14 of a completed traverse and a B.S. on station 13. A level B.S. of 4.72 is shot on B.M.1 which has an elevation of 1036.47. All horizontal angles are turned to the right. This traverse connects station 14 with station 22 of the completed traverse. Necessary data follows:

Sta.   14 H∡ = 131°–37', V∡ = 3°–04', S' = 1.96, h.i. = 5.10

Sta. 101 H∡ = 175°–18', V∡ = 6°–29', S' = 2.09, h.i. = 4.96

Sta. 102 H∡ = 164°–22', V∡ = −0°–08', S' = 2.55, h.i. = 4.59

Sta. 103 H∡ = 105°–54', V∡ = −0°–47', S' = 1.49, h.i. − 5.21

b. Sideshots of various objects are taken from station 1 with a B.S. on station 2. H.I. is obtained by taking a level B.S. of 10.49 on a B.M. with elevation 2376.44. The h.i. is 4.77. All angles are to the right. Necessary data follows:

Fence corner	H∢ = 37°, V∢ = 18°–42′, S′ = 2.37	
Edge of pavement	H∢ = 18°, V∢ = −7°–13′, S′ = 1.90	
Edge of pavement	H∢ = 115°, V∢ = 0°–48′, S′ = 2.70	
North end culvert	H∢ = 297°, V∢ = 5°–31′, S′ = 0.21	
South end culvert	H∢ = 331°, V∢ = −0°–18′, S′ = 1.05	

c. A connecting traverse of two stations is run, starting with the instrument set up at station 3 of a completed traverse and a B.S. on station 2. A level B.S. of 7.96 is shot on a B.M. of elevation 229.26. This traverse connects station 3 with station 11 of the completed traverse and sideshots are taken for mapping. All angles are to the right. Necessary data follows:

sta. 3, h.i. = 5.34

To sta. A   H∢ = 92°–16′, V∢ = 1°–18′, S′ = 2.26

To ₵ stream H∢ = 18½°,   V∢ = −0°–10′, S′ = 3.11

To ₵ stream H∢ = 68½°,   V∢ = −2°–06′, S′ = 0.82

sta. A, h.i. = 5.22

To sta. B   H∢ = 181°–06′, V∢ = 2°–59′, S′ −2.56

To ₵ stream H∢ = 91°, V∢ = −0°–37′, S′ = 1.46

sta. B, h.i. = 5.49

To sta. 11   H∢ = 217°–14′, V∢ = 0°–57′, S′ = 3.03

To ₵ stream H∢ = 134°, V∢ = −1–08′, S′ −1.21

sta. 11, h.i. = 5.38

To sta. 10   H∢ = 78°–43′, V∢ = 0° = 00′, S′ = 2.07

2/ Trace the maps onto a separate sheet of paper and plot contour lines.

a. Contours at one foot intervals

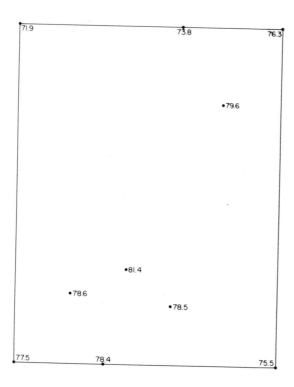

b. Contours at five-foot intervals

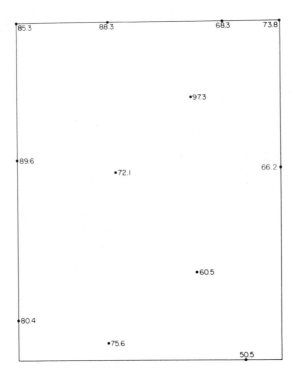

INSTRUCTIONAL OBJECTIVES OF CHAPTER 8

1/ *Given outside dimensions of a building and its distance from a parallel line, desired offset distance, and a point for the transit setup, the student should be able to prepare a sketch showing all dimensions needed to stake out the building by the baseline and offset method.*

2/ *Given the same data the student should be able to calculate angles and distances to stake out the building by the angle and distance method.*

3/ *Given a transit set up over a point, backsight, and distance to set a construction stake, tape, hammer, stake, and nail, the student should be able to act as instrumentman, rear tapeman, or head tapeman in setting a point for construction control.*

4/ *Given a set of construction stakes in place, a benchmark, a finished grade for construction, an engineer's level, and a level rod, the student should be able to act as instrumentman, rodman, or notekeeper in determining the elevation of staketops and should be able to compute cut or fill for each stake.*

5/ *Given elevation of construction stake, finished grade, and desired grade rod length, the student should be able to determine the distance above or below the construction stake to build a batter board.*

6/ *Given original elevations and final elevations on a grid pattern plus other necessary key points, the student should be able to compute earth volume of excavation or fill.*

chapter eight

Construction Surveys —General

Construction drawings show size and location of improvements to be built. The improvements, ranging from large bridges and buildings to fences and traffic signs, are positioned on a plot plan by directions and distances from existing objects. It is a surveyor's job to use surveying equipment and methods to provide reference marks close enough to the proposed construction so that carpenters, masons, and other tradesmen can build in the right location, using their own equipment and methods. He transfers ideas of architects or engineers, called *designers* in this book, from their drawings to the land in a form useful to the builder.

8-1 INTRODUCTION

The surveyor is responsible for supplying reference marks so that each individual improvement is started at the right horizontal and vertical location on the land. Measuring from the reference marks to start construction is the responsibility of the builder and, except in complex structures, internal measurements within each improvement are his responsibility also. Much of the surveying control is through stakes hammered into the ground and construction surveying is often called *construction stakeout*.

The one who designs a facility prepares an overall plan view of it on a copy of the plot plan. This is called a *site plan* and its purpose is to show relationships between the land and all the improvements that are to be constructed. Locations of proposed buildings, drives, parking lots, pipelines, and any other improvements to the land are shown. Arrangements within buildings are shown on other drawings.

This overall plan provides much of the information the surveyor needs. The improvements are tied down by directions and distances. The more important buildings are positioned from points on the site such as property corners or traverse stations. Less important improvements are positioned from the more important ones. The dimensions of buildings are not shown on the site plan, but dimensions are provided for many of the other improvements.

The surveyor finds additional information on the foundation plan, on elevation views which show final elevations called *final grades* or *finished grades*, and on detail sheets. Some knowledge of construction procedures is necessary to provide stakes in the best positions to control the work and to provide them at the right time. Reference marks must be provided for each phase as construction progresses from start to finish, but they cannot be provided too early or other construction work will destroy them.

8–2 CONSTRUCTION STAKEOUT

An example of simple construction stakeout is the placing of a stake to indicate the location for a telephone pole. Poles must be installed at definite locations to support the lines properly, but they need not be located with great accuracy. A stake is driven into the ground at the desired centerline location for the pole and a crew later removes the stake, drills a hole centered on the stake hole, and installs the pole.

Residential construction generally does not require highly accurate control. It is common for local governments to require houses to be set back certain distances from property lines. In many cases these *building lines* are defined by surveyor's stakes and the builder places the house where he chooses within the lines. An example is shown in Fig. 8-1.

Most work must be controlled more closely than this. Stakes must be located some distance away from the object to be built so that they will not be disturbed by construction operations and will be in their original positions as long as needed. Usually earth must be excavated or built up because bottom elevations of proposed construction do not coincide with the ground surface. Stakes may be set to guide the earthwork and other stakes set for construction after earthmoving is completed. As an alternative, stakes may be set with an offset great enough to be clear of the earthwork. Offsets vary from one to 10 ft and are occasionally more.

The stake indicates direction and distance horizontally and distance vertically from a point on the stake to a reference point on the object to be built. The point on the stake may be a nail or tack driven flush with the top. Horizontal distance and vertical distance are determined by the builder with a tape or rule. Both distances are measured in relation to the stake top unless the side of the stake is marked with a line from which the vertical distance is to be measured. The horizontal distance is still measured from the nail in the stake top. If there is no nail, it is measured from the mark on the side of the stake.

The equipment used to transfer line and grade from stakes to the improve-

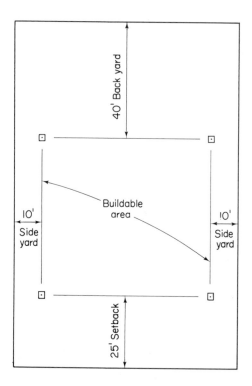

Figure 8-1 Surveyor's stakes to define building lines

ment being built includes six foot folding rules, steel or reinforced cloth tapes, several types of levels, plumb bobs, and string lines. The rules and tapes are usually calibrated in ft and in. to a sixteenth of an inch.

A builder's level, used with a level rod or sometimes used with a six ft folding rule as a rod, is a simplified version of the engineer's level and is used the same way. It has a smaller field of vision, less magnification, and a less sensitive level bubble. It is accurate enough to transfer grades for construction over distances up to about 50 ft and costs much less than an engineer's level.

Carpenter's levels and mason's levels consist of long wooden or metal frames in which two level vials are fixed, one parallel to the long edge of the level and one perpendicular to it so that the edge can be aligned level or plumb. A line level consists of a level vial with a hook at each end so that it can be hung from a string line to indicate whether or not the line is level. It must be placed at the middle of the line because its weight makes the line

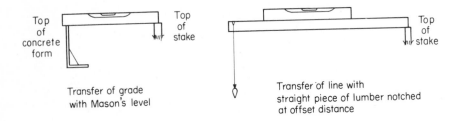

Top of concrete form

Top of stake

Transfer of grade with Mason's level

Top of stake

Transfer of line with straight piece of lumber notched at offset distance

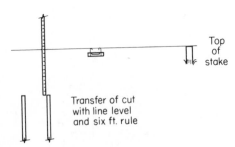

Top of stake

Transfer of cut with line level and six ft. rule

Figure 8-2 Builder's equipment for transferring line and grade

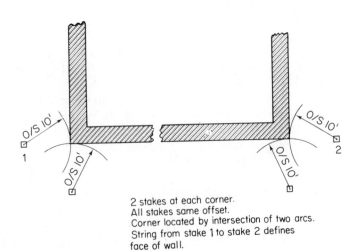

O/S 10'   O/S 10'

O/S 10'   O/S 10'

1   2

2 stakes at each corner.
All stakes same offset.
Corner located by intersection of two arcs.
String from stake 1 to stake 2 defines face of wall.

Figure 8-3 Construction stakes for building walls

sag so that it will hang level only at the center of a level string line It is placed at the middle of the string line by eye. These levels are illustrated in Fig. 8-2. The line level is useful for longer distances up to 20 or 30 ft. A hand level of the kind shown in Fig. 1-1 is also used.

These levels are used to extend the offset distance from the stake in a level line, and a plumb bob is used to plumb down to grade. A carpenter's or mason's level can be used to plumb up to grade. Methods are illustrated in Fig. 8-2.

Key points ordinarily referenced from construction stakes are center or four corners of column footings at their top elevation, outside corners of foundation walls at the first floor elevation, face of street curbs at the top elevation, centerline or edge of pavement with centerline elevations for pavement without curbs, and face of retaining walls at the top elevation. For a building, stakes may be set to locate each corner in such a way that strings between stakes can be used to align the walls as shown in Fig. 8-3.

8-3 ESTABLISHING CONTROL

An improvement to be built must be located with respect to the land, and various parts of any construction project must be located with respect to each other. The relationships must be established through an overall reference system. Several are available.

Baseline and Offset Method

A project may be staked out by locating all stakes by right angle offsets from a control line called a baseline. Often this line is the one from which the designer positions the building on the plot plan. An example is shown in Fig. 8-4 in which a building is to be located with reference to two property lines which are defined by corner markers. The building is to be constructed parallel to both property lines. Stakes are to have 10 ft offsets.

The transit is set up over one property corner and line is taken by sighting the other. Distances are measured along the property line from the southeast corner and nails put into the ground at proper locations to measure the offsets to the stakes. Backsights are set at each of the property corners unless the corner markers can be seen with the transit when set up over the nails. The transit is then set up over each nail, backsight taken on whichever property corner is farther away, and stakes set at right angles at the correct distance.

Angle and Distance Method

The stake locations can be designated by angle and distance using the southeast corner as the vertex and the baseline as a B.S. Angles and distances are computed from coordinates by inversing. The method is illustrated in Fig. 8-5.

This method permits more stakes to be put in at one instrument setting and therefore saves time for a field party at the cost of extra calculation time for one man in the office. The inversing can be done very quickly with a computer. Conditions of the site may limit visibility, making this method impossible, or the size of the project may require measuring very long distances. The baseline and offset method may be preferable for either reason.

It is easier to visualize what is being done when the baseline and offset method is used and this helps to prevent mistakes. Results can be checked by measuring diagonals in either case. The correct length of the diagonal may be computed before going into the field, or two diagonals may be measured to check that they are equal. The diagonals may be from nails set at the actual corner locations or from stake to stake.

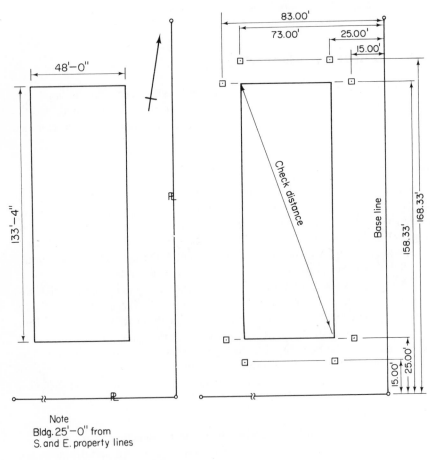

Figure 8-4 Baseline and offset stakeout

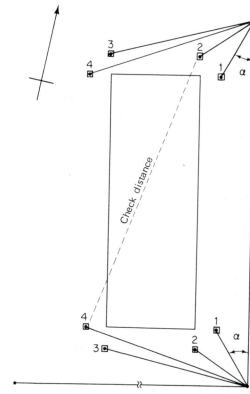

Stake	N/S	W/E	tan α = W/N / E/S	α	sin α	L = W/sin α / E/sin α
1	25	15				
2	15	25				
3	15	73				
4	25	83				

Figure 8-5 Angle and distance stakeout

Coordinate Method

Designers of complex facilities, such as a chemical processing plant which includes buildings, large concrete tanks, and many pipes running from buildings to tanks, often provide coordinates at key construction points based on two mutually perpendicular baselines. The surveyor establishes the baselines with monuments. They should be permanent (iron rods set in a concrete base) so they will be available for control of future repairs and alterations after the plant is built.

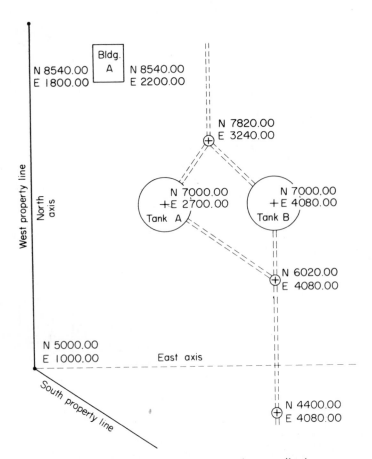

Figure 8-6 Locations of key points by coordinates

Construction stakes are set as they are needed throughout the construction period. They can be set by baseline and offset or by angle and distance using points on a baseline for the instrument setups. Figure 8-6 shows an example with coordinates on key points. The surveyor must set stakes at many other points over the construction period and must compute coordinates for them.

Vertical Control

Bench marks must be set throughout the site and should be made permanent for large projects where they may be needed for several years during construction. They should be set where they can be used conveniently and are not likely to be disturbed by construction operations. A brass plate convex upward set in concrete provides a satisfactory permanent B.M. At least three should be set so that if one is disturbed, agreement between the other two will indicate which of the three has moved. When all B.M.s are set, a level circuit is run starting and ending at the B.M. which is the origin for construction elevations. All the new B.M.s are used as T.P.s to establish their elevations. Level circuits are covered in Chap. 4.

8-4 FIELD METHODS

Wooden stakes are cut from lumber of various sizes and lengths. Stakes cut from 1 × 3 or 2 × 2 lumber and 18 in. long are typical. When accuracy requires it, a tack or nail is driven into the stake flush with the top. In some cases, the entire stake top provides satisfactory control. If additional stakes are to be set by measuring distances from previously set stakes, nails or tacks must be used to provide accurate measurements without excessive accumulated error.

Instructions to the builder are marked on the stakes. The construction object the stake refers to is noted with abbreviations such as "S.E. cor" for southeast corner, or "M.H." for manhole. The distance above or below the stake is noted and preceded by the letter "F" for *fill* if the finished elevation is above the stake and "C" for *cut* if the finished elevation is below the stake. For example, C-6.55 means the reference point of the object to be built is 6.55 ft below the stake. The horizontal distance is called an offset distance and is abbreviated o/s or ⌀. For example, o/s 10 ft means the reference point is 10 ft horizontally from the stake.

Generally, dimensions are written in ft and in. because the builder uses these units. Offsets are almost always in full feet but vertical distances are in hundredths of a ft when the surveyor determines them and he must convert them to ft and in. before writing them on the stakes. Conversion factors to convert decimals of a foot to inches and fractions are listed in Table VI.

Ties should be provided for stakes where the difficulty of resetting the stake justifies the time spent in setting the ties. *Ties* are marks placed at known locations in relation to an important point so that if the important point is moved, its location can be reestablished from the ties. They may be located by distance from the point or by angle from a B.S. in addition to distance. Ties are usually nails driven into trees, pavement, or stakes and located where they are unlikely to be disturbed.

Theoretically, any combination of two directions or distances from one or two points locates another point as discussed in Chap. 2. In practice, three ties are established to fix the position more surely and as a precaution against loss of one of them. The tie locations should be sketched in the field notebook as shown in Fig. 8-7.

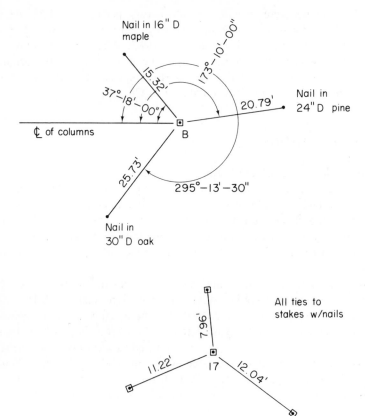

Figure 8-7 Ties in field notebook

Setting a point can be a challenge when the point must be on the top of a stake. A two or three man party is customary, The instrumentman puts the transit on line and directs preliminary placing of the stake. The head tapeman setting the stake holds the tape horizontal if he can and holds the stake alongside the tape at the correct distance. If the tape is on a slope he holds the stake a little beyond the correct tape mark so that the stake is more nearly at the correct horizontal distance. The rear tapeman holds the tape at the point under the instrument.

In a two man party the instrumentman is also the rear tapeman and can keep the tape in the correct position by holding it under his foot while sighting with the transit. He should stand on the leather thong attached to the zero end of the tape, never on the part that is calibrated for measuring.

The stake is driven slightly into the ground with a hammer, and the distance is checked. This time the tape should be held level by use of plumb bobs. The instrumentman should watch the stake as driving begins and should signal to keep it on line. The head tapeman calls for a distance check as often as he needs it and adjusts the stake top as necessary for line and distance. He drives until the stake is deep enough to be solidly in position. The instrumentman provides a continuous check on line.

If the stake is driven out of position the best way to move the top horizontally is by hitting the ground next to the stake. Hitting the top loosens the stake. Pounding stones into the ground next to the stake is necessary to move it in dry or sandy soil.

The tapeman determines the point for the nail with plumb bob and tape while being directed on line by the instrumentman. In a two man party the tapeman takes line with a pencil or plumb bob at two points on the staketop and draws a straight line between them using the tape as a straightedge. He then measures distance and marks where it falls on the line. The nail is driven there. Two distances may be measured first, a straight line drawn between them, and line taken if this procedure is preferred.

After the stakes are placed in the desired locations a level circuit is run with an engineer's level and rod shots are taken on all staketops. The procedure is the same as that for profile leveling. Closing the circuit on another B.M. provides a check that the starting B.M. was not disturbed and is usually more convenient. Elevations are computed for staketops and cuts and fills are determined by the difference between staketop elevation and finished grade of the reference point. Sample notes are shown in Fig. 8-8.

In order to control construction from the surveyor's stakes it is often convenient for the builder to establish a horizontal line at a certain number of full feet above or below the finished elevation of a portion of his work. This is done by building a *batter board* of two rods or stakes stuck in the ground with a horizontal board between them at a distance above (or below) the construction stake so that the distance from top of board to finished grade is a number of whole feet.

A nail is driven into the board directly above the stake. Figure 8-9 shows

Sta.	B.S.(+)	H.I.	F.S. (−)	Rod	Elev.	Fin. Grade	Fill
BM –1	1.21	101.21			100.00		
Stk – 1				4.73	96.48	97.00	0.52
Stk –2				5.55	95.66	97.00	1.34
BM–2			12.34		88.87		

Note: Finished grade is top of wall.

Figure 8-8 Notekeeping for grade stakes

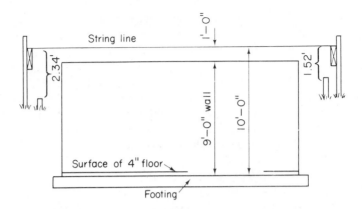

Figure 8-9 Batter boards (grade stakes are in Fig. 8-8)

batter boards arranged above two construction stakes so that the cut to the top of foundation wall is one ft. A stringline between batter boards controls all elevations and defines the outside face of the wall. The top of footing is 10 ft below the stringline at all points along the line. The basement floor is 9 ft. 8 in. below the stringline at all points and the top of wall is 1 ft. below at all points. The first floor elevation can also be controlled by the stringline.

A *grade rod* may be prepared with marks on it so that when the bottom of the rod is on finished grade a mark coincides with the string. A grade rod for the construction shown in Fig. 8-9 would have marks at 10 ft., 9 ft. 8 in., and 1 ft. so that it could be used to determine three finished grades from one string line. A level rod could be used, but the key marks would have to be memorized. If finished grade is above the stringline, marks are located from the top of the rod.

At times the builder wants surveyor's stakes set at a certain number of full feet above finished grade. This is also accomplished by running a level circuit with rod shots on the staketops. Instead of recording the rod shots and computing cuts and fills, the desired cut or fill is recorded and the neces-

Sta.	+	H.I.	—	Rod	Elev.	Fin. Grade	Cut
B.M.–1	1.21	101.21			100.00		
Stk –1				2.21	99.00	97.00	2.00
Stk –2				2.21	99.00	97.00	2.00
B.M.–2			12.34		88.87		

Note: Stakes set for same wall as in Fig. 8-8 and 8-9

Figure 8-10 Notekeeping for grade stakes with specified cut of two feet

sary rod shot is computed. Then the stake is driven until the computed rod shot is read with the rod on top of the stake. The rod is read with the stake too high and then the stake is driven and the rod read until the desired reading is obtained without driving past the correct elevation. As an alternative, the rod may be slid down the side of the stake until the computed value is read and the side of the stake marked at that elevation. Either procedure requires some trials and adjustments. It is helpful for the instrumentman to signal the number of hundredths lower or higher with the number of fingers on the right hand indicating tenths and fingers on the left hand indicating hundredths. Signals for this purpose vary greatly in different areas. Sample field notes are shown in Fig. 8-10.

8-5 GIVING LINE AND GRADE

Some types of construction require such accuracy that the actual final alignment is guided by surveying. Examples include steel structural members and large machinery which is completely fabricated before being delivered to the jobsite. The construction at the site must be accurate enough so that the prefabricated items will fit into place. Allowable errors are only a few hundredths of a foot even over distances of several hundred feet. Since the transit is set up on line and rod elevations are read for grade this type of operation is called *giving line and grade*.

Steel columns or beams are set in place on steel plates resting on a concrete base. The steel plates are bolted to the concrete with *anchor bolts* which must be set in a pattern to fit the holes in the plates. The distance from center to center of column or beam bearings is critical and is controlled to within a few hundredths of a ft by surveying methods. The spacing of bolts about the center point is also critical and is controlled by ordinary measuring methods because it involves short distances. See Fig. 8-11 for illustration.

Anchor bolts may be imbedded in the fresh concrete before it solidifies. In this case the transit is kept in place and anchor bolts are placed with constant checking of line and distance. Elevation of the concrete is checked at this time. If anchor bolts are set in drill holes in the hardened concrete, the centers are marked accurately on the concrete and drill holes located with templates from the center mark.

The elevations of the plates on which the columns or beams will rest are critical, especially in multi-story buildings, since all elevations above depend on lower elevations. Plates are adjusted in elevation using an engineer's level with the rod held on the plate. The H.I. is determined and the rod shot needed to put the plate at the correct elevation is computed. The plate is set on a bed of *grout* which is built up a specified height above the concrete for a better pressure distribution. The grout thickness is on the order of a half

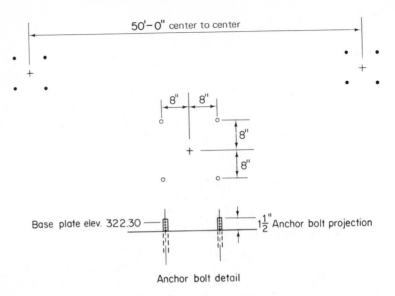

Anchor bolt detail

Figure 8-11 Anchor bolt layout

inch. The plate is placed over the bolts and its elevation checked. If too high, it is lowered by cutting away the grout and if too low, it is raised with thin steel shims under the plate. See Fig. 8-12 for illustration. The four corners of large plates may be checked and shimmed to the correct elevation. If the concrete and grout are placed as they should be, the plates will be close to

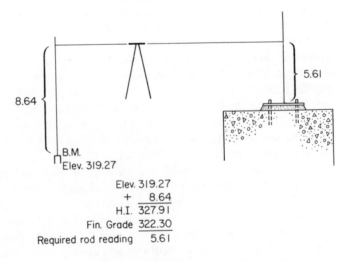

Elev.	319.27
+	8.64
H.I.	327.91
Fin. Grade	322.30
Required rod reading	5.61

Figure 8-12 Setting a base plate

Spectra-Physics Model 611 Transit and Theodolite Laser System

Figure 8-13 Transit with laser attachment

grade but below it so that only a small amount of shimming is needed and no grout need be cut away.

Columns are installed plumb by aligning the top of column with the transit on the same line it was on to align the base plate.

Giving line and grade with a transit requires that an instrumentman remain with the instrument for long periods of time even though the instrument is stationary. By using a laser attachment the instrumentman is able to set the line of sight and leave the transit until a new line is needed.

The *laser*, named for its description "light amplification by stimulated emission and radiation," is used with very low power to provide control for construction. The instrumentman aims the telescope at a desired point and clamps horizontal and vertical motions. He then directs the laser beam through the telescope and the very narrow beam follows the path of the line of sight showing a dot of light on any object in its way. The instrumentman can set the telescope on a level line and leave to hold the rod on a baseplate being set. He can then read the rod while the plate is raised until the light dot is at the correct rod reading. The telescope can be set on line and two tapemen can set points on line using the beam to guide them at various locations along the line. No instrumentman is needed. Adapters are available to provide a narrow vertical or horizontal line. The vertical line is useful for setting and checking columns or any other construction that must be plumb and the horizontal line is useful for checking level construction. A laser attachment on a transit is shown in Fig. 8-13.

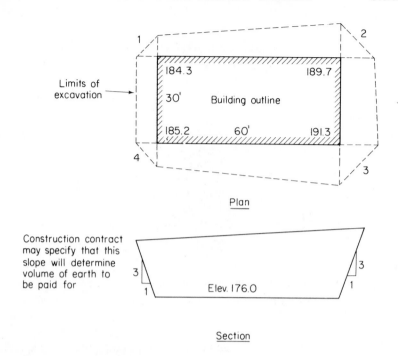

Figure 8-14 Earth volume of building excavation

8–6 EARTHWORK

The surface of the earth is changed somewhat by each construction project. Earth must be moved from one part of the site to another and often earth must be excavated and hauled away from the site or brought in to fill the site. Large quantities of earthwork are paid for by the cubic yard and must be measured to determine the price.

A volume of earth is measured by determining the shape of the ground surface before and after the earth moving operation and computing the volume difference. The procedure is the same whether the earth is added or removed. Elevations are determined throughout the area at grid locations before earthmoving begins and are determined at the same locations after earthmoving is completed. The grid size is selected to suit the roughness of the ground surface. The more irregular the ground is, the smaller the grid size must be to produce accurate results. Common grid sizes are 25, 50, and 100 ft.

The volume is computed by assuming that a square area the size of a grid square and centered at each grid intersection point has a constant depth equal

	Avg. Height	Length	Avg. Width	Volume	Cubic ft
Cube	8.3 13.7 15.3 9.2 4$\overline{)46.5}$ 11.6	60'	30'	h x l x w	20,900
Wedges					
1–2	$\frac{8.3+13.7}{2}=11'$	60'	$\frac{8.3+13.7}{3.2}=3.3'$	$\frac{1}{2}$ x hlw	1090
2–3	$\frac{13.7+15.3}{2}=14.5'$	30'	$\frac{13.7+15.3}{3.2}=4.8'$		1040
3–4	$\frac{15.3+9.2}{2}=12.2'$	60'	$\frac{15.3+9.2}{3.2}=4.1'$		1500
4–1	$\frac{9.2+8.3}{2}=8.8'$	30'	$\frac{9.2+8.3}{3.2}=2.9'$		380
Pyramids					
1	8.3	$\frac{8.3}{3}=2.8'$	$\frac{8.3}{3}=2.8'$	$\frac{1}{3}$ x h x $\frac{lw}{2}$	11
2	13.7	$\frac{13.7}{3}=4.6'$	$\frac{13.7}{3}=4.6'$		48
3	15.3	$\frac{15.3}{3}=5.1'$	$\frac{15.3}{3}=5.1'$		66
4	9.2	$\frac{9.2}{3}=3.1'$	$\frac{9.2}{3}=3.1'$		15

Total $\dfrac{25,050}{27}=928$ C.Y.

Figure 8-14 (Continued)

to the difference between the two elevations taken at that point. The result of this assumption is that at each grid intersection a volume is computed equal to a cube with surface area the size of a grid square and height equal to the difference between original and final elevations.

This method is sufficiently accurate for the central part of the earth volume where each surface square is complete. However, at the edges, triangular or other surface areas must be used to approximate the total area. In addition, the edge areas will be on a slope, whether cut or fill, so that volumes at the edges are wedges and pyramids. These volumes are computed and added to the cubes. The volume of a wedge is $\frac{1}{2}$ height × base and the volume of a pyramid is $\frac{1}{3}$ height × base.

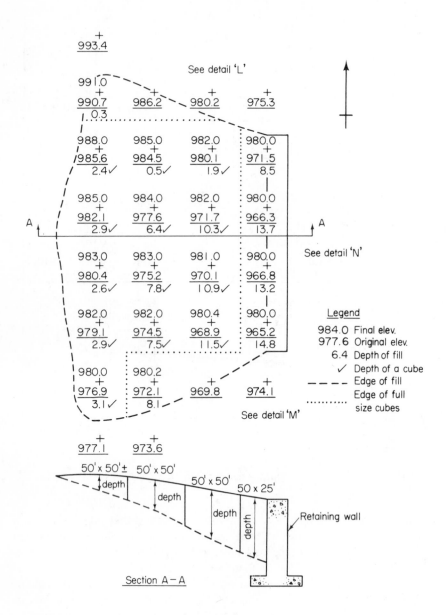

Figure 8-15 Earth volume—general case

Final elevations are not needed at the edge of the fill because the difference between original and final elevations is zero. Each volume bounded by an edge is considered a wedge or pyramid whichever more nearly approximates its shape. Distances from coordinate points to edges are needed to get the sizes of wedges and pyramids.

The volume of full size cubes is determined by totaling the "average depth of fill" for all cubes and multiplying by the surface area of the 50 ft by 50 ft grid squares. This is equivalent to piling the cubes one on top of the other and computing one volume.

Volumes along the west edge are wedges but are computed as 50 ft by 50 ft cubes with one edge of zero depth and are included in the total volume of cubes.

Along the wall are cubes with surface area of one half grid square. Depths of fill along the wall are shown and depths at the opposite side are equal to the average of the depth at the wall and the depth at the next coordinate point.

At the north and south edges are cubes, wedges and pyramids. Volumes of all are computed by the formula, Volume = area x average fill. This formula becomes $V = \frac{height}{3}$ x base for pyramids and $V = \frac{height}{2}$ x base for wedges.

Figure 8-15 (Continued)

Original grades are taken in a grid pattern that extends beyond the edges of the proposed earthwork. If edge locations are known before construction, elevations also may be obtained at the edges. A specific application where these elevations are obtained is covered in Chap. 9. *Final grades* are taken on the same grid pattern plus key points needed to divide the volume into wedges and pyramids. In general the key points are those needed to define the top and bottom of slope.

Two examples are worked. Figure 8-14 illustrates how to determine volume of a simple excavation for a building basement. A grid pattern is not needed. Original elevations are determined at the four building corners. Final elevation is the grade at the bottom of the basement floor and is obtained from the construction drawings. Volume of excavation over the slopes is divided into a pyramid at each corner and a wedge along each side. In an excavation of this kind the builder is often paid for a specific volume of earthwork such as this whether he actually excavates more or less in doing the work.

Figure 8-15 illustrates how to determine volume of an embankment where the limits are not known ahead of time. In this example a retaining wall is built at the foot of a steep slope so that the ground can be leveled. Original grades are taken beyond the area to be filled. Final grades are taken on the same grid pattern plus key points on the edges. Wedges and pyramids are determined at the edges by interpolating between known elevations for the necessary original elevations.

Volume calculations

Full size cubes (50' x 50')

```
   2.4
   0.5
   1.9
   2.9
   6.4
  10.3
   2.6
   7.8
  10.9
   2.9
   7.5
  11.5
   3.1
```
70.7 x 50 x 50 = 176,750 C.F.

Adjacent to wall

Corner	Calculations	Fill	Explanation
A	$\frac{5.7+0}{2}$	2.8	Avg. of adjacent fills.
B	$\frac{11.5+14.8}{2}$	13.2	Avg. of adjacent fills.
C	$\frac{10.9+13.2}{2}$	12.0	Avg. of adjacent fills.
D	$\frac{10.3+13.7}{2}$	12.0	Avg. of adjacent fills.
E	$\frac{1.9+8.5}{2}$	5.2	Avg. of adjacent fills.
F		0	Edge of fill.
G		0	Edge of fill.
H		8.5	Known fill.
J		13.7	Known fill.
K		13.2	Known fill.
L		14.8	Known fill.
M		0	Edge of fill.

E
from
detail "M"   Detail "N"
fill 5.7

Surface	Calculations	Volume C.F.
ABLM	$\frac{2.8+13.2+14.8+0}{4}$ x 25 x 25	4,810
BCKL	$\frac{13.2+12.0+13.2+14.8}{4}$ x 25 x 50	620
CDJK	$\frac{12.0+12.0+13.7+13.2}{4}$ x 25 x 50	15,880
DEHJ	$\frac{12.0+5.2+8.5+13.7}{4}$ x 25 x 50	12,380
EFGH	$\frac{5.2+0+0+8.5}{4}$ x 25 x 30	2,550
Total		52,240

Figure 8-15 (Continued)

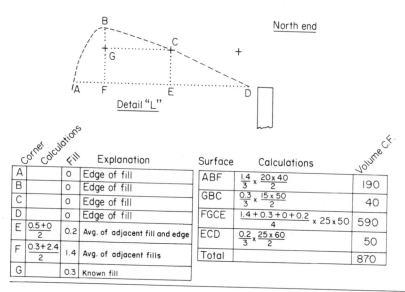

North end

Detail "L"

Corner	Calculations	Fill	Explanation
A		0	Edge of fill
B		0	Edge of fill
C		0	Edge of fill
D		0	Edge of fill
E	$\frac{0.5+0}{2}$	0.2	Avg. of adjacent fill and edge
F	$\frac{0.3+2.4}{2}$	1.4	Avg. of adjacent fills
G		0.3	Known fill

Surface	Calculations	Volume C.F.
ABF	$\frac{1.4}{3} \times \frac{20 \times 40}{2}$	190
GBC	$\frac{0.3}{3} \times \frac{15 \times 50}{2}$	40
FGCE	$\frac{1.4+0.3+0+0.2}{4} \times 25 \times 50$	590
ECD	$\frac{0.2}{3} \times \frac{25 \times 60}{2}$	50
Total		870

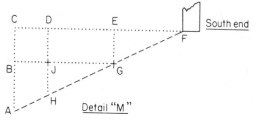

South end

Detail "M"

Corner	Calculations	Fill	Explanation
A		0	Edge of fill
B	$\frac{3.1+8.1}{2}$	5.6	Avg. of adjacent fills
C	$\frac{2.9+7.5+3.1+8.1}{4}$	5.4	Avg. of adjacent fills
D	$\frac{7.5+8.1}{2}$	7.8	Avg. of adjacent fills
E	$\frac{11.5+0}{2}$	5.7	Avg. of adjacent fill and edge
F		0	Edge of fill
G		0	Edge of fill
H		0	Edge of fill
J		8.1	Known fill

Surface	Calculations	Volume C.F.
ABJH	$\frac{0.+5.6+8.1+0}{4} \times 25 \times 25$	2,250
BCDJ	$\frac{5.6+5.4+7.8+8.1}{4} \times 25 \times 25$	4,190
JDEG	$\frac{8.1+7.8+5.7+0}{4} \times 25 \times 50$	6,750
HJG	$\frac{8.1}{3} \times \frac{25 \times 50}{2}$	1,690
GEF	$\frac{5.7}{3} \times \frac{25 \times 50}{2}$	1,190
Total		16,070

Figure 8-15 (Continued)

Total volume

Full size cubes   176,750
Adjacent to wall   52,240
North end   870
South end   16,070
$$\frac{245,930\ \text{C.F.}}{27} = 9,110\ \text{C.Y.}$$

Figure 8-15 (Continued)

PROBLEMS

1/ Draw a layout sketch suitable for the field showing construction stakes with every dimension needed to set them by baseline and offset method. Do not leave any addition or subtraction for the field.

a.

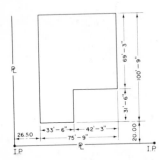

Provide a stake at each corner with no offset. Property lines are perpendicular. Only two iron pins are available.

b.

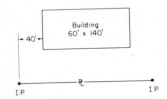

Provide two stakes at each corner with 10 ft offset. Building is to be parallel to property line and 20 ft from it.

2/ Draw a sketch and provide angles and distances from the instrument to each stake for staking the buildings of Problem 1 by the angle and distance method. *Note* that some of the distances are long for taping. In practice the instrument would probably be set up at two points and angles and distances prepared for those two setups.

3/ Finish the following grade staking field notes:

a.

Sta.	B.S.	H.I.	F.S.	Rod	Elev.	Fin Gr.	Cor F.
BM–1	9.73				186.43		
#1				8.41		189.50	
#2				10.72		189.50	
#3				4.86		189.50	
#4				6.21		189.50	
BM–1			9.73				

b.

Sta.	B.S.	H.I.	F.S.	Rod	Elev.	Fin Gr.	Cor F.
BM–1	4.88				597.63		
#1						595.00	
#2						595.00	
#3						595.00	
TP–1	5.87		2.97				
#4						596.50	
#5						596.50	
TP–2	5.51		3.84				
#6						596.50	
TP–3	3.71		9.03				
BM–1			4.12				

4/ A contractor wants stake tops to be a whole number of ft above foundation forms. Top of form elevation is 144.00. H.I. is 161.17. A stake is driven and a rod reading of 11.84 is read on the stake. The stake must be driven deeper until it is a whole number of ft above elevation 144.00. What are final rod reading and cut or fill?

5/ A stake is to be set with fill of 10.00 ft to the top of wall. Finished elevation of top of wall is 336.50 and the H.I. is 334.27. What rod reading is needed to set the stake at proper elevation?

6/ Design elevation of a footing is 483.30. A stake is set at elevation 494.23. What cut or fill should be marked on the stake? At what distance above and below the stake can a batter board be built to provide a cut or fill of a whole number of feet and what will cut or fill be at each of the two settings?

7/ Finished grade is 153.00, a grade stake is at 157.96, and a grade rod of 6.00 ft is desired. How far above or below the grade stake should a batter board be built?

8/ Original and final elevations are given for the 50 ft grid pattern shown. Compute the volume of earth removed.

Sta.	Original Elev.	Final Elev.
A1	224.6	224.6
A2	223.5	223.5
A3	222.3	222.3
A4	221.1	221.1
B1	225.2	225.2
B2	224.2	216.6
B3	223.1	215.5
B4	222.0	222.0
C1	226.0	226.0
C2	224.8	224.8
C3	223.6	223.6
C4	222.5	222.5

9/ An embankment is built to an elevation of 40.00 with a top width of 200 ft and length of 500 ft. Side slopes are 1:2. The 100 ft grid pattern is shown with the embankment superimposed. The original ground elevation could be interpolated at the toe of embankment slope but the ground is nearly level and such a refinement would make very little difference in the answer.

	1	2	3	4	5
A	36.4	36.8	37.8	38.2	39.2
B	35.2	35.6	36.5	37.1	38.0
C	34.2	34.5	35.5	36.2	37.2
D	33.1	33.2	34.0	35.3	36.3
E	32.1	32.2	33.0	34.1	35.1
F	30.7	30.2	32.1	33.2	34.4
G	30.1	30.2	30.9	31.2	33.3
H	29.7	30.0	30.8	31.1	32.0

10/ Original ground elevations are given at the corners of a proposed 100 ft by 80 ft building. The subgrade for the building is 100.00. Excavation will have slopes of 3:1 and fill will have slopes of 1:1. Compute volume of fill, volume of excavation; and volume of waste or borrow.

INSTRUCTIONAL OBJECTIVES OF CHAPTER 9

1/ *Given a starting elevation and slope for a construction project, the student should be able to:*
   a. Determine the elevation at any station.
   b. Prepare a grade sheet.

2/ *Given cuts or fills at stakes, the student should be able to determine how far above or below stakes to construct batter boards for a grade rod of a given length.*

3/ *Given stake elevations and cuts or fills at two stations and a rod shot on one stake, the student should be able to show mathematically how to align the transit so that the line of sight is parallel to finished grade and how to determine the grade rod.*

4/ *Given an elevation and cut or fill at one stake and the slope, the student should be able to show mathematically how to align the transit so that the line of sight is parallel to finished grade and how to determine the grade rod.*

5/ *Given base width, finished grade, side slope, and center-line stakes, the student should be able to determine locations for slope stakes with the assistance of an instrumentman and tapeman. He should also be able to determine cut or fill at stakes and keep field notes for slope staking.*

6/ *Given cross sections drawn to scale or field data, the student should be able to compute earth volume between two stations by the average end area method and by using the prismoidal formula.*

chapter nine

Construction Surveys Dealing with Slopes

Many construction projects are long and narrow with constantly changing elevation and consist of repetitive construction for much of their length. Examples are pipelines, highways, and tracks. Construction stakeout procedures for these projects are discussed in this chapter.

9–1 SLOPES

Slopes in civil engineering projects are designated by a percentage or decimal which is equal to the tangent of the angle formed between the sloping line and a horizontal line. The slope when designated this way is often called a grade. The term slope is used instead in this book to prevent confusion with the term grade meaning elevation. Grade is used throughout this book to mean elevation. A slope of 1.15% or .0115 means the sloping line changes elevation 1.15 ft in a horizontal distance of 100 ft. A plus slope rises in a forward direction and a minus slope is downhill in a forward direction.

9–2 PIPELINES

When construction stakeout is considered there are two categories of pipeline—pressure and gravity. Liquid or gas which fills a pipeline under pressure, will flow upward as readily as downward and slope is of little importance. Water and natural gas lines are of this type and it is customary to construct them at a certain depth below the surface without regard to the slope of the pipe. Line is staked at an offset for this type of pipeline and grade is measured from the ground surface at the edge of the trench.

Gravity pipelines are only partially full of liquid and the liquid flows from a higher elevation to a lower one. It flows only as far as the pipe continues to slope downward. The steepness of the slope determines the velocity at which the liquid flows and therefore the quantity that flows in a given time. The slope is an important factor in the design and construction of these pipelines. Storm drains and sanitary sewers are of this type, and line and grade must be indicated for these pipes without regard to the grade of the ground surface.

LINE AND GRADE

A plan and profile of a sanitary sewer are shown in Fig. 9-1. It is the surveyor's task to stake it so that it can be built to proper line and slope. Stakes are shown arranged at 50 ft intervals as needed to control the horizontal alignment of the sewer. A large offset is needed because of the sewer trench. Note that stationing starts from the lower end of a gravity line.

In order for the surveyor to mark a cut on each stake he must determine the grade of the sewer at the station of the stake. The pipe invert is the control point for grade. The invert is the low point of the inside circumference of the sewer. The liquid flowing in the pipe flows on this surface so it is a logical point of control. Pipes vary a little in size and shape due to manufacturing imperfections and therefore do not fit together precisely. Controlling the invert assures that the irregularities are at the top where they do not impede flow.

The grade at any point of the sewer is determined by adding to the known

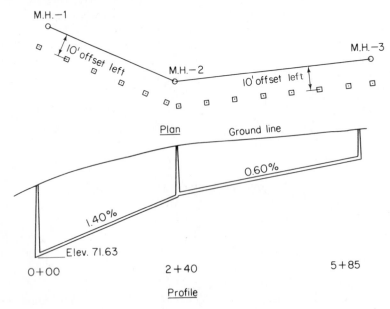

Figure 9-1 Plan and profile of sanitary sewer showing surveyor's stakes

Description	Station	Slope	Invert Grade
MH – 1	0+00		71.63
		.0140	.70
	0+50		72.33
		.0140	.70
	1+00		73.03
		.0140	.70
	1+50		73.73
		.0140	.70
	2+00		74.43
		.0140	.56
MH–2	2+40		74.99 out/75.09 in
		.0060	.06
	2+50		75.15
		.0060	.30
	3+00		75.45
		.0060	.30
	3+50		75.75
		.0060	.30
	4+00		76.05
		.0060	.30
	4+50		76.35
		.0060	.30
	5+00		76.65
		.0060	.30
	5+50		76.95
		.0060	.21
MH–3	5+85		77.16

Check

$$240' @ .0140 = 3.36'$$
$$345' @ .0060 = \underline{2.07'}$$
$$5.43$$
$$+ \ \underline{.10} \ \text{M.H. drop}$$
$$5.53$$

$$71.63$$
$$+ \ \underline{5.53}$$
$$77.16$$

Figure 9-2 Grade sheet for sewer of Fig. 9-1

grade of a lower point an increase in elevation determined by the horzontal distance from the lower point and the slope of the sewer. The work should be tabulated and performed in an orderly way with suitable checks as shown on the *grade sheet* in Fig. 9-2.

The grade or elevation of the sewer is calculated at each station where a stake is to be set. Then when elevations of stake tops are known, cuts can be computed.

Baxter Ave. Sewer, Reed City

STA	BS(+)	H.I.	FS(-)	Rod	Elev.	Fin Gr.	Cut		Date	Page
BM-1	3.21	81.56			78.35					H. Hill inst.
0+00				4.28	77.28	71.63	5.65	MH-1		A. Bakalar
0+50				4.10	77.46	72.33	5.13			rod.
1+00				3.22	78.34	73.03	5.31			W. Higgins
TP-1	12.01	92.63	0.94		80.62					Chief
1+50				12.90	79.73	73.73	6.00			Wild transit
2+00				11.80	80.83	74.43	6.40			Wild level
2+40				10.85	81.78	74.99 out / 75.09 in	6.01 / 6.11	MH-2		Rod - 13
2+50				10.78	81.85	75.15	6.70			Tape - 11
3+00				9.71	82.92	75.45	7.47			clear, cool,
3+50				8.63	84.00	75.75	8.25			calm.
4+00				7.55	85.08	76.05	9.03			
4+50				6.51	86.12	76.35	9.77			
TP-2	5.72	91.95	6.40		86.23			MH-2		
5+00				5.82	86.13	76.65	9.48			
5+50				5.33	86.62	76.95	9.67			
5+85				5.36	86.59	77.16	9.43	MH-3		
TP-3	2.90	84.06	10.79		81.16					
BM-1			5.71		78.35					
	+23.84		-23.84							

check

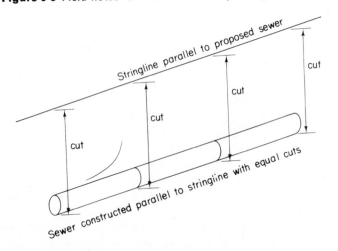

MH-3

Cut from here

Sewer

Stakes

All offsets are 10' left of stakes

MH-1

Figure 9-3 Field notes for sewer stakeout (see Figs. 9-1 and 9-2)

Stringline parallel to proposed sewer

cut

cut

cut

cut

Sewer constructed parallel to stringline with equal cuts

Figure 9-4 Pipe laid with stringline as a guide

Construction Stakeout

Stakeout should be performed in two stages. First, stakes should be set at correct station and offset as described in Chap. 8. Then a level circuit should be run with rod shots on all stakes. Stakes may be used as T.P.s also, but there will be less likelihood of a mistake if a rod shot is recorded for each stake; and, when a T.P. is read on a stake, a separate F.S. is recorded in addition to the rod shot for that stake.

Sample field notes are shown in Fig. 9-3. Cuts are computed in the field book. The station number, offset, and cut are then marked on each stake. Offset is marked on the side toward proposed construction or it is marked right or left, meaning the construction is right or left of the stake while looking forward.

Construction Methods

The traditional method of building a sewer to correct line and slope is to establish a stringline at a vertical distance above the proposed sewer and parallel to it. The stringline must therefore have the design slope of the sewer. The pipe is laid section by section starting at the lowest end with each section of pipe fitting into the previous one at the joint. The first piece of pipe is checked at both ends with a *grade rod* for proper distance below the stringline and its horizontal alignment is checked with a plumb bob hung from the stringline.

The next piece of pipe is joined to the first and laid so that the opposite end is the correct distance below the stringline and on line. See Fig. 9-4 for illustration.

The stringline is put into position by building a *batter board* at the correct height above each stake top to require a cut of a predetermined length to grade. The length is normally a whole number of feet and a grade rod is prepared for this length. The batter board is built crossing the trench with the top level and at the required elevation. A nail is driven into the top of the batter board at the correct offset to put it on line. A stringline stretched from nail to nail is on line at the predetermined height above the sewer invert at all points. See Fig. 9-5 for illustration. See Fig. 9-6 for illustration of a grade rod and how it is used.

When a stringline is used, two sections of line at the same line and slope should always be in place as a check against mistakes. They form one continuous straight line if the three batter boards and nails are correctly positioned.

A *manhole* is required at a change of slope or line in a sewer and at certain spacing when there is no change in slope or line. At the center of the manhole a vertical drop is needed to permit proper flow. Thus at a manhole two cuts are recorded on the construction stake, one for the outgoing sewer

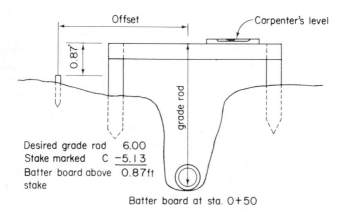

Desired grade rod   6.00
Stake marked   C   −5.13
Batter board above   0.87ft
stake

Batter board at sta. 0+50

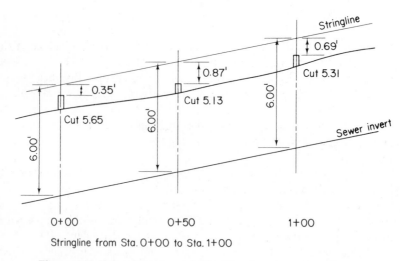

Stringline from Sta. 0+00 to Sta. 1+00

Figure 9-5 Batter boards and stringline for sewer (see Fig. 9-3)

and one for the incoming one, and the stringline leading downstream and upstream start at different elevations. One tenth of a ft is a typical drop for small size sewers.

The stringline can be replaced by a transit located on a platform over the centerline of a manhole (or on the sewer centerline opposite any stake).

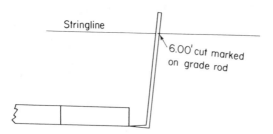

Stringline

6.00' cut marked
on grade rod

Figure 9-6 Grade rod in use

It is not practical to align the transit for a whole foot cut. The grade rod must be marked to conform to the height of the transit. Line can be taken from a plumb line held over the next manhole or over another point on line. The point on line must be located by offset from the construction stake.

The line of sight can be adjusted to correct slope by sighting the level rod at the correct reading as shown in Fig. 9-7, or a vertical angle can be cal-

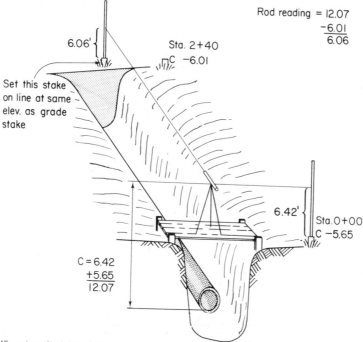

Rod reading = 12.07
$$\frac{-6.01}{6.06}$$

6.06'

Sta. 2+40
C −6.01

Set this stake
on line at same
elev. as grade
stake

6.42'

Sta.0+00
C −5.65

C = 6.42
$$\frac{+5.65}{12.07}$$

When transit sights 6.06 on new stake, the line of sight is on line and slope 12.07' above proposed invert line. Grade rod should be marked at 12.07'

Figure 9-7 Transit aligned to line and slope

culated from the known slope and the transit set on line at that vertical angle using a range pole or plumb bob string for line. The level rod or range pole need not remain in place after the instrument is clamped. The angle should be recorded when set and checked periodically during construction.

Slope is converted to a vertical angle as follows:

$$\tan \text{ of angle} = \text{slope}$$
$$\tan \alpha = .014$$
$$\alpha = 0° 48'$$

The tan of 0° 48′ is .01396 when carried to five decimal places. The vertical vernier has a least count of one min so the transit cannot be aimed more accurately. The error in this case is .00004 multiplied by the horizontal distance, 0.01 ft at 240 ft. It could be as high as 0.03 ft at 240 ft. Errors of this size are not significant for ordinary sewer construction.

Use of Laser

Once the transit is aligned, the line of sight can be fixed by a laser beam directed through the transit as described in Chap. 8 and it can be read on the grade rod by the crew installing the pipe.

A laser is available which can be set in a manhole location on line and leveled with the beam at the center of the proposed pipeline. The beam is then elevated to a vertical angle equal to the slope for the sewer line. The dial with which the angle is set is calibrated in percent slope so that no conversion is needed. When properly aligned the beam defines the centerline of the pipe up to the next manhole as shown in Fig. 9-8.

The trench can be dug using the laser beam as a guide for line and approximate depth. Pipe is laid using a template the size of the inside cross section of the pipe. The template has a translucent target at the center through

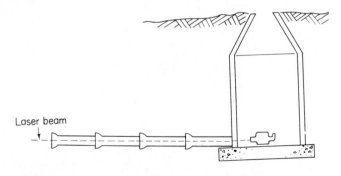

Laser beam

Figure 9-8 Laser positioned in manhole to define centerline for pipelaying

which the light beam can be seen. The template is needed at both ends of the first piece of pipe to place it in position. Each piece after that is fitted to the joint of the previous piece and the opposite end is aligned with the template and the laser beam. See Figs. 9-9 and 9-10 for illustration of the laser and template.

The templates are useful for small sewers up to about 12 in. in diameter. Using a template results in a sewer built with a straight centerline rather than a straight invert although the variation at the invert is small. Larger pipes are aligned with the target set at a specified height above the invert for each piece of pipe and the result is a more accurate invert. Construction stakes are required only at each change in slope or direction when laser is used to align a sewer.

9-3 ROADWAYS AND TRACKS

Highways, streets, and tracks for vehicles must be built at design slopes. The shape of the earth precludes building them level, yet economy of vehicle operation dictates that slopes not be too steep. Excavating earth and building earth embankments are both expensive and are kept to a minimum when designing. Also an effort is made to economize by matching embankment size with quantity of excavation. All these factors are involved in the decision to build at the design slope. Pavement construction is not highly accurate compared to buildings or even sewers. Nevertheless, stakes should be set and marked to one hundredth of a foot and precautions taken to avoid an accumulation of errors. Tracks must be more accurately controlled than pavement slope because the movement of the vehicles using tracks is completely controlled by the slopes and alignments of the tracks.

Surveyor's stakes are needed at 25, 50, or 100 ft stations and in a few cases the actual work can be guided by laser beam with stakes farther apart. Grade sheet computations are the same as for sewer work. Stakes are set on the centerline for highway pavement and at offsets of two to four feet outside the construction for streets and tracks.

For streets, the top of curb is the reference grade and stakes are driven by the paving crew at the correct offset and a stringline stretched from stake to stake, so that it duplicates the line and slope of the back of the proposed curb. A line of surveyor's stakes is often required for each curb because grade is not always the same on both sides of the street.

If the curb is to be of concrete, a long form is installed with its top edge duplicating the stringline and the concrete is placed into this form. If stone curb is to be installed, each piece is placed with its back edge touching the stringline along its length. Usually, both curbs are built first and pavement between curbs is built at the correct distance below the tops of curbs.

Track construction includes several steps. *Ballast*, consisting of crushed

Spectra-Physics Model 855 Dialgrade Laser System

Figure 9-9 Laser for construction of sewer lines

Spectra-Physics Model 855 Dialgrade Laser System

Figure 9-10 Template for aligning pipe with laser beam

stone or similar material, is placed and compacted to an elevation so that wood or concrete ties can be placed on the ballast and rails attached to the ties with top of rail approximately at correct grade.

Stakes for track construction are usually provided at finished grade. The rails are aligned by pushing long steel bars into the ground next to the rails and forcing the rails transversely and are lowered or raised by removing or adding ballast under the ties until the rails are at line and grade as determined from the surveyor's stakes with a rule and carpenter's level. The rails are aligned between stakes by eye or with a stringline stretched at the edge of the rail.

Tracks are also built by track laying machines which lay rails and spike them in place at finished grade while being guided by a line at grade and at a predetermined offset. The line is of cord or wire stretched from one surveyor's stake to the next. The stakes may be required at 10 ft spacing for accurate alignment of high speed tracks. Only one line of stakes is needed to control a pair of rails.

A variety of methods may be used to transfer line and grade from construction stakes for highway paving.

Bituminous concrete is placed by paving machines which place a continuous strip of pavement while following a line placed to define the edge of pavement or else at grade a foot or two off line. The machine follows the line with a sensor device which controls the paving to conform to the line. The line is a cord or wire stretched between surveyor's stakes 10 ft. apart. One control line is sufficient for pavements up to 30 ft in width. If bituminous curbs are built, they are constructed on top of the pavement edge after paving.

Portland cement concrete pavement is placed in forms similar to street paving but without curbs and requires one line of construction stakes at 50 or 100 ft spacing on straight sections and two lines at 25 or 50 ft on curves. Centerline grade is the reference grade for one line of stakes and pavement edges are referenced when two lines are staked. Grade is transferred up to 20 or 30 ft by line level from construction stakes. Portland cement concrete is also placed by a method called slip forming which is similar to bituminous concrete paving and is staked out the same way.

9-4 EARTHWORK STAKEOUT

Before construction stakes are set for paving or laying track, the earth must usually be rearranged, sometimes to great depths in *cuts* or *excavations* or to great heights in *fills* or *embankments*. Stakes must be set to control the earthwork and must be set at the extremities of the proposed excavation or embankment area. Topsoil must be removed before fill is placed and stakeout for fill indicates the edge of the fill at an elevation below the existing top soil where the edge of fill meets natural ground.

The customary method is to stake the centerline of the improvement at 50 or 100 ft stations and at points where the earthwork final grade coincides with the existing grade. The designer's profile drawing shows where these points are. These points are the transition points between cut and fill and are important to the builder's operation. Stakes called *slope stakes* are set at the same stations as the centerline stakes at points at the edge of the proposed embankment or excavation.

The finished sides of the embankment or excavation are called *side slopes*. Their slopes are much steeper than the longitudinal centerline slopes. They are designated by the tangent of the angle between the slope and a horizontal line and are expressed as a ratio. Typical side slopes are from 1 on 1 to 1 on 3.

The horizontal distance from centerline to edge of earthwork, whether in cut or fill, depends on width of the finished surface, on the slope of the sides of the earthwork, and on the difference between elevation of original ground at the limit of the earthwork and the finished grade of the earthwork. The finished earthwork surface, whether in cut or fill, is called finished *base* because it is the base for pavement or tracks. See Fig. 9-11 for the relationship among these factors. Note that the width of earthwork is related to grade of base above or below original ground only at the earthwork limits.

The distance from centerline to edge of earthwork is equal to one half the finished base width plus the horizontal component of the earthwork side slopes. The trick is to locate the point at which the side slope of the proposed earthwork will intersect the original ground. This is where the slope stake is driven. Fortunately, it does not have to be located with great accuracy and is measured only to the nearest one tenth of a ft.

Stakeout requires two steps. Centerline stakes are set first using the preliminary survey traverse as a base for their location. The connecting traverse of Chap. 6 is an example of the type of preliminary traverse used to establish line for stakeout. A cross section leveling circuit is then run to set slope stakes and also obtain other offsets and elevations needed to plot ground cross sections.

The design drawings show the relationship between the traverse and proposed centerline. They also show finished grades at 50 or 100 ft stations. Finished grade is top of rail or top of pavement and top of earth base is a constant distance below that. This distance is shown on the track or pavement cross section which is part of the design drawings.

Centerline stakes will be lost because of earthmoving operations. Sometimes they are referenced by ties. Whether they are referenced or not, the only practical place to mark cuts and fills is on stakes outside the embankment or excavation area. Slope stakes are marked with cut or fill computed from the ground adjacent to the stake. Cut or fill for slope stakes is figured the same as other cuts and fills except that they are measured to the tenth of a ft from the ground surface, not from the stake top.

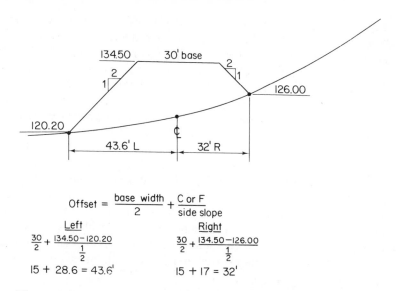

Figure 9-11 Relationships: base width, fill, side slopes, slope state offsets

It is convenient to compute the cuts and fills from rod readings without converting to elevations. With an H.I. determined from a B.M., the B.S. reading that would be read on a level rod if it could be held on the final grade of the earthwork is computed. This figure is called the *grade rod* and it is plus if final grade is below the H.I. and minus if final grade is above the H.I. These signs are logical because a backsight is plus when the bottom of the rod is below H.I. and minus when the bottom of the rod is above H.I. and the rod is upside down. Computing the grade rod is illustrated in Fig. 9-12.

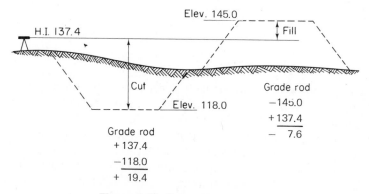

Figure 9-12 Computing grade rod

The zero end of a tape is held over the centerline stake and the rodman walks at a right angle to the centerline with the rod and other end of the tape to the point where he judges the embankment or excavation will meet the existing ground and a rod shot is taken there. At the correct point the horizontal distance read on the tape will equal one half the base width plus the cut or fill divided by the side slope. The cut or fill is equal to the difference between grade rod and the rod shot which is called the *ground rod*. The relationship is illustrated in Fig. 9-13.

The rodman must compute mentally and adjust his position until the rod is at the point where the horizontal distance and ground elevation satisfy the relationship expressed by the formula, distance = one half the base width + (C or F) ÷ side slope.

To obtain cut or fill from the point where the rod is, the rod shot (ground rod) is subtracted from grade rod. Ground rod is always plus. A plus answer indicates a cut and a minus answer indicates a fill. See Fig. 9-14 for illustration.

Mental arithmetic for the first trial and for two adjustments to locate the correct distance in Fig. 9-13 is as follows:

Base width of 40 ft and side slope of 1 on 2

Try 35'

$$35' \neq 20 + (7.6 - 1.7)\,2$$
$$35' \neq 31.8'$$

Try 28'

$$28' \neq 20 + (7.6 - 3.2)\,2$$
$$28' \neq 28.8'$$

Try 29.2'

$$29.2' = 20 + (7.6 - 3.0)\,2$$
$$29.2' = 29.2'$$

The mental calculations are actually easier with a little practice than they appear to be in print. Nevertheless, the rodman's job requires skill and he is the key man. The party chief often handles this job.

Notes are usually started at the bottom of the page and continue up so that the notes and sketch coincide with the field locations while proceeding forward. The notekeeper is less likely to confuse right and left when using this procedure. Figure 9-15 shows typical notes. Cut and fill are written over the line and distance from the centerline is written under the line. Additional

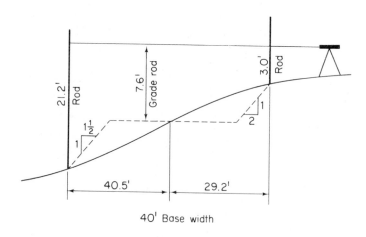

$$40.5 = 2.0 + (21.2 - 7.6)1\tfrac{1}{2}$$
$$40.5 = 40.4 \ \text{O.K.}$$

$$29.2 = 20 + (7.6 - 3.0)2$$
$$29.2 = 29.2 \ \text{O.K.}$$

Figure 9-13 Computing distance to edge of cut and fill

shots are taken at breaks in the ground surface as in the sample cross section notes of Chap. 4. It is understood that the farthest shot represents the limit of earthwork. A slope stake is driven there on a slant to differentiate it from the centerline stakes and it is marked with cut or fill and station. The notes provide the data necessary to plot a cross section of the ground surface which will be used to compute the quantity of earthwork.

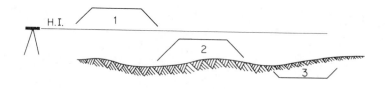

	1	2	3
Grade rod	− 3.4	+ 2.6	+ 13.7
Ground rod	− 8.2	− 8.2	− 8.2
Cut or fill	− 11.6 fill	− 5.6 fill	+ 5.5 cut

Figure 9-14 Cut and fill computed from grade rod and ground rod

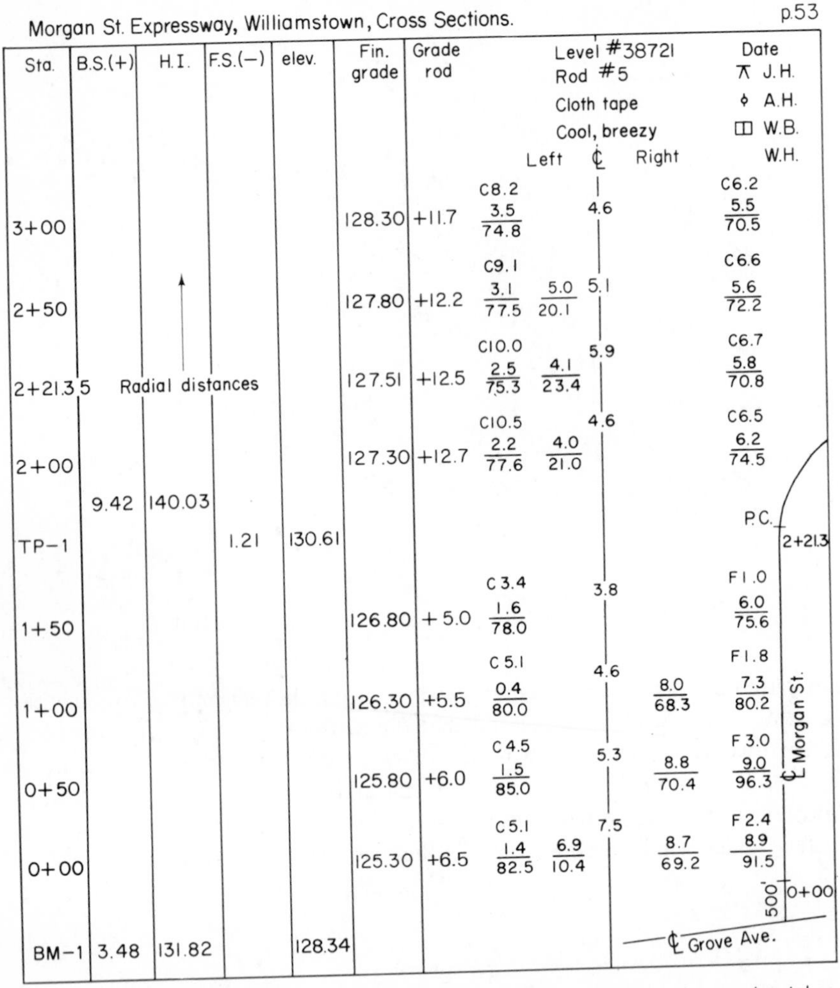

Morgan St. Expressway, Williamstown, Cross Sections.   p.53

Sta.	B.S.(+)	H.I.	F.S.(−)	elev.	Fin. grade	Grade rod	Left	¢	Right	Date
										Level #38721 ⊼ J.H.
										Rod #5 ◊ A.H.
										Cloth tape ▢ W.B.
										Cool, breezy W.H.
3+00				128.30	+11.7	$\frac{3.5}{74.8}$	C8.2	4.6	C6.2 $\frac{5.5}{70.5}$	
2+50				127.80	+12.2	$\frac{3.1}{77.5}$	C9.1	5.0 5.1 $\frac{}{20.1}$	C6.6 $\frac{5.6}{72.2}$	
2+21.35	Radial distances			127.51	+12.5	$\frac{2.5}{75.3}$	C10.0	4.1 5.9 $\frac{}{23.4}$	C6.7 $\frac{5.8}{70.8}$	
2+00				127.30	+12.7	$\frac{2.2}{77.6}$	C10.5	4.0 4.6 $\frac{}{21.0}$	C6.5 $\frac{6.2}{74.5}$	
TP−1	9.42	140.03	1.21	130.61					P.C. 2+21.3	
1+50				126.80	+5.0	$\frac{1.6}{78.0}$	C3.4	3.8	F1.0 $\frac{6.0}{75.6}$	
1+00				126.30	+5.5	$\frac{0.4}{80.0}$	C5.1	4.6	$\frac{8.0}{68.3}$ F1.8 $\frac{7.3}{80.2}$	
0+50				125.80	+6.0	$\frac{1.5}{85.0}$	C4.5	5.3	$\frac{8.8}{70.4}$ F3.0 $\frac{9.0}{96.3}$	¢ Morgan St.
0+00				125.30	+6.5	$\frac{1.4}{82.5}$	C5.1	6.9 7.5 $\frac{}{10.4}$	$\frac{8.7}{69.2}$ F2.4 $\frac{8.9}{91.5}$	500' 0+00
BM−1	3.48	131.82		128.34				¢ Grove Ave.		

Note: Cut and fill are computed in the field and marked on the grade stakes. Elevations are computed and original cross sections plotted in the office.

Figure 9-15 Field notes for grade stakes

9–5 EARTH VOLUME

The cross sections of original ground plotted to scale are known as *original cross sections*. These are kept until earthwork is complete. Field data are then obtained to plot *final cross sections* at the same stations. These are plotted with the original cross sections and together show the upper and lower boundaries of the earth volume that was placed or removed at that cross section. Thus the cross sectional area of the earthwork is plotted to scale at each station.

In most cases the volume of earthwork between stations is a *prismoid* (nearly a prism) with two ends parallel and the sides defined by lines which are approximately straight. The volume between cross sections is approximately equal to the average of the two end areas multiplied by the distance between them. This approximation is called the *average end area method* and is accurate enough to be the most common way of determining volume of earthwork for payment to the builder when he is being paid by the cubic yard.

The *prismoidal formula* gives more accurate results but requires a cross section midway between the two end areas. Thus, more office time is spent on calculations and the added accuracy is usually not justified since field accuracy is not high and the price of earthwork is not high compared to other construction items. The prismoidal formula is:

$$V = \frac{(A_0 + 4M + A_1)}{6} \times L$$

where A_0 and A_1 are the two end areas, M is the area at the middle, and L is the total length. The shape of the middle area is determined by averaging the lengths of all sides of the two end areas. Its area is not the average of the two end areas. All data are in ft so that the answer is in cubic ft. To obtain cubic yards, the usual unit for earthwork, the answer is divided by 27.

The necessary areas may be determined in various ways. If the cross sections are rather simple they can be divided into rectangles, trapezoids, and triangles and the areas determined mathematically. The areas can be plotted on coordinate paper and the squares counted and the total number of squares multiplied by the area of one square. The areas can be determined with a planimeter which is a device for measuring irregular areas. The outline of the area is traced and the planimeter indicates the area in square in. This area is then converted to square ft according to the scale of the cross section. Calculations are illustrated in Fig. 9-16.

The first and last volume sections of an embankment or excavation have one end with an area of zero at the locations where the earthwork meets original ground. Earthwork may begin or come to an end by gradually merging with the original ground, but often the end of embankment is the start of excavation or vice versa. In either situation, the earthwork coincides with the original ground at a line as illustrated in Fig. 9-17.

Special staking procedures are required. The line where earthwork coincides with original ground must be located. This line of transition does not occur at a station nor is it perpendicular to the axis of the earthwork. Its center is staked as part of the centerline stakeout. Its ends are located at an offset on either side of the centerline of one half the base width at points that

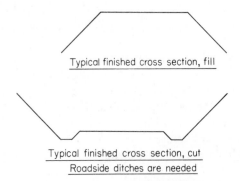

Typical finished cross section, fill

Typical finished cross section, cut

Roadside ditches are needed

If cross section areas are determined by planimeter it is necessary to plot final cross sections superimposed on original cross sections. It is helpful to do this no matter what method is used to determined areas. Either final cross sections are plotted from field leveling data or templates of the various specified final cross sections are prepared and the appropriate one is traced onto the original cross section at the correct distance above or below it.

Sta.	Planimeter area sq. in.	Area sq. ft.	Calculation	Volume, C.Y.
0+00	34.3	3430		
			$\frac{3430 + 4140}{2} \times \frac{50}{27}$	7010
0+50	41.4	4140		
			$\frac{4140 + 5650}{2} \times \frac{50}{27}$	9060
1+00	56.5	5650		
			$\frac{5650 + 4820}{2} \times \frac{50}{27}$	9700
1+50	48.2	4820		
			$\frac{4820 + 3970}{2} \times \frac{50}{27}$	8140
2+00	39.7	3970		
			Total	33,910 C.Y.

Figure 9-16 Determination of earth volume

are at the same elevation as the ground at the centerline stake. They are located by successive trials with a level rod until the rod shot is the same as at the center stake. At these points the final base grade coincides with the grade of the existing ground. Slope stakes are set at these points and together with the centerline stakes define the transition line.

The volume of an end section can be determined by treating it as a wedge or pyramid, or a combination of the two, whichever most nearly approximates its shape. See Fig. 9-18 for illustration.

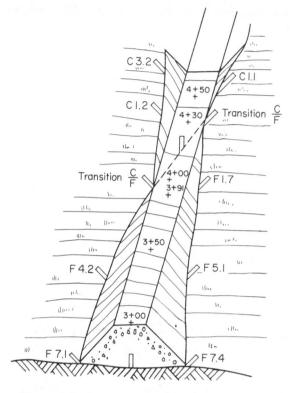

Figure 9-17 Earthwork showing transition from cut to fill

Sta.	Area		Calculation		Volume C.Y.		
	Cut	Fill	Cut	Fill	Cut	Fill	
3+00		1260					
				$\frac{1260+1040}{2} \times \frac{50}{27}$		2130	
3+50		1040					
				$\frac{1040+160}{2} \times \frac{41}{27}$		910	
3+91 Transition.	0	160					
				$160 \times \frac{39}{3} \times \frac{1}{27}$		80	
4+00	not	used					
			$140 \times \frac{39}{3} \times \frac{1}{27}$		70		
4+30 Transition	140	0					
			$\frac{140+360}{2} \times \frac{20}{27}$			190	
4+50	360						
				TOTALS	260	3120	

Figure 9-18 Earth volume at transition between cut and fill (see Figure 9-17)

PROBLEMS

1/ A line slopes up hill at 2.1% from station $0+00$ at elevation 123.57. What is the elevation of the line at station $3+62$?

2/ A line slopes down hill at 1.7% from station $7+50$ at elevation 2340.17. What is the elevation of the line at station $9+23$?

3/ Prepare a grade sheet at 50 ft stations for a sewer line with a slope of 1.0% from station $0+00$ to station $1+40$ and 0.6% from station $1+40$ to station $2+00$. Allow a drop of 0.1 ft at the M.H. station $0+00$ has an elevation of 321.06.

4/ Prepare a grade sheet at 50 ft stations for a gravity pipeline from station $0+00$ with elevation 119.24 to station $1+71$ with elevation 121.05.

5/ A stake is marked C–3'–9½". How far above or below the stake should a batter board be built for a five-ft grade rod?

6/ A stake is marked C–7'–5". How far above or below the stake should a batter board be built for a six-ft grade rod?

7/ A pipeline is to be constructed at a constant slope. A transit over station $0+00$ is 5.19 ft above a stake marked C–6.46. A stake at $2+00$ is marked C–8.37. In order to align the transit line of sight parallel to the proposed pipeline, a level rod is held on the stake at station $2+00$. What will the rod reading be when the transit is properly aligned?

8/ In order to set the line of sight parallel to a pipeline with a slope of 2.7% what vertical angle should be used?

9/ A pipeline is to be constructed with a slope of 6%. A transit is set up 4.72 ft above a stake marked C–9.13. What vertical angle should be set into the transit to align it parallel to the pipeline and what will the grade rod be when using the transit line of sight?

10/ Find volume of earth fill in cubic yards between stations 2+00 and 3+00 by average end area method.

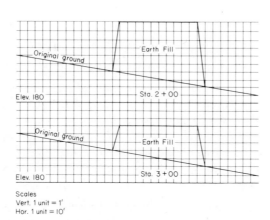

Scales
Vert. 1 unit = 1'
Hor. 1 unit = 10'

11/ Find volume of earth fill in cubic yards by average end area method and by prismoidal formula between stations 113 and 114 if the embankment has a 30 ft base width and side slopes of 1 on 1½. Cross section grade stake notes are given.

Sta.	L	₵	R
113	F6.2	F3.3	F1.0
	6.3		1.1
	———		———
	24.3		16.5
114	F7.8	F5.0	F3.4
	6.4		2.0
	———		———
	26.7		20.1

INSTRUCTIONAL OBJECTIVES OF CHAPTER 10

1/ *Given the angle of intersection between two streets, pavement width, curb radius, and offset distance, the student should be able to determine the necessary angles and distances to set stakes at the centers of the curb arcs and on the radii to the P.C. and P.T.*

2/ *Given the radius, angle of intersection, desired spacing of stakes on the curve, and station of P.I., the student should be able to determine deflection angles and distances for staking a circular curve either with stakes at equal spaces or with stakes at specified stations. Distances should be calculated for taping from the P.C. and for taping between adjacent stakes.*

3/ *Given the slopes of the two tangents, the station and elevation of the PVI, and length of curve, the student should be able to determine elevations on a vertical curve at designated stations.*

chapter ten

Construction Curves

Curves are often required in construction. The simplest curve used is an arc of a circle and its most frequent use is in pavement construction where a curve is preferable to an angular change of direction. A curve is a necessity for safety on high speed highways and is also used for changes in direction on low speed streets because of its more pleasing appearance. A curve is designed for the speed at which it will be used and must therefore be constructed accurately. Vehicles at high speeds and vehicles riding on rails at any speed require transition curves so that they can gradually ease from straight line travel to a circular curve and from the curve to the new straight line direction. Only circular curves are covered in this book.

10–1 CIRCULAR CURVE GEOMETRY

The centerline of a vehicular route is designed with bearings and distances between angle points. A change in direction is measured by deflection angle designated I and called the *angle of intersection*. When dividing a tract of land into streets and building lots, instead of the centerline, the boundaries of the streets, called *right-of-way lines*, are designed with bearings, distances, and angle points. Curves are placed at the angle points as illustrated in Fig. 10-1. Each curve is tangent to the two straight lines. The straight line segments between curves are called *tangents*. When proceeding forward, the point at which a curve starts is a *point of curvature* (P.C.) and the point at which the next tangent starts is a *point of tangency* (P.T.)

Because the curve is part of a circle, radii at the P.C. and P.T. are perpendicular to the tangents and intersect at the center of the circle. Construction of these two radii illustrates some relationships shown in Fig. 10-2.

10–2 CIRCULAR CURVE STAKEOUT

The radius is selected by the designer and from it other relationships are determined so that the curve can be staked out. The station of the point of

229

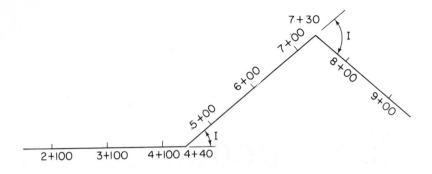

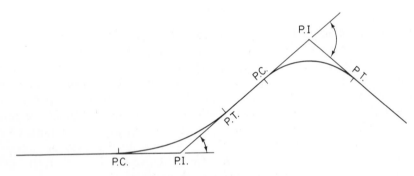

Figure 10-1 Route with curves

intersection (P.I.) and the angle I are also fixed by the designer. The rest of this chapter deals with street and highway pavement. However, the computations and stakeout procedures for circular curves are useful for staking right-of-way lines on curves and the principles apply to railroad track curves, although the method used for them is different.

Street Curb

An example of a circular curve on a vehicular route is the curved curb, called a *curb return* or *radius curb*, at the intersection of two streets. The curb return is built on a circular arc of short radius to facilitate traffic movement around the corner. The radius of the curb depends on the speed and volume of traffic. A longer radius provides easier traffic movement but is more costly, so it is not used unless volume and speed of traffic justify the cost.

The designer of the street intersection selects a radius length for the curb returns. The method of stakeout and the required computations are the surveyor's responsibility. The builder usually requires offset stakes at 25

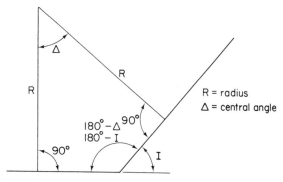

a. Relationships showing Δ and I are equal.

R = radius
Δ = central angle

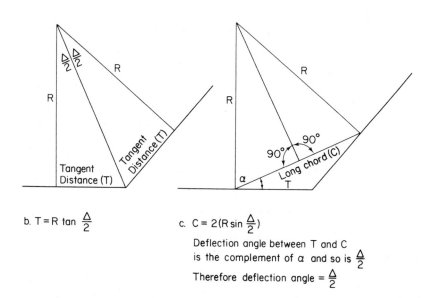

b. $T = R \tan \dfrac{\Delta}{2}$

c. $C = 2(R \sin \dfrac{\Delta}{2})$

Deflection angle between T and C
is the complement of α and so is $\dfrac{\Delta}{2}$

Therefore deflection angle = $\dfrac{\Delta}{2}$

Figure 10-2 Circular curve relationships

or 50 ft stations for curbs of both streets plus an additional stake at each end of the curve. Another stake is set at the center of the circle so that the builder can swing a radius from this stake with a tape to locate the radius curb. Finished grade is commonly a straight slope from P.C. to P.T. and is determined by the builder. See Fig. 10-3 for illustration.

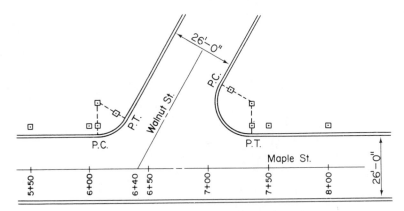

Requirements:
> Place stakes at 50ft stations, P.C. and P.T. with 5ft offsets and at center of curves for Maple St. curbs.

Procedure:
> 1. Set up on offset line and set stakes up to P.C.
> 2. Set up on P.C. stake, back sight on offset line, turn 90° and set center stake at distance R−offset, turn to deflection angle and set P.T. stake at chord distance (based on R−offset), turn 180° and set P.T. stake for opposite radius curb.
> 3. Set up on P.T. stake for opposite radius curb, backsight on offset line and set stakes similarly to step 2.

Calculations:
> Given: Station of intersection of Maple ₵ and Walnut ₵.
> Find: Station of P.C. of first radius curb.
> Method: Distance back from ₵ intersection to P.C. is "T" of a curve of radius equal to the curb radius plus half the street width. See following example.

Figure 10-3 Stakeout for radius curb

Highway Pavement

A survey party staking out highway pavement usually proceeds forward along the centerline setting stakes at 50 or 100 ft intervals and sets a stake at the P.C. The station of the P.C. is determined by subtracting the tangent distance (T) from the station of the P.I. With the transit at the P.C. and a backsight on line to the rear, the telescope can be plunged and the P.I. staked. Then the deflection angle $\dfrac{\Delta}{2}$ can be laid off and the P.T. located on line at the *long chord* distance (C). The transit can then be set up on the P.T. and a backsight taken on the P.I. Plunging the telescope aligns the transit on the next tangent. The station of the P.T. is determined by adding the length of the curve (L)

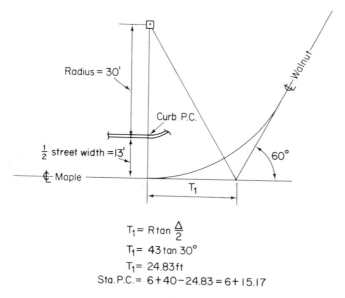

$$T_1 = R \tan \frac{\Delta}{2}$$
$$T_1 = 43 \tan 30°$$
$$T_1 = 24.83 \, \text{ft}$$
$$\text{Sta. P.C.} = 6+40-24.83 = 6+15.17$$

Find: Station of P.T. of second radius curb.
Method: Distance ahead from ℄ intersection to P.T. is "T" of a curve with the same radius and a central angle which is the complement of the previous central angle.

$$T_2 = R \tan \frac{\Delta}{2}$$
$$T_2 = 43 \tan 60°$$
$$T = 74.48 \, \text{ft}$$
$$\text{Sta. P.T.} = 6+40+74.48 = 7+14.48$$

Figure 10-3 (Continued)

to the station of the P.C. Length of curve is determined by proportion. The curve is a part of a complete circle and its length is proportional to its central angle. A complete circle has a central angle of 360° and a length of $2\pi R$.

Therefore, the length of a circular curve is $\dfrac{\Delta}{360} \times 2\pi R$. Stationing on circular curves of railroad tracks is determined by the length in 100 ft chords. Stationing by curve length is covered in this book.

It is usually necessary to set stakes on the curve. This is done by setting the transit at the P.C. and positioning stakes on the curve by deflection angle and distance from the P.C. In order to set stakes at intermediate points, the curve may be considered to be divided by the stakes into a number of arcs. Each arc from P.C. to stake has a central angle which can be used to deter-

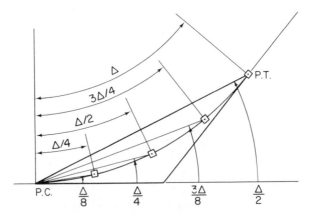

Figure 10-4 Deflection angles to intermediate points on a curve

mine a deflection angle and chord distance from P.C. to stake using the formulas for locating the P.T. as given in Fig. 10-2.

For example, the partial curve to the midpoint of a full curve has a central angle one half the size of the central angle for the full curve. The deflection angle is therefore one half the deflection angle for the full curve or $\dfrac{\Delta}{4}$ and the length of the chord to that point is $2\left(R\sin\dfrac{\Delta}{4}\right)$. See Fig. 10-4 for illustration.

Sample calculations are shown in Fig. 10-5 for a case in which stakes are desired on the curve at spacing no greater than 25 ft. The length of curve is determined and divided into the minimum number of equal parts necessary to make the spacing less than 25 ft. The chord from the transit at the P.C. to each stake is computed in Fig. 10-5. Stakes can thus be set with one end of the tape held at the P.C.

The chord from any stake to an adjacent stake is equal to the chord from P.C. to stake #1 because the curve lengths between stakes are equal. The curve can thus be staked out by taping a distance equal to the first chord length from each stake to the succeeding stake. Angles are turned from the P.C. in either case.

The P.T. must be accurately located because it is the point from which the next tangent starts. It may be located by the long chord from the P.C., or by a succession of short chords from the P.C., or by setting up the transit at the P.I. and measuring from the P.I. The method requiring fewest tape measurements is the most accurate, but obstacles may sometimes prevent using it.

A circular curve by its construction is symmetrical about a line connecting its center with the P.I. Therefore, the curve of Fig. 10-4 or 10-5 could be staked out from either P.C. or P.T. with the same angles and distances. To put the transit on line in the direction of the forward tangent, it can be set up on the P.T., backsighted on the P.C., plunged, and the original deflection angle turned to the new tangent. Therefore, it is not necessary to set the P.I. to stake the forward tangent. The forward tangent is staked at the first station beyond the P.T. and then stakes are set at regular intervals on the tangent.

Deflection angles and chords for stakeout can be computed from any stake on the curve. The transit can be set up over any stake and a B.S. taken on an adjacent stake to set other stakes. See Fig. 10-6 for illustration. The original deflection angle is turned to the left to put the transit on line tangent to the curve, the scope is plunged and the original deflection angle laid off to the left and the original subchord measured to locate the next stake. Double the deflection angle can be laid off in one step either before or after plunging instead of turning the deflection angle twice.

In most cases the curve which is to be staked out is designed on a slope. The stakes must be marked with cuts and so must be located at points where the finished grade is known. It is customary to compute finished grades at 25 or 50 ft intervals on a curve and set a stake at each of these points.

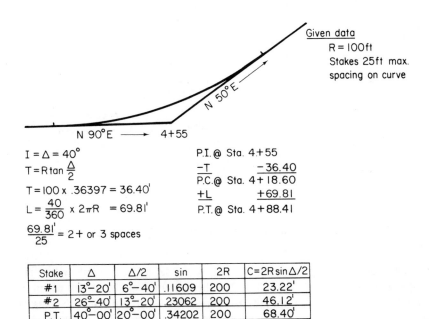

Given data
$R = 100$ ft
Stakes 25ft max. spacing on curve

N 50°E

N 90°E ⟶   4+55

$I = \Delta = 40°$

$T = R \tan \dfrac{\Delta}{2}$

$T = 100 \times .36397 = 36.40'$

$L = \dfrac{40}{360} \times 2\pi R = 69.81'$

$\dfrac{69.81'}{25} = 2 + \text{ or } 3 \text{ spaces}$

P.I. @ Sta. 4+55

$\begin{array}{ll} -T & -36.40 \\ \hline \text{P.C.@ Sta. } 4+18.60 \\ +L & +69.81 \\ \hline \text{P.T.@ Sta. } 4+88.41 \end{array}$

Stake	Δ	Δ/2	sin	2R	C=2R sin Δ/2
#1	13°–20'	6°–40'	.11609	200	23.22'
#2	26°–40'	13°–20'	.23062	200	46.12'
P.T.	40°–00'	20°–00'	.34202	200	68.40'

Figure 10-5 Computations for curve stakeout—equal short chords

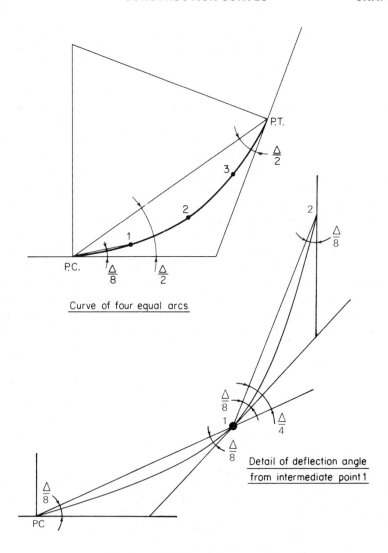

Figure 10-6 Deflection angles from intermediate point on a curve

If the curve of Fig. 10-5 has to have stakes set at 25 ft intervals the first stake beyond the P.C. is at sta 4 + 25. The tangent distance, length of curve, and P.C. station are computed the same way as in Fig. 10-5. Necessary calculations for setting stakes at predetermined points are shown in Fig. 10-7. The central angle for the subchord from P.C. to station 4 + 25 is proportional to the length of curve that subtends it. This applies to the central angle for any chord. Central angles are computed by proportion and chords are computed from the angles.

It is usually advantageous to tape from stake to stake instead of taping all chords from the P.C. The subchords necessary to do this can be calculated as follows:

$$C = 2R \sin \frac{\Delta}{2}$$

From sta. 4 + 25 to sta. 4 + 50, Δ = 17°59′ less 3°40′ (see Fig. 10-7)

$$\Delta = 14°19' \text{ and } \frac{\Delta}{2} = 7°09'30''$$

$$C = 200 \sin 7°09'30'' \text{ or } 24.92 \text{ ft.}$$

C from sta 4 + 50 to sta 4 + 75 is the same

From sta 4 + 75 to P.T., Δ = 40° less 32°18′ (see Fig. 10-7)

$$\Delta = 7°42' \text{ and } \frac{\Delta}{2} = 3°51'$$

$$C = 200 \sin 3°51' \text{ or } 13.40 \text{ ft.}$$

From these calculations and Fig. 10-7, deflection angles and chord lengths

Given: I = Δ = 40°
       T   = 36.40′
       L   = 69.81′
       P.I. sta. = 4+55
       P.C. sta. = 4+18.60
       P.T. sta. = 4+88.41

Calculations: Curve length P.C. to sta 4+25 = 6.40′

Central angles

$$\text{P.C.} - \text{sta. } 4+25 \quad \frac{6.40}{69.81} \times 40° = 3°- 40'$$

$$\text{P.C.} - \text{sta. } 4+50 \quad \frac{6.40+25}{69.81} \times 40° = 17°- 59'$$

$$\text{P.C.} - \text{sta. } 4+75 \quad \frac{6.40+50}{69.81} \times 40° = 32°- 18'$$

$$\text{P.C.} - \text{P.T.} \qquad\qquad\qquad = 40°$$

Stake	Δ	$\Delta/2$	sin	2R	$C = 2R \sin \Delta/2$
4+25	3°–40′	1°–50′	.03199	200	6.40′
4+50	17°–59′	8°–59′30″	.15629	200	31.26′
4+75	32°–18′	16°–09′	.27829	200	55.66′
4+88.41	40°	20°	.34202	200	68.40′

Figure 10-7 Calculation of subchords

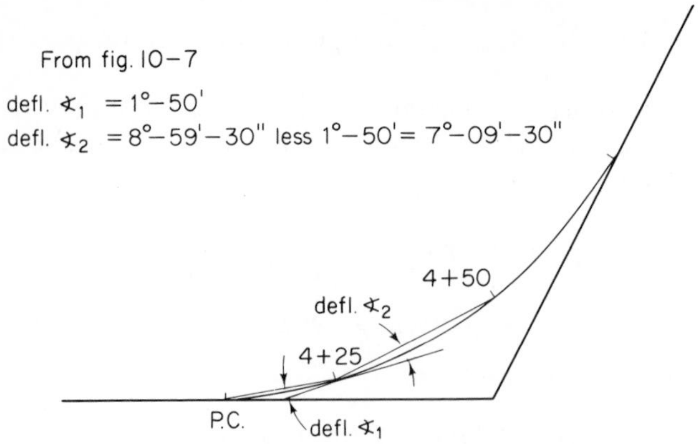

From fig. 10−7

defl. x_1 = 1°−50'
defl. x_2 = 8°−59'−30" less 1°−50'= 7°−09'−30"

To set a stake at 4+50 with the instrument at 4+25, backsight P.C., turn 8°59'30" (1°50' plus 7°09') to left, plunge scope and set stake on line at the subchord distance.

Rule: With instrument at any point on the curve, the sum of deflection angles to set a point with another point as a B.S. is one half the central angle between the B.S. point and the F.S. point.

Figure 10-8 Deflection angle from one intermediate point to another

can be obtained between any two adjacent stakes on the curve. The deflection angle is the same from either end of any chord. With the transit at any stake and a backsight on either adjacent stake, turning the deflection angle for that stake puts the transit on line on the tangent to the curve. The scope can then be plunged and the deflection angle for the other stake can be laid off.

P.C. 4 + 18.60	defl. $\sphericalangle$	subchord
	1°− 50'	6.40'
+ 25	1°− 50'	6.40'
	7°−09'−30"	24.92'
+ 50	8°−59'−30"	31.26'
	7°−09'−30"	24.92'
+ 75	16°−09'	55.66'
	3°−51'	13.40'
P.T. 4+88.41	20°−00'	68.40'

Figure 10-9 Field note arrangement, deflection angles, and subchords

This can be done in one less step by backsighting one adjacent stake, turning an angle equal to the sum of the two deflection angles and plunging the scope. It is then on line to set the other adjacent stake. See Fig. 10-8 for illustration.

Field notes arranged so the transit can be set up at any stake are shown in Fig. 10-9. Notes should be set up before going into the field. They provide information so that the curve can be staked even if it is impossible to sight all points from the P.C.

The radius for the curve of stakes is not necessarily the design radius. The design radius is normally to the centerline of pavement or the right-of-way line, but stakes may be set at the edge of pavement or offset from the edge of pavement. Calculations for stakeout are similar to those of Figs. 10-5 and 10-7 except that the radius for the line of stakes is used. See Fig. 10-10 for illustration.

10-3 VERTICAL CURVE

The designer of a vehicle route chooses the most advantageous slopes according to the ground surface. The route is not designed with continuous changes in slope, but is designed with one straight line slope to a point, a different slope from that point to another point and one slope for each section of the route between points.

Transition from one straight slope to the next is eased by a curve in a vertical plane similar to the curve between tangents in a horizontal plane. The vertical curve is a parabola with formula $y = kx^2$. It departs from a straight line at a rate increasing as the square of the distance traveled along the straight line and returns to the next straight line at the same rate, but decreasing. Thus, it provides a smooth change in direction for vehicles and also provides increased sight distance for the driver. See Fig. 10-11 for illustration.

Stationing is measured in a horizontal direction as usual and offsets to the curve from the straight lines are computed in a vertical direction. The offsets added to or subtracted from the elevations on the straight lines give the finished grades. Elevations are needed every 25 ft. or 50 ft. for stakeout.

The point at which the curve begins is the *point of vertical curvature* (PVC); the point of intersection of the two straight lines is the *point of vertical intersection* (PVI); and the point at which the curve ends is the *point of vertical tangency* (PVT). The two straight lines are called the *back tangent* and the *forward tangent*.

Finished grades at the points to be staked are computed as follows:

<u>To set offset stakes for a curve</u>

1. Determine deflection angles on the design curve. If the central angle remains constant, deflection angles are the same for a curve of any radius. Therefore deflection angles can be calculated on the design curve. It is convenient to do so because the design length has already been determined for stationing and the length for any other radius would have to be calculated. Using only the design curve helps eliminate mistakes caused by working with several curves.

2. Determine short chord lengths for a curve of desired radius to set stakes.

Given: The curve of Fig. 10-7 as the centerline of a 24 ft pavement
Required: Stakeout at 25 ft stations with three ft offsets on both sides

| From fig. 10-7 | | | Stakes at inside edge | | Stakes at outside edge | |
sta	Δ/2	sin	2R	$c = 2R\sin\Delta/2$	2R	$c = 2R\sin\Delta/2$
P.C. 4 + 18.60						
4 + 25	1°-50'	.03199	170 ft	5.44	230 ft	7.36
4 + 50	8°-59'-30"	.15629	170 ft	26.57	230 ft	35.95
4 + 75	16°-09'	.27829	170 ft	47.31	230 ft	64.01
P.T. 4 + 88.41	20°	.34202	170 ft	58.14	230 ft	78.66

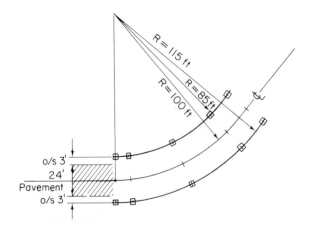

Figure 10-10 Stakeout of curve with a different radius

1. Compute elevation at A over the PVT as if the back tangent continues forward at the same slope and determine the vertical distance from point A to the PVT. The distance can be determined by multiplying the rate of divergence between the two grades by the horizontal length from PVI to PVT.
2. Compute offsets from the back tangent and back tangent extended at as many stations as needed for construction. These offsets vary according to the relationship $y = kx^2$ with x measured horizontally forward from the PVC and y measured in a vertical direction from the back tangent and back tangent extended. The offsets can be computed by proportions, each offset being proportional to the square of its horizontal distance from the PVC.
3. Determine elevations at the stations using the offset and the elevation of the back tangent and the back tangent extended.
   See Fig. 10-12 for illustration.

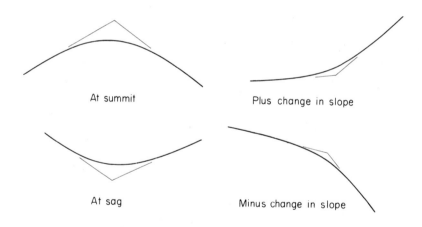

At summit   Plus change in slope

At sag   Minus change in slope

Figure 10-11 Vertical curves

The vertical curve may also be considered to be symmetrical about a centerline through the PVI and offsets computed for stations on both sides of the centerline according to their distances from the centerline. The center-line offset is determined and other offsets computed using the rule that the offsets vary in proportion to the square of the distance from the PVC and PVT. See Fig. 10-13 for illustration.

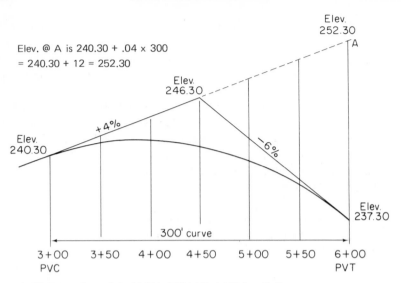

Elev. @ A is 240.30 + .04 × 300

= 240.30 + 12 = 252.30

1. Distance from A to PVT is $150(4\% + 6\%) = 15$ ft
2. Number of spaces is $\dfrac{300}{50} = 6$
3. Vertical offsets vary inversely as the square of the distance
4. If each 50 ft length is considered one unit, then offsets are to be computed at 1,2,3,4, and 5.
5. The proportions used for determining offsets are

$$\frac{\phi_1}{1^2} = \frac{15}{6^2} \text{ or } \phi_1 = \frac{15}{36}$$

$$\frac{\phi_2}{2^2} = \frac{15}{6^2} \text{ or } \phi_2 = \frac{15}{36} \times 4 \text{ etc.}$$

Sta.	Back tan Elev.	Offset factor	ϕ	Elev.
3+00	240.30	O		240.30
3+50	2.00 242.30	$\frac{1}{36}$ × 15	.42	241.88
4+00	2.00 244.30	$\frac{4}{36}$ × 15	1.67	242.63
4+50	2.00 246.30	$\frac{9}{36}$ × 15	3.75	242.55
5+00	2.00 248.30	$\frac{16}{36}$ × 15	6.66	241.64
5+50	2.00 250.30	$\frac{25}{36}$ × 15	10.42	239.88
6+00	2.00 252.30	$\frac{36}{36}$ × 15	15	237.30

Figure 10-12 Elevations for vertical curve stakeout—first method

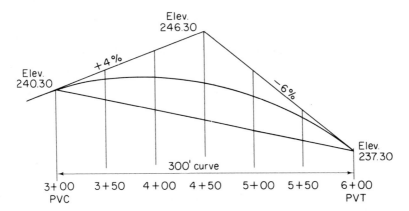

1. Elevation of a chord at the centerline through PVI is the average of PVC and PVT or $\dfrac{240.30 + 237.30}{2} = 238.80$

2. The vertical curve elevation at the centerline is halfway between chord and PVI or $\dfrac{238.80 + 246.30}{2} = 242.55$

3. The offset from PVI to curve is $246.30 - 242.55 = 3.75$

4. Offsets at all stations are proportional to the station's distance from PVC or PVT and are calculated as fractions of the offset at PVI

Sta.	Tan. elev.	Distance from PVC or PVT	Offset factor	Offset	Elev.
3 + 00	240.30	O	O	O	240.30
3 + 50	+2.00 242.30	50	$\frac{1}{9}$	.42	241.88
4 + 00	+2.00 244.30	100	$\frac{4}{9}$	1.67	242.63
4 + 50	+2.00 246.30	150	1	3.75	242.55
5 + 00	−3.00 243.30	100	$\frac{4}{9}$	1.67	241.63
5 + 50	−3.00 240.30	50	$\frac{1}{9}$	.42	239.88
6 + 00	−3.00 237.30	O	O	O	237.30

Figure 10-13 Elevations for vertical curve stakeout—second method

PROBLEMS

1/ Two streets intersect as shown here. Each has 30 ft pavement width and the curves at the intersection have a radius of 50 ft. Determine stations of P.C. and P.T. on Proctor St. and of P.T. and P.C. on Hill St.

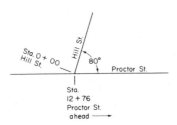

2/ Two streets intersect as shown here. Each has 36 ft pavement width and the curves at the intersection have a radius of 50 ft. Determine stations of P.C. and P.T. on Lincoln St. and of P.T. and P.C. on Ogden Ave.

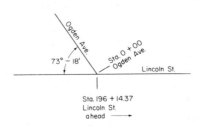

3/ Find deflection angles and distances to P.T. and to middle of circular curve from P.C. for a curve with radius of 500 ft and angle of intersection of 34°.

4/ A curve of 300 ft radius and 45° angle of intersection is to be staked out. The P.I. is at station 93+50. Find stations of P.C. and P.T. Determine deflection angles and subchords for stakeout at 50 ft stations.

5/ A curve of 100 ft radius and 40° angle of intersection is to be staked out. The P.I. is at station 4+55. Find stations of P.C. and P.T. Determine deflection angles and subchords for stakes at equal spacing not to exceed 25 ft between stakes.

6/ A street has a change in slope at station 16+50 from +1.3% to +4.8%. The PVI at 16+50 is at elevation 117.36. Determine elevations at 50 ft stations for a 200 ft vertical curve.

7/ A street has a change in slope at station 37+00 from −7.0% to −2.3%. The P.V.I. at station 37+00 is at elevation 846.35. Determine elevations at full stations for a 400 ft vertical curve.

8/ A highway has a change in slope from −1.6% to +2.1% at station 3+00. The P.V.I. at station 3+00 is at elevation 79.28. Determine elevations at full stations for a 500 ft vertical curve.

INSTRUCTIONAL OBJECTIVE OF CHAPTER 11

The objective of this chapter is to list major employers in the surveying field and the types of work and opportunities for advancement that are available.

chapter eleven
Employment in the Surveying Field

Not everyone engaged in surveying work is a surveyor. Certain skills are needed and those not yet possessing sufficient skills should be considered in training. Various organizations have programs for advancement by steps in the surveying field. Experience on the job and sometimes written examinations are required.

11-1 CIVIL ENGINEERING AND SURVEYING

Much surveying work is performed in connection with civil engineering projects and most civil engineers are familiar with the principles of surveying as a necessary part of their work. In fact, surveying was at one time regarded as a part of the field of civil engineering.

The type of surveying most readily associated with civil engineering is construction stakeout. However, preliminary surveying and preparation of maps and plot plans for construction planning and design are also important to civil engineering.

Increased knowledge and more sophisticated equipment have necessitated specialization in various fields once considered within the broad field of civil engineering. Surveying is one of these. Larger and more complex construction projects require more accurate control and modern, sophisticated equipment is capable of providing it. However, keeping up with new equipment and techniques is a full time job and so specialization in surveying is necessary. Even so, those who consider themselves surveyors should be familiar with principles of civil engineering design and construction as a necessary part of their work.

Every large civil engineering or construction organization employs surveyors who are expected to be able to work in the field and also plot field information to scale and perform the types of calculations shown in this book. It is necessary for the surveyor to be able to do some office work since it is not possible to work outside in all types of weather. State transportation departments or departments of public works, county highway departments, city and town public works departments, consulting civil engineering firms, and construction contractors all employ large numbers of surveyors.

11–2 MAPPING AND SURVEYING

Field information for the mapping of large areas requires special surveying techniques to obtain needed accuracy. In addition, computations must take into account the curvature of the earth. Mapping of this type is done in the United States by two federal government organizations, the National Geodetic Survey and the Geological Survey. The National Geodetic Survey establishes and maintains networks of horizontal and vertical control stations throughout the United States. The Geological Survey is in the process of preparing topographic maps of the entire country at scales of one in. to 2000 ft or one in. to one mile. Most of the work is complete, but the maps must be periodically revised.

These two organizations and many other federal government organizations employ surveyors and mapmakers. The Army Corps of Engineers, Forest Service, National Park Service, Bureau of Land Management, and various agencies of less extensive operation also employ surveyors and mapmakers.

11–3 LAND SURVEYING

The surveyor who determines the location of property boundaries requires a knowledge of legal principles in addition to the mathematical knowledge and surveying skill required of all surveyors. Experience and good judgment are also needed in this important phase of surveying work.

The land surveyor searches for all evidence indicating where property boundaries lie. This evidence is found by searching records kept in county court houses, highway departments, city engineer's offices and other offices, and is also found by establishing a traverse in the field and locating all fences, previous surveyor's marks and other evidence of property boundaries in relation to the traverse. The evidence, which is often conflicting, must be evaluated according to legal principles and a decision reached as to where the property lines are. The land surveyor then marks the property corners.

The land surveyor is in a position of public trust since he deals in matters beyond the understanding of his clients, which affect not only their properties, but also property belonging to others. In order to protect the public, nearly every state in the United States has a law requiring that a person be registered by the state before he can offer his services as a land surveyor and also requiring that a person have certain knowledge, skills, and experience in order to be registered as a land surveyor. In a few states, the holder of an engineer's license is considered qualified for property surveying.

States generally require a certain number of years of suitable experience in land surveying work, plus the ability to pass a written examination, before granting a license to practice the profession of land surveying. Requirements differ from state to state. Once a surveyor has earned such a license, he may establish a business of his own. This is probably the most satisfying and best paying opportunity in the surveying field.

Becoming licensed is the key to owning a surveying business. The land surveyor can perform any other surveying work that clients might want in addition to property surveys; however, a skilled surveyor who does not have a land surveyor's license would find it difficult if not impossible to obtain clients, even though he offered all types of surveying services except property surveying.

Money lending institutions, developers, and builders often want assurance from a land surveyor that property is of adequate size and in the expected location before they invest money in it, especially if they intend to increase the value of the land by building on it. If additional surveying work is needed for a plot plan or construction stakeout the same land surveyor will most likely be retained for the additional work.

11-4 SURVEYOR'S UNIONS

Surveyor's unions operate for the same purpose and in the same way as other construction trade unions. In order to obtain better wages and better working conditions for members, the union signs agreements with employers in the construction industry to supply surveying personnel at specified pay rates. The union is responsible for supplying properly trained personnel to the employers.

The union sends men with proper qualifications to fill specific positions, such as party chief, instrumentman, rodman, and apprentice rodman; and the union runs training programs and administers qualification examinations for the membership to advance to these grades.

Union bargaining power improves the pay scale for surveyors. Pay is now more in line with the substantial contribution the surveyor makes to the construction effort. A career as a union surveyor is an attractive one for a man who likes outdoor work. Union training programs increase the level of competence of the membership and so assist the construction industry as a whole.

TABLE I

Natural Sines and Cosines

′	0° Sine	0° Cosine	1° Sine	1° Cosine	2° Sine	2° Cosine	3° Sine	3° Cosine	4° Sine	4° Cosine	′
0	.00000	1.	.01745	.99985	.03490	.99939	.05234	.99863	.06976	.99756	60
1	.00029	1.	.01774	.99984	.03519	.99938	.05263	.99861	.07005	.99754	59
2	.00058	1.	.01803	.99984	.03548	.99937	.05292	.99860	.07034	.99752	58
3	.00087	1.	.01832	.99983	.03577	.99936	.05321	.99858	.07063	.99750	57
4	.00116	1.	.01862	.99983	.03606	.99935	.05350	.99857	.07092	.99748	56
5	.00145	1.	.01891	.99982	.03635	.99934	.05379	.99855	.07121	.99746	55
6	.00175	1.	.01920	.99982	.03664	.99933	.05408	.99854	.07150	.99744	54
7	.00204	1.	.01949	.99981	.03693	.99932	.05437	.99852	.07179	.99742	53
8	.00233	1.	.01978	.99980	.03723	.99931	.05466	.99851	.07208	.99740	52
9	.00262	1.	.02007	.99980	.03752	.99930	.05495	.99849	.07237	.99738	51
10	.00291	1.	.02036	.99979	.03781	.99929	.05524	.99847	.07266	.99736	50
11	.00320	.99999	.02065	.99979	.03810	.99927	.05553	.99846	.07295	.99734	49
12	.00349	.99999	.02094	.99978	.03839	.99926	.05582	.99844	.07324	.99731	48
13	.00378	.99999	.02123	.99977	.03868	.99925	.05611	.99842	.07353	.99729	47
14	.00407	.99999	.02152	.99977	.03897	.99924	.05640	.99841	.07382	.99727	46
15	.00436	.99999	.02181	.99976	.03926	.99923	.05669	.99839	.07411	.99725	45
16	.00465	.99999	.02211	.99976	.03955	.99922	.05698	.99838	.07440	.99723	44
17	.00495	.99999	.02240	.99975	.03984	.99921	.05727	.99836	.07469	.99721	43
18	.00524	.99999	.02269	.99974	.04013	.99919	.05756	.99834	.07498	.99719	42
19	.00553	.99998	.02298	.99974	.04042	.99918	.05785	.99833	.07527	.99716	41
20	.00582	.99998	.02327	.99973	.04071	.99917	.05814	.99831	.07556	.99714	40
21	.00611	.99998	.02356	.99972	.04100	.99916	.05844	.99829	.07585	.99712	39
22	.00640	.99998	.02385	.99972	.04129	.99915	.05873	.99827	.07614	.99710	38
23	.00669	.99998	.02414	.99971	.04159	.99913	.05902	.99826	.07643	.99708	37
24	.00698	.99998	.02443	.99970	.04188	.99912	.05931	.99824	.07672	.99705	36
25	.00727	.99997	.02472	.99969	.04217	.99911	.05960	.99822	.07701	.99703	35
26	.00756	.99997	.02501	.99969	.04246	.99910	.05989	.99821	.07730	.99701	34
27	.00785	.99997	.02530	.99968	.04275	.99909	.06018	.99819	.07759	.99699	33
28	.00814	.99997	.02560	.99967	.04304	.99907	.06047	.99817	.07788	.99696	32
29	.00844	.99996	.02589	.99966	.04333	.99906	.06076	.99815	.07817	.99694	31
30	.00873	.99996	.02618	.99966	.04362	.99905	.06105	.99813	.07846	.99692	30
31	.00902	.99996	.02647	.99965	.04391	.99904	.06134	.99812	.07875	.99689	29
32	.00931	.99996	.02676	.99964	.04420	.99902	.06163	.99810	.07904	.99687	28
33	.00960	.99995	.02705	.99963	.04449	.99901	.06192	.99808	.07933	.99685	27
34	.00989	.99995	.02734	.99963	.04478	.99900	.06221	.99806	.07962	.99683	26
35	.01018	.99995	.02763	.99962	.04507	.99898	.06250	.99804	.07991	.99680	25
36	.01047	.99995	.02792	.99961	.04536	.99897	.06279	.99803	.08020	.99678	24
37	.01076	.99994	.02821	.99960	.04565	.99896	.06308	.99801	.08049	.99676	23
38	.01105	.99994	.02850	.99959	.04594	.99894	.06337	.99799	.08078	.99673	22
39	.01134	.99994	.02879	.99959	.04623	.99893	.06366	.99797	.08107	.99671	21
40	.01164	.99993	.02908	.99958	.04653	.99892	.06395	.99795	.08136	.99668	20
41	.01193	.99993	.02938	.99957	.04682	.99890	.06424	.99793	.08165	.99666	19
42	.01222	.99993	.02967	.99956	.04711	.99889	.06453	.99792	.08194	.99664	18
43	.01251	.99992	.02996	.99955	.04740	.99888	06482	.99790	.08223	.99661	17
44	.01280	.99992	.03025	.99954	.04769	.99886	.06511	.99788	.08252	.99659	16
45	.01309	.99991	.03054	.99953	.04798	.99885	.06540	.99786	.08281	.99657	15
46	.01338	.99991	.03083	.99952	.04827	.99883	.06569	.99784	.08310	.99654	14
47	.01367	.99991	.03112	.99952	.04856	.99882	.06598	.99782	.08339	.99652	13
48	.01396	.99990	.03141	.99951	.04885	.99881	.06627	.99780	.08368	.99649	12
49	.01425	.99990	.03170	.99950	.04914	.99879	.06656	.99778	.08397	.99647	11
50	.01454	.99989	.03199	.99949	.04943	.99878	.06685	.99776	.08426	.99644	10
51	.01483	.99989	.03228	.99948	.04972	.99876	.06714	.99774	.08455	.99642	9
52	.01513	.99989	.03257	.99947	.05001	.99875	.06743	.99772	.08484	.99639	8
53	.01542	.99988	.03286	.99946	.05030	.99873	.06773	.99770	.08513	.99637	7
54	.01571	.99988	.03316	.99945	.05059	.99872	.06802	.99768	.08542	.99635	6
55	.01600	.99987	.03345	.99944	.05088	.99870	.06831	.99766	.08571	.99632	5
56	.01629	.99987	.03374	.99943	.05117	.99869	.06860	.99764	.08600	.99630	4
57	.01658	.99986	.03403	.99942	.05146	.99867	.06889	.99762	.08629	.99627	3
58	.01687	.99986	.03432	.99941	.05175	.99866	.06918	.99760	.08658	.99625	2
59	.01716	.99985	.03461	.99940	.05205	.99864	.06947	.99758	.08687	.99622	1
60	.01745	.99985	.03490	.99939	.05234	.99863	.06976	.99756	.08716	.99619	0
′	Cosine	Sine	Cosine	Sine	Cosine	Sine	Cosine	Sine	Cosine	Sine	′
	89°		88°		87°		86°		85°		

TABLE 1 cont.

Natural Sines and Cosines

′	5° Sine	5° Cosine	6° Sine	6° Cosine	7° Sine	7° Cosine	8° Sine	8° Cosine	9° Sine	9° Cosine	′
0	.08716	.99619	.10453	.99452	.12187	.99255	.13917	.99027	.15643	.98769	60
1	.08745	.99617	.10482	.99449	.12216	.99251	.13946	.99023	.15672	.98764	59
2	.08774	.99614	.10511	.99446	.12245	.99248	.13975	.99019	.15701	.98760	58
3	.08803	.99612	.10540	.99443	.12274	.99244	.14004	.99015	.15730	.98755	57
4	.08831	.99609	.10569	.99440	.12302	.99240	.14033	.99011	.15758	.98751	56
5	.08860	.99607	.10597	.99437	.12331	.99237	.14061	.99006	.15787	.98746	55
6	.08889	.99604	.10626	.99434	.12360	.99233	.14090	.99002	.15816	.98741	54
7	.08918	.99602	.10655	.99431	.12389	.99230	.14119	.98998	.15845	.98737	53
8	.08947	.99599	.10684	.99428	.12418	.99226	.14148	.98994	.15873	.98732	52
9	.08976	.99596	.10713	.99424	.12447	.99222	.14177	.98990	.15902	.98728	51
10	.09005	.99594	.10742	.99421	.12476	.99219	.14205	.98986	.15931	.98723	50
11	.09034	.99591	.10771	.99418	.12504	.99215	.14234	.98982	.15959	.98718	49
12	.09063	.99588	.10800	.99415	.12533	.99211	.14263	.98978	.15988	.98714	48
13	.09092	.99586	.10829	.99412	.12562	.99208	.14292	.98973	.16017	.98709	47
14	.09121	.99583	.10858	.99409	.12591	.99204	.14320	.98969	.16046	.98704	46
15	.09150	.99580	.10887	.99406	.12620	.99200	.14349	.98965	.16074	.98700	45
16	.09179	.99578	.10916	.99402	.12649	.99197	.14378	.98961	.16103	.98695	44
17	.09208	.99575	.10945	.99399	.12678	.99193	.14407	.98957	.16132	.98690	43
18	.09237	.99572	.10973	.59396	.12706	.99189	.14436	.98953	.16160	.98686	42
19	.09266	.99570	.11002	.99393	.12735	.99186	.14464	.98948	.16189	.98681	41
20	.09295	.99567	.11031	.99390	.12764	.99182	.14493	.98944	.16218	.98676	40
21	.09324	.99564	.11060	.99386	.12793	.99178	.14522	.98940	.16246	.98671	39
22	.09353	.99562	.11089	.99383	.12822	.99175	.14551	.98936	.16275	.98667	38
23	.09382	.99559	.11118	.99380	.12851	.99171	.14580	.98931	.16304	.98662	37
24	.09411	.99556	.11147	.99377	.12880	.99167	.14608	.98927	.16333	.98657	36
25	.09440	.99553	.11176	.99374	.12908	.99163	.14637	.98923	.16361	.98652	35
26	.09469	.99551	.11205	.99370	.12937	.99160	.14666	.98919	.16390	.98648	34
27	.09498	.99548	.11234	.99367	.12966	.99156	.14695	.98914	.16419	.98643	33
28	.09527	.99545	.11263	.99364	.12995	.99152	.14723	.98910	.16447	.98638	32
29	.09556	.99542	.11291	.99360	.13024	.99148	.14752	.98906	.16476	.98633	31
30	.09585	.99540	.11320	.99357	.13053	.99144	.14781	.98902	.16505	.98629	30
31	.09614	.99537	.11349	.99354	.13081	.99141	.14810	.98897	.16533	.98624	29
32	.09642	.99534	.11378	.99351	.13110	.99137	.14838	.98893	.16562	.98619	28
33	.09671	.99531	.11407	.99347	.13139	.99133	.14867	.98889	.16591	.98614	27
34	.09700	.99528	.11436	.99344	.13168	.99129	.14896	.98884	.16620	.98609	26
35	.09729	.99526	.11465	.99341	.13197	.99125	.14925	.98880	.16648	.98604	25
36	.09758	.99523	.11494	.99337	.13226	.99122	.14954	.98876	.16677	.98600	24
37	.09787	.99520	.11523	.99334	.13254	.99118	.14982	.98871	.16706	.98595	23
38	.09816	.99517	.11552	.99331	.13283	.99114	.15011	.98867	.16734	.98590	22
39	.09845	.99514	.11580	.99327	.13312	.99110	.15040	.98863	.16763	.98585	21
40	.09874	.99511	.11609	.99324	.13341	.99106	.15069	.98858	.16792	.98580	20
41	.09903	.99508	.11638	.99320	.13370	.99102	.15097	.98854	.16820	.98575	19
42	.09932	.99506	.11667	.99317	.13399	.99098	.15126	.98849	.16849	.98570	18
43	.09961	.99503	.11696	.99314	.13427	.99094	.15155	.98845	.16876	.98565	17
44	.09990	.99500	.11725	.99310	.13456	.99091	.15184	.98841	.16906	.98561	16
45	.10019	.99497	.11754	.99307	.13485	.99087	.15212	.98836	.16935	.98556	15
46	.10048	.99494	.11783	.99303	.13514	.99083	.15241	.98832	.16964	.98551	14
47	.10077	.99491	.11812	.99300	.13543	.99079	.15270	.98827	.16992	.98546	13
48	.10106	.99488	.11840	.99297	.13572	.99075	.15299	.98823	.17021	.98541	12
49	.10135	.99485	.11869	.99293	.13600	.99071	.15327	.98818	.17050	.98536	11
50	.10164	.99482	.11898	.99290	.13629	.99067	.15356	.98814	.17078	.98531	10
51	.10192	.99479	.11927	.99286	.13658	.99063	.15385	.98809	.17107	.98526	9
52	.10221	.99476	.11956	.99283	.13687	.99059	.15414	.98805	.17136	.98521	8
53	.10250	.99473	.11985	.99279	.13716	.99055	.15442	.98800	.17164	.98516	7
54	.10279	.99470	.12014	.99276	.13744	.99051	.15471	.98796	.17193	.98511	6
55	.10308	.99467	.12043	.99272	.13773	.99047	.15500	.98791	.17222	.98506	5
56	.10337	.99464	.12071	.99269	.13802	.99043	.15529	.98787	.17250	.98501	4
57	.10366	.99461	.12100	.99265	.13831	.99039	.15557	.98782	.17279	.98496	3
58	.10395	.99458	.12129	.99262	.13860	.99035	.15586	.98778	.17308	.98491	2
59	.10424	.99455	.12158	.99258	.13889	.99031	.15615	.98773	.17336	.98486	1
60	.10453	.99452	.12187	.99255	.13917	.99027	.15643	.98769	.17365	.98481	0
′	Cosine	Sine	Cosine	Sine	Cosine	Sine	Cosine	Sine	Cosine	Sine	′
	84°		83°		82°		81°		80°		

TABLE 1 cont.

Natural Sines and Cosines

′	10° Sine	Cosine	11° Sine	Cosine	12° Sine	Cosine	13° Sine	Cosine	14° Sine	Cosine	′
0	.17365	.98481	.19081	.98163	.20791	.97815	.22495	.97437	.24192	.97030	60
1	.17393	.98476	.19109	.98157	.20820	.97809	.22523	.97430	.24220	.97023	59
2	.17422	.98471	.19138	.98152	.20848	.97803	.22552	.97424	.24249	.97015	58
3	.17451	.98466	.19167	.98146	.20877	.97797	.22580	.97417	.24277	.97008	57
4	.17479	.98461	.19195	.98140	.20905	.97791	.22608	.97411	.24305	.97001	56
5	.17508	.98455	.19224	.98135	.20933	.97784	.22637	.97404	.24333	.96994	55
6	.17537	.98450	.19252	.98129	.20962	.97778	.22665	.97398	.24362	.96987	54
7	.17565	.98445	.19281	.98124	.20990	.97772	.22693	.97391	.24390	.96980	53
8	.17594	.98440	.19309	.98118	.21019	.97766	.22722	.97384	.24418	.96973	52
9	.17623	.98435	.19338	.98112	.21047	.97760	.22750	.97378	.24446	.96966	51
10	.17651	.98430	.19366	.98107	.21076	.97754	.22778	.97371	.24474	.96959	50
11	.17680	.98425	.19395	.98101	.21104	.97748	.22807	.97365	.24503	.96952	49
12	.17708	.98420	.19423	.98096	.21132	.97742	.22835	.97358	.24531	.96945	48
13	.17737	.98414	.19452	.98090	.21161	.97735	.22863	.97351	.24559	.96937	47
14	.17766	.98409	.19481	.98084	.21189	.97729	.22892	.97345	.24587	.96930	46
15	.17794	.98404	.19509	.98079	.21218	.97723	.22920	.97338	.24615	.96923	45
16	.17823	.98399	.19538	.98073	.21246	.97717	.22948	.97331	.24644	.96916	44
17	.17852	.98394	.19566	.98067	.21275	.97711	.22977	.97325	.24672	.96909	43
18	.17880	.98389	.19595	.98061	.21303	.97705	.23005	.97318	.24700	.96902	42
19	.17909	.98383	.19623	.98056	.21331	.97698	.23033	.97311	.24728	.96894	41
20	.17937	.98378	.19652	.98050	.21360	.97692	.23062	.97304	.24756	.96887	40
21	.17966	.98373	.19680	.98044	.21388	.97686	.23090	.97298	.24784	.96880	39
22	.17995	.98368	.19709	.98039	.21417	.97680	.23118	.97291	.24813	.96873	38
23	.18023	.98362	.19737	.98033	.21445	.97673	.23146	.97284	.24841	.96866	37
24	.18052	.98357	.19766	.98027	.21474	.97667	.23175	.97278	.24869	.96858	36
25	.18081	.98352	.19794	.98021	.21502	.97661	.23203	.97271	.24897	.96851	35
26	.18109	.98347	.19823	.98016	.21530	.97655	.23231	.97264	.24925	.96844	34
27	.18138	.98341	.19851	.98010	.21559	.97648	.23260	.97257	.24954	.96837	33
28	.18166	.98336	.19880	.98004	.21587	.97642	.23288	.97251	.24982	.96829	32
29	.18195	.98331	.19908	.97998	.21616	.97636	.23316	.97244	.25010	.96822	31
30	.18224	.98325	.19937	.97992	.21644	.97630	.23345	.97237	.25038	.96815	30
31	.18252	.98320	.19965	.97987	.21672	.97623	.23373	.97230	.25066	.96807	29
32	.18281	.98315	.19994	.97981	.21701	.97617	.23401	.97223	.25094	.96800	28
33	.18309	.98310	.20022	.97975	.21729	.97611	.23429	.97217	.25122	.96793	27
34	.18338	.98304	.20051	.97969	.21758	.97604	.23458	.97210	.25151	.96786	26
35	.18367	.98299	.20079	.97963	.21786	.97598	.23486	.97203	.25179	.96778	25
36	.18395	.98294	.20108	.97958	.21814	.97592	.23514	.97196	.25207	.96771	24
37	.18424	.98288	.20136	.97952	.21843	.97585	.23542	.97189	.25235	.96764	23
38	.18452	.98283	.20165	.97946	.21871	.97579	.23571	.97182	.25263	.96756	22
39	.18481	.98277	.20193	.97940	.21899	.97573	.23599	.97176	.25291	.96749	21
40	.18509	.98272	.20222	.97934	.21928	.97566	.23627	.97169	.25320	.96742	20
41	.18538	.98267	.20250	.97928	.21956	.97560	.23656	.97162	.25348	.96734	19
42	.18567	.98261	.20279	.97922	.21985	.97553	.23684	.97155	.25376	.96727	18
43	.18595	.98256	.20307	.97916	.22013	.97547	.23712	.97148	.25404	.96719	17
44	.18624	.98250	.20336	.97910	.22041	.97541	.23740	.97141	.25432	.96712	16
45	.18652	.98245	.20364	.97905	.22070	.97534	.23769	.97134	.25460	.96705	15
46	.18681	.98240	.20393	.97899	.22098	.97528	.23797	.97127	.25488	.96697	14
47	.18710	.98234	.20421	.97893	.22126	.97521	.23825	.97120	.25516	.96690	13
48	.18738	.98229	.20450	.97887	.22155	.97515	.23853	.97113	.25545	.96682	12
49	.18767	.98223	.20478	.97881	.22183	.97508	.23882	.97106	.25573	.96675	11
50	.18795	.98218	.20507	.97875	.22212	.97502	.23910	.97100	.25601	.96667	10
51	.18824	.98212	.20535	.97869	.22240	.97496	.23938	.97093	.25629	.96660	9
52	.18852	.98207	.20563	.97863	.22268	.97489	.23966	.97086	.25657	.96653	8
53	.18881	.98201	.20592	.97857	.22297	.97483	.23995	.97079	.25685	.96645	7
54	.18910	.98196	.20620	.97851	.22325	.97476	.24023	.97072	.25713	.96638	6
55	.18938	.98190	.20649	.97845	.22353	.97470	.24051	.97065	.25741	.96630	5
56	.18967	.98185	.20677	.97839	.22382	.97463	.24079	.97058	.25769	.96623	4
57	.18995	.98179	.20706	.97833	.22410	.97457	.24108	.97051	.25798	.96615	3
58	.19024	.98174	.20734	.97827	.22438	.97451	.24136	.97044	.25826	.96608	2
59	.19052	.98168	.20763	.97821	.22467	.97444	.24164	.97037	.25854	.96600	1
60	.19081	.98163	.20791	.97815	.22495	.97437	.24192	.97030	.25882	.96593	0
′	Cosine	Sine	Cosine	Sine	Cosine	Sine	Cosine	Sine	Cosine	Sine	′
	79°		78°		77°		76°		75°		

TABLE 1 cont.

Natural Sines and Cosines

′	15° Sine	15° Cosine	16° Sine	16° Cosine	17° Sine	17° Cosine	18° Sine	18° Cosine	19° Sine	19° Cosine	′
0	.25882	.96593	.27564	.96126	.29237	.95630	.30902	.95106	.32557	.94552	60
1	.25910	.96585	.27592	.96118	.29265	.95622	.30929	.95097	.32584	.94542	59
2	.25938	.96578	.27620	.96110	.29293	.95613	.30957	.95088	.32612	.94533	58
3	.25966	.96570	.27648	.96102	.29321	.95605	.30985	.95079	.32639	.94523	57
4	.25994	.96562	.27676	.96094	.29348	.95596	.31012	.95070	.32667	.94514	56
5	.26022	.96555	.27704	.96086	.29376	.95588	.31040	.95061	.32694	.94504	55
6	.26050	.96547	.27731	.96078	.29404	.95579	.31068	.95052	.32722	.94495	54
7	.26079	.96540	.27759	.96070	.29432	.95571	.31095	.95043	.32749	.94485	53
8	.26107	.96532	.27787	.96062	.29460	.95562	.31123	.95033	.32777	.94476	52
9	.26135	.96524	.27815	.96054	.29487	.95554	.31151	.95024	.32804	.94466	51
10	.26163	.96517	.27843	.96046	.29515	.95545	.31178	.95015	.32832	.94457	50
11	.26191	.96509	.27871	.96037	.29543	.95536	.31206	.95006	.32859	.94447	49
12	.26219	.96502	.27899	.96029	.29571	.95528	.31233	.94997	.32887	.94438	48
13	.26247	.96494	.27927	.96021	.29599	.95519	.31261	.94988	.32914	.94428	47
14	.26275	.96486	.27955	.96013	.29626	.95511	.31289	.94979	.32942	.94418	46
15	.26303	.96479	.27983	.96005	.29654	.95502	.31316	.94970	.32969	.94409	45
16	.26331	.96471	.28011	.95997	.29682	.95493	.31344	.94961	.32997	.94399	44
17	.26359	.96463	.28039	.95989	.29710	.95485	.31372	.94952	.33024	.94390	43
18	.26387	.96456	.28067	.95981	.29737	.95476	.31399	.94943	.33051	.94380	42
19	.26415	.96448	.28095	.95972	.29765	.95467	.31427	.94933	.33079	.94370	41
20	.26443	.96440	.28123	.95964	.29793	.95459	.31454	.94924	.33106	.94361	40
21	.26471	.96433	.28150	.95956	.29821	.95450	.31482	.94915	.33134	.94351	39
22	.26500	.96425	.28178	.95948	.29849	.95441	.31510	.94906	.33161	.94342	38
23	.26528	.96417	.28206	.95940	.29876	.95433	.31537	.94897	.33189	.94332	37
24	.26556	.96410	.28234	.95931	.29904	.95424	.31565	.94888	.33216	.94322	36
25	.26584	.96402	.28262	.95923	.29932	.95415	.31593	.94878	.33244	.94313	35
26	.26612	.96394	.28290	.95915	.29960	.95407	.31620	.94869	.33271	.94303	34
27	.26640	.96386	.28318	.95907	.29987	.95398	.31648	.94860	.33298	.94293	33
28	.26668	.96379	.28346	.95898	.30015	.95389	.31675	.94851	.33326	.94284	32
29	.26696	.96371	.28374	.95890	.30043	.95380	.31703	.94842	.33353	.94274	31
30	.26724	.96363	.28402	.95882	.30071	.95372	.31730	.94832	.33381	.94264	30
31	.26752	.96355	.28429	.95874	.30098	.95363	.31758	.94823	.33408	.94254	29
32	.26780	.96347	.28457	.95865	.30126	.95354	.31786	.94814	.33436	.94245	28
33	.26808	.96340	.28485	.95857	.30154	.95345	.31813	.94805	.33463	.94235	27
34	.26836	.96332	.28513	.95849	.30182	.95337	.31841	.94795	.33490	.94225	26
35	.26864	.96324	.28541	.95841	.30209	.95328	.31868	.94786	.33518	.94215	25
36	.26892	.96316	.28569	.95832	.30237	.95319	.31896	.94777	.33545	.94206	24
37	.26920	.96308	.28597	.95824	.30265	.95310	.31923	.94768	.33573	.94196	23
38	.26948	.96301	.28625	.95816	.30292	.95301	.31951	.94758	.33600	.94186	22
39	.26976	.96293	.28652	.95807	.30320	.95293	.31979	.94749	.33627	.94176	21
40	.27004	.96285	.28680	.95799	.30348	.95284	.32006	.94740	.33655	.94167	20
41	.27032	.96277	.28708	.95791	.30376	.95275	.32034	.94730	.33682	.94157	19
42	.27060	.96269	.28736	.95782	.30403	.95266	.32061	.94721	.33710	.94147	18
43	.27088	.96261	.28764	.95774	.30431	.95257	.32089	.94712	.33737	.94137	17
44	.27116	.96253	.28792	.95766	.30459	.95248	.32116	.94702	.33764	.94127	16
45	.27144	.96246	.28820	.95757	.30486	.95240	.32144	.94693	.33792	.94118	15
46	.27172	.96238	.28847	.95749	.30514	.95231	.32171	.94684	.33819	.94108	14
47	.27200	.96230	.28875	.95740	.30542	.95222	.32199	.94674	.33846	.94098	13
48	.27228	.96222	.28903	.95732	.30570	.95213	.32227	.94665	.33874	.94088	12
49	.27256	.96214	.28931	.95724	.30597	.95204	.32254	.94656	.33901	.94078	11
50	.27284	.96206	.28959	.95715	.30625	.95195	.32282	.94646	.33929	.94068	10
51	.27312	.96198	.28987	.95707	.30653	.95186	.32309	.94637	.33956	.94058	9
52	.27340	.96190	.29015	.95698	.30680	.95177	.32337	.94627	.33983	.94049	8
53	.27368	.96182	.29042	.95690	.30708	.95168	.32364	.94618	.34011	.94039	7
54	.27396	.96174	.29070	.95681	.30736	.95159	.32392	.94609	.34038	.94029	6
55	.27424	.96166	.29098	.95673	.30763	.95150	.32419	.94599	.34065	.94019	5
56	.27452	.96158	.29126	.95664	.30791	.95142	.32447	.94590	.34093	.94009	4
57	.27480	.96150	.29154	.95656	.30819	.95133	.32474	.94580	.34120	.93999	3
58	.27508	.96142	.29182	.95647	.30846	.95124	.32502	.94571	.34147	.93989	2
59	.27536	.96134	.29209	.95639	.30874	.95115	.32529	.94561	.34175	.93979	1
60	.27564	.96126	.29237	.95630	.30902	.95106	.32557	.94552	.34202	.93969	0
′	Cosine	Sine	Cosine	Sine	Cosine	Sine	Cosine	Sine	Cosine	Sine	′
	74°		73°		72°		71°		70°		

TABLE 1 cont.

Natural Sines and Cosines

′	20° Sine	20° Cosine	21° Sine	21° Cosine	22° Sine	22° Cosine	23° Sine	23° Cosine	24° Sine	24° Cosine	′
0	.34202	.93969	.35837	.93358	.37461	.92718	.39073	.92050	.40674	.91355	60
1	.34229	.93959	.35864	.93348	.37488	.92707	.39100	.92039	.40700	.91343	59
2	.34257	.93949	.35891	.93337	.37515	.92697	.39127	.92028	.40727	.91331	58
3	.34284	.93939	.35918	.93327	.37542	.92686	.39153	.92016	.40753	.91319	57
4	.34311	.93929	.35945	.93316	.37569	.92675	.39180	.92005	.40780	.91307	56
5	.34339	.93919	.35973	.93306	.37595	.92664	.39207	.91994	.40806	.91295	55
6	.34366	.93909	.36000	.93295	.37622	.92653	.39234	.91982	.40833	.91283	54
7	.34393	.93899	.36027	.93285	.37649	.92642	.39260	.91971	.40860	.91272	53
8	.34421	.93889	.36054	.93274	.37676	.92631	.39287	.91959	.40886	.91260	52
9	.34448	.93879	.36081	.93264	.37703	.92620	.39314	.91948	.40913	.91248	51
10	.34475	.93869	.36108	.93253	.37730	.92609	.39341	.91936	.40939	.91236	50
11	.34503	.93859	.36135	.93243	.37757	.92598	.39367	.91925	.40966	.91224	49
12	.34530	.93849	.36162	.93232	.37784	.92587	.39394	.91914	.40992	.91212	48
13	.34557	.93839	.36190	.93222	.37811	.92576	.39421	.91902	.41019	.91200	47
14	.34584	.93829	.36217	.93211	.37838	.92565	.39448	.91891	.41045	.91188	46
15	.34612	.93819	.36244	.93201	.37865	.92554	.39474	.91879	.41072	.91176	45
16	.34639	.93809	.36271	.93190	.37892	.92543	.39501	.91868	.41098	.91164	44
17	.34666	.93799	.36298	.93180	.37919	.92532	.39528	.91856	.41125	.91152	43
18	.34694	.93789	.36325	.93169	.37946	.92521	.39555	.91845	.41151	.91140	42
19	.34721	.93779	.36352	.93159	.37973	.92510	.39581	.91833	.41178	.91128	41
20	.34748	.93769	.36379	.93148	.37999	.92499	.39608	.91822	.41204	.91116	40
21	.34775	.93759	.36406	.93137	.38026	.92488	.39635	.91810	.41231	.91104	39
22	.34803	.93748	.36434	.93127	.38053	.92477	.39661	.91799	.41257	.91092	38
23	.34830	.93738	.36461	.93116	.38080	.92466	.39688	.01787	.41284	.91080	37
24	.34857	.93728	.36488	.93106	.38107	.92455	.39715	.91775	.41310	.91068	36
25	.34884	.93718	.36515	.93095	.38134	.92444	.39741	.91764	.41337	.91056	35
26	.34912	.93708	.36542	.93084	.38161	.92432	.39768	.91752	.41363	.91044	34
27	.34939	.93698	.36569	.93074	.38188	.92421	.39795	.91741	.41390	.91032	33
28	.34966	.93688	.36596	.93063	.38215	.92410	.39822	.91729	.41416	.91020	32
29	.34993	.93677	.36623	.93052	.38241	.92399	.39848	.91718	.41443	.91008	31
30	.35021	.93667	.36650	.93042	.38268	.92388	.39875	.91706	.41469	.90996	30
31	.35048	.93657	.36677	.93031	.38295	.92377	.39902	.91694	.41496	.90984	29
32	.35075	.93647	.36704	.93020	.38322	.92366	.39928	.91683	.41522	.90972	28
33	.35102	.93637	.36731	.93010	.38349	.92355	.39955	.91671	.41549	.90960	27
34	.35130	.93626	.36758	.92999	.38376	.92343	.39982	.91660	.41575	.90948	26
35	.35157	.93616	.36785	.92988	.38403	.92332	.40008	.91648	.41602	.90936	25
36	.35184	.93606	.36812	.92978	.38430	.92321	.40035	.91636	.41628	.90924	24
37	.35211	.93596	.36839	.92967	.38456	.92310	.40062	.91625	.41655	.90911	23
38	.35239	.93585	.36867	.92956	.38483	.92299	.40088	.91613	.41681	.90899	22
39	.35266	.93575	.36894	.92945	.38510	.92287	.40115	.91601	.41707	.90887	21
40	.35293	.93565	.36921	.92935	.38537	.92276	.40141	.91590	.41734	.90875	20
41	.35320	.93555	.36948	.92924	.38564	.92265	.40168	.91578	.41760	.90863	19
42	.35347	.93544	.36975	.92913	.38591	.92254	.40195	.91566	.41787	.90851	18
43	.35375	.93534	.37002	.92902	.38617	.92243	.40221	.91555	.41813	.90839	17
44	.35402	.93524	.37029	.92892	.38644	.92231	.40248	.91543	.41840	.90826	16
45	.35429	.93514	.37056	.92881	.38671	.92220	.40275	.91531	.41866	.90814	15
46	.35456	.93503	.37083	.92870	.38698	.92209	.40301	.91519	.41892	.90802	14
47	.35484	.93493	.37110	.92859	.38725	.92198	.40328	.91508	.41919	.90790	13
48	.35511	.93483	.37137	.92849	.38752	.92186	.40355	.91496	.41945	.90778	12
49	.35538	.93472	.37164	.92838	.38778	.92175	.40381	.91484	.41972	.90766	11
50	.35565	.93462	.37191	.92827	.38805	.92164	.40408	.91472	.41998	.90753	10
51	.35592	.93452	.37218	.92816	.38832	.92152	.40434	.91461	.42024	.90741	9
52	.35619	.93441	.37245	.92805	.38859	.92141	.40461	.91449	.42051	.90729	8
53	.35647	.93431	.37272	.92794	.38886	.92130	.40488	.91437	.42077	.90717	7
54	.35674	.93420	.37299	.92784	.38912	.92119	.40514	.91425	.42104	.90704	6
55	.35701	.93410	.37326	.92773	.38939	.92107	.40541	.91414	.42130	.90692	5
56	.35728	.93400	.37353	.92762	.38966	.92096	.40567	.91402	.42156	.90680	4
57	.35755	.93389	.37380	.92751	.38993	.92085	.40594	.91390	.42183	.90668	3
58	.35782	.93379	.37407	.92740	.39020	.92073	.40621	.91378	.42209	.90655	2
59	.35810	.93368	.37434	.92729	.39046	.92062	.40647	.91366	.42235	.90643	1
60	.35837	.93358	.37461	.92718	.39073	.92050	.40674	.91355	.42262	.90631	0
′	Cosine	Sine	Cosine	Sine	Cosine	Sine	Cosine	Sine	Cosine	Sine	′
	69°		68°		67°		66°		65°		

TABLE 1 cont.

Natural Sines and Cosines

′	25° Sine	25° Cosine	26° Sine	26° Cosine	27° Sine	27° Cosine	28° Sine	28° Cosine	29° Sine	29° Cosine	′
0	.42262	.90631	.43837	.89879	.45399	.89101	.46947	.88295	.48481	.87462	60
1	.42288	.90618	.43863	.89867	.45425	.89087	.46973	.88281	.48506	.87448	59
2	.42315	.90606	.43889	.89854	.45451	.89074	.46999	.88267	.48532	.87434	58
3	.42341	.90594	.43916	.89841	.45477	.89061	.47024	.88254	.48557	.87420	57
4	.42367	.90582	.43942	.89828	.45503	.89048	.47050	.88240	.48583	.87406	56
5	.42394	.90569	.43968	.89816	.45529	.89035	.47076	.88226	.48608	.87391	55
6	.42420	.90557	.43994	.89803	.45554	.89021	.47101	.88213	.48634	.87377	54
7	.42446	.90545	.44020	.89790	.45580	.89008	.47127	.88199	.48659	.87363	53
8	.42473	.90532	.44046	.89777	.45606	.88995	.47153	.88185	.48684	.87349	52
9	.42499	.90520	.44072	.89764	.45632	.88981	.47178	.88172	.48710	.87335	51
10	.42525	.90507	.44098	.89752	.45658	.88968	.47204	.88158	.48735	.87321	50
11	.42552	.90495	.44124	.89739	.45684	.88955	.47229	.88144	.48761	.87306	49
12	.42578	.90483	.44151	.89726	.45710	.88942	.47255	.88130	.48786	.87292	48
13	.42604	.90470	.44177	.89713	.45736	.88928	.47281	.88117	.48811	.87278	47
14	.42631	.90458	.44203	.89700	.45762	.88915	.47306	.88103	.48837	.87264	46
15	.42657	.90446	.44229	.89687	.45787	.88902	.47332	.88089	.48862	.87250	45
16	.42683	.90433	.44255	.89674	.45813	.88888	.47358	.88075	.48888	.87235	44
17	.42709	.90421	.44281	.89662	.45839	.88875	.47383	.88062	.48913	.87221	43
18	.42736	.90408	.44307	.89649	.45865	.88862	.47409	.88048	.48938	.87207	42
19	.42762	.90396	.44333	.89636	.45891	.88848	.47434	.88034	.48964	.87193	41
20	.42788	.90383	.44359	.89623	.45917	.88835	.47460	.88020	.48989	.87178	40
21	.42815	.90371	.44385	.89610	.45942	.88822	.47486	.88006	.49014	.87164	39
22	.42841	.90358	.44411	.89597	.45968	.88808	.47511	.87993	.49040	.87150	38
23	.42867	.90346	.44437	.89584	.45994	.88795	.47537	.87979	.49065	.87136	37
24	.42894	.90334	.44464	.89571	.46020	.88782	.47562	.87965	.49090	.87121	36
25	.42920	.90321	.44490	.89558	.46046	.88768	.47588	.87951	.49116	.87107	35
26	.42946	.90309	.44516	.89545	.46072	.88755	.47614	.87937	.49141	.87093	34
27	.42972	.90296	.44542	.89532	.46097	.88741	.47639	.87923	.49166	.87079	33
28	.42999	.90284	.44568	.89519	.46123	.88728	.47665	.87909	.49192	.87064	32
29	.43025	.90271	.44594	.89506	.46149	.88715	.47690	.87896	.49217	.87050	31
30	.43051	.90259	.44620	.89493	.46175	.88701	.47716	.87882	.49242	.87036	30
31	.43077	.90246	.44646	.89480	.46201	.88688	.47741	.87868	.49268	.87021	29
32	.43104	.90233	.44672	.89467	.46226	.88674	.47767	.87854	.49293	.87007	28
33	.43130	.90221	.44698	.89454	.46252	.88661	.47793	.87840	.49318	.86993	27
34	.43156	.90208	.44724	.89441	.46278	.88647	.47818	.87826	.49344	.86978	26
35	.43182	.90196	.44750	.89428	.46304	.88634	.47844	.87812	.49369	.86964	25
36	.43209	.90183	.44776	.89415	.46330	.88620	.47869	.87798	.49394	.86949	24
37	.43235	.90171	.44802	.89402	.46355	.88607	.47895	.87784	.49419	.86935	23
38	.43261	.90158	.44828	.89389	.46381	.88593	.47920	.87770	.49445	.86921	22
39	.43287	.90146	.44854	.89376	.46407	.88580	.47946	.87756	.49470	.86906	21
40	.43313	.90133	.44880	.89363	.46433	.88566	.47971	.87743	.49495	.86892	20
41	.43340	.90120	.44906	.89350	.46458	.88553	.47997	.87729	.49521	.86878	19
42	.43366	.90108	.44932	.89337	.46484	.88539	.48022	.87715	.49546	.86863	18
43	.43392	.90095	.44958	.89324	.46510	.88526	.48048	.87701	.49571	.86849	17
44	.43418	.90082	.44984	.89311	.46536	.88512	.48073	.87687	.49596	.86834	16
45	.43445	.90070	.45010	.89298	.46561	.88499	.48099	.87673	.49622	.86820	15
46	.43471	.90057	.45036	.89285	.46587	.88485	.48124	.87659	.49647	.86805	14
47	.43497	.90045	.45062	.89272	.46613	.88472	.48150	.87645	.49672	.86791	13
48	.43523	.90032	.45088	.89259	.46639	.88458	.48175	.87631	.49697	.86777	12
49	.43549	.90019	.45114	.89245	.46664	.88445	.48201	.87617	.49723	.86762	11
50	.43575	.90007	.45140	.89232	.46690	.88431	.48226	.87603	.49748	.86748	10
51	.43602	.89994	.45166	.89219	.46716	.88417	.48252	.87589	.49773	.86733	9
52	.43628	.89981	.45192	.89206	.46742	.88404	.48277	.87575	.49798	.86719	8
53	.43654	.89968	.45218	.89193	.46767	.88390	.48303	.87561	.49824	.86704	7
54	.43680	.89956	.45243	.89180	.46793	.88377	.48328	.87546	.49849	.86690	6
55	.43706	.89943	.45269	.89167	.46819	.88363	.48354	.87532	.49874	.86675	5
56	.43733	.89930	.45295	.89153	.46844	.88349	.48379	.87518	.49899	.86661	4
57	.43759	.89918	.45321	.89140	.46870	.88336	.48405	.87504	.49924	.86646	3
58	.43785	.89905	.45347	.89127	.46896	.88322	.48430	.87490	.49950	.86632	2
59	.43811	.89892	.45373	.89114	.46921	.88308	.48456	.87476	.49975	.86617	1
60	.43837	.89879	.45399	.89101	.46947	.88295	.48481	.87462	.50000	.86603	0
′	Cosine	Sine	Cosine	Sine	Cosine	Sine	Cosine	Sine	Cosine	Sine	′
	64°		63°		62°		61°		60°		

TABLE 1 cont.
Natural Sines and Cosines

′	30° Sine	30° Cosine	31° Sine	31° Cosine	32° Sine	32° Cosine	33° Sine	33° Cosine	34° Sine	34° Cosine	′
0	.50000	.86603	.51504	.85717	.52992	.84805	.54464	.83867	.55919	.82904	60
1	.50025	.86588	.51529	.85702	.53017	.84789	.54488	.83851	.55943	.82887	59
2	.50050	.86573	.51554	.85687	.53041	.84774	.54513	.83835	.55968	.82871	58
3	.50076	.86559	.51579	.85672	.53066	.84759	.54537	.83819	.55992	.82855	57
4	.50101	.86544	.51604	.85657	.53091	.84743	.54561	.838c4	.56016	.82839	56
5	.50126	.86530	.51628	.85642	.53115	.84728	.54586	.83788	.56040	.82822	55
6	.50151	.86515	.51653	.85627	.53140	.84712	.54610	.83772	.56064	.82806	54
7	.50176	.86501	.51678	.85612	.53164	.84697	.54635	.83756	.56088	.82790	53
8	.50201	.86486	.51703	.85597	.53189	.84681	.54659	.83740	.56112	.82773	52
9	.50227	.86471	.51728	.85582	.53214	.84666	.54683	.83724	.56136	.82757	51
10	.50252	.86457	.51753	.85567	.53238	.84650	.54708	.83708	.56160	.82741	50
11	.50277	.86442	.51778	.85551	.53263	.84635	.54732	.83692	.56184	.82724	49
12	.50302	.86427	.51803	.85536	.53288	.84619	.54756	.83676	.56208	.82708	48
13	.50327	.86413	.51828	.85521	.53312	.84604	.54781	.83660	.56232	.82692	47
14	.50352	.86398	.51852	.85506	.53337	.84588	.54805	.83645	.56256	.82675	46
15	.50377	.86384	.51877	.85491	.53361	.84573	.54829	.83629	.56280	.82659	45
16	.50403	.86369	.51902	.85476	.53386	.84557	.54854	.83613	.56305	.82643	44
17	.50428	.86354	.51927	.85461	.53411	.84542	.54878	.83597	.56329	.82626	43
18	.50453	.86340	.51952	.85446	.53435	.84526	.54902	.83581	.56353	.82610	42
19	.50478	.86325	.51977	.85431	.53460	.84511	.54927	.83565	.56377	.82593	41
20	.50503	.86310	.52002	.85416	.53484	.84495	.54951	.83549	.56401	.82577	40
21	.50528	.86295	.52026	.85401	.53509	.84480	.54975	.83533	.56425	.82561	39
22	.50553	.86281	.52051	.85385	.53534	.84464	.54999	.83517	.56449	.82544	38
23	.50578	.86266	.52076	.85370	.53558	.84448	.55024	.83501	.56473	.82528	37
24	.50603	.86251	.52101	.85355	.53583	.84433	.55048	.83485	.56497	.82511	36
25	.50628	.86237	.52126	.85340	.53607	.84417	.55072	.83469	.56521	.82495	35
26	.50654	.86222	.52151	.85325	.53632	.84402	.55097	.83453	.56545	.82478	34
27	.50679	.86207	.52175	.85310	.53656	.84386	.55121	.83437	.56569	.82462	33
28	.50704	.86192	.52200	.85294	.53681	.84370	.55145	.83421	.56593	.82446	32
29	.50729	.86178	.52225	.85279	.53705	.84355	.55169	.83405	.56617	.82429	31
30	.50754	.86163	.52250	.85264	.53730	.84339	.55194	.83389	.56641	.82413	30
31	.50779	.86148	.52275	.85249	.53754	.84324	.55218	.83373	.56665	.82396	29
32	.50804	.86133	.52299	.85234	.53779	.84308	.55242	.83356	.56689	.82380	28
33	.50829	.86119	.52324	.85218	.53804	.84292	.55266	.83340	.56713	.82363	27
34	.50854	.86104	.52349	.85203	.53828	.84277	.55291	.83324	.56736	.82347	26
35	.50879	.86089	.52374	.85188	.53853	.84261	.55315	.83308	.56760	.82330	25
36	.50904	.86074	.52399	.85173	.53877	.84245	.55339	.83292	.56784	.82314	24
37	.50929	.86059	.52423	.85157	.53902	.84230	.55363	.83276	.56808	.82297	23
38	.50954	.86045	.52448	.85142	.53926	.84214	.55388	.83260	.56832	.82281	22
39	.50979	.86030	.52473	.85127	.53951	.84198	.55412	.83244	.56856	.82264	21
40	.51004	.86015	.52498	.85112	.53975	.84182	.55436	.83228	.56880	.82248	20
41	.51029	.86000	.52522	.85096	.54000	.84167	.55460	.83212	.56904	.82231	19
42	.51054	.85985	.52547	.85081	.54024	.84151	.55484	.83195	.56928	.82214	18
43	.51079	.85970	.52572	.85066	.54049	.84135	.55509	.83179	.56952	.82198	17
44	.51104	.85956	.52597	.85051	.54073	.84120	.55533	.83163	.56976	.82181	16
45	.51129	.85941	.52621	.85035	.54097	.84104	.55557	.83147	.57000	.82165	15
46	.51154	.85926	.52646	.85020	.54122	.84088	.55581	.83131	.57024	.82148	14
47	.51179	.85911	.52671	.85005	.54146	.84072	.55605	.83115	.57047	.82132	13
48	.51204	.85896	.52696	.84989	.54171	.84057	.55630	.83098	.57071	.82115	12
49	.51229	.85881	.52720	.84974	.54195	.84041	.55654	.83082	.57095	.82098	11
50	.51254	.85866	.52745	.84959	.54220	.84025	.55678	.83066	.57119	.82082	10
51	.51279	.85851	.52770	.84943	.54244	.84009	.55702	.83050	.57143	.82065	9
52	.51304	.85836	.52794	.84928	.54269	.83994	.55726	.83034	.57167	.82048	8
53	.51329	.85821	.52819	.84913	.54293	.83978	.55750	.83017	.57191	.82032	7
54	.51354	.85806	.52844	.84897	.54317	.83962	.55775	.83001	.57215	.82015	6
55	.51379	.85792	.52869	.84882	.54342	.83946	.55799	.82985	.57238	.81999	5
56	.51404	.85777	.52893	.84866	.54366	.83930	.55823	.82969	.57262	.81982	4
57	.51429	.85762	.52918	.84851	.54391	.83915	.55847	.82953	.57286	.81965	3
58	.51454	.85747	.52943	.84836	.54415	.83899	.55871	.82936	.57310	.81949	2
59	.51479	.85732	.52967	.84820	.54440	.83883	.55895	.82920	.57334	.81932	1
60	.51504	.85717	.52992	.84805	.54464	.83867	.55919	.82904	.57358	.81915	0
′	Cosine	Sine	Cosine	Sine	Cosine	Sine	Cosine	Sine	Cosine	Sine	′
	59°		58°		57°		56°		55°		

TABLE 1 cont.

Natural Sines and Cosines

′	35° Sine	35° Cosine	36° Sine	36° Cosine	37° Sine	37° Cosine	38° Sine	38° Cosine	39° Sine	39° Cosine	′
0	.57358	.81915	.58779	.80902	.60182	.79864	.61566	.78801	.62932	.77715	60
1	.57381	.81899	.58802	.80885	.60205	.79846	.61589	.78783	.62955	.77696	59
2	.57405	.81882	.58826	.80867	.60228	.79829	.61612	.78765	.62977	.77678	58
3	.57429	.81865	.58849	.80850	.60251	.79811	.61635	.78747	.63000	.77660	57
4	.57453	.81848	.58873	.80833	.60274	.79793	.61658	.78729	.63022	.77641	56
5	.57477	.81832	.58896	.80816	.60298	.79776	.61681	.78711	.63045	.77623	55
6	.57501	.81815	.58920	.80799	.60321	.79758	.61704	.78694	.63068	.77605	54
7	.57524	.81798	.58943	.80782	.60344	.79741	.61726	.78676	.63090	.77586	53
8	.57548	.81782	.58967	.80765	.60367	.79723	.61749	.78658	.63113	.77568	52
9	.57572	.81765	.58990	.80748	.60390	.79706	.61772	.78640	.63135	.77550	51
10	.57596	.81748	.59014	.80730	.60414	.79688	.61795	.78622	.63158	.77531	50
11	.57619	.81731	.59037	.80713	.60437	.79671	.61818	.78604	.63180	.77513	49
12	.57643	.81714	.59061	.80696	.60460	.79653	.61841	.78586	.63203	.77494	48
13	.57667	.81698	.59084	.80679	.60483	.79635	.61864	.78568	.63225	.77476	47
14	.57691	.81681	.59108	.80662	.60506	.79618	.61887	.78550	.63248	.77458	46
15	.57715	.81664	.59131	.80644	.60529	.79600	.61909	.78532	.63271	.77439	45
16	.57738	.81647	.59154	.80627	.60553	.79583	.61932	.78514	.63293	.77421	44
17	.57762	.81631	.59178	.80610	.60576	.79565	.61955	.78496	.63316	.77402	43
18	.57786	.81614	.59201	.80593	.60599	.79547	.61978	.78478	.63338	.77384	42
19	.57810	.81597	.59225	.80576	.60622	.79530	.62001	.78460	.63361	.77366	41
20	.57833	.81580	.59248	.80558	.60645	.79512	.62024	.78442	.63383	.77347	40
21	.57857	.81563	.59272	.80541	.60668	.79494	.62046	.78424	.63406	.77329	39
22	.57881	.81546	.59295	.80524	.60691	.79477	.62069	.78405	.63428	.77310	38
23	.57904	.81530	.59318	.80507	.60714	.79459	.62092	.78387	.63451	.77292	37
24	.57928	.81513	.59342	.80489	.60738	.79441	.62115	.78369	.63473	.77273	36
25	.57952	.81496	.59365	.80472	.60761	.79424	.62138	.78351	.63496	.77255	35
26	.57976	.81479	.59389	.80455	.60784	.79406	.62160	.78333	.63518	.77236	34
27	.57999	.81462	.59412	.80438	.60807	.79388	.62183	.78315	.63540	.77218	33
28	.58023	.81445	.59436	.80420	.60830	.79371	.62206	.78297	.63563	.77199	32
29	.58047	.81428	.59459	.80403	.60853	.79353	.62229	.78279	.63585	.77181	31
30	.58070	.81412	.59482	.80386	.60876	.79335	.62251	.78261	.63608	.77162	30
31	.58094	.81395	.59506	.80368	.60899	.79318	.62274	.78243	.63630	.77144	29
32	.58118	.81378	.59529	.80351	.60922	.79300	.62297	.78225	.63653	.77125	28
33	.58141	.81361	.59552	.80334	.60945	.79282	.62320	.78206	.63675	.77107	27
34	.58165	.81344	.59576	.80316	.60968	.79264	.62342	.78188	.63698	.77088	26
35	.58189	.81327	.59599	.80299	.60991	.79247	.62365	.78170	.63720	.77070	25
36	.58212	.81310	.59622	.80282	.61015	.79229	.62388	.78152	.63742	.77051	24
37	.58236	.81293	.59646	.80264	.61038	.79211	.62411	.78134	.63765	.77033	23
38	.58260	.81276	.59669	.80247	.61061	.79193	.62433	.78116	.63787	.77014	22
39	.58283	.81259	.59693	.80230	.61084	.79176	.62456	.78098	.63810	.76996	21
40	.58307	.81242	.59716	.80212	.61107	.79158	.62479	.78079	.63832	.76977	20
41	.58330	.81225	.59739	.80195	.61130	.79140	.62502	.78061	.63854	.76959	19
42	.58354	.81208	.59763	.80178	.61153	.79122	.62524	.78043	.63877	.76940	18
43	.58378	.81191	.59786	.80160	.61176	.79105	.62547	.78025	.63899	.76921	17
44	.58401	.81174	.59809	.80143	.61199	.79087	.62570	.78007	.63922	.76903	16
45	.58425	.81157	.59832	.80125	.61222	.79069	.62592	.77988	.63944	.76884	15
46	.58449	.81140	.59856	.80108	.61245	.79051	.62615	.77970	.63966	.76866	14
47	.58472	.81123	.59879	.80091	.61268	.79033	.62638	.77952	.63989	.76847	13
48	.58496	.81106	.59902	.80073	.61291	.79016	.62660	.77934	.64011	.76828	12
49	.58519	.81089	.59926	.80056	.61314	.78998	.62683	.77916	.64033	.76810	11
50	.58543	.81072	.59949	.80038	.61337	.78980	.62706	.77897	.64056	.76791	10
51	.58567	.81055	.59972	.80021	.61360	.78962	.62728	.77879	.64078	.76772	9
52	.58590	.81038	.59995	.80003	.61383	.78944	.62751	.77861	.64100	.76754	8
53	.58614	.81021	.60019	.79986	.61406	.78926	.62774	.77843	.64123	.76735	7
54	.58637	.81004	.60042	.79968	.61429	.78908	.62796	.77824	.64145	.76717	6
55	.58661	.80987	.60065	.79951	.61451	.78891	.62819	.77806	.64167	.76698	5
56	.58684	.80970	.60089	.79934	.61474	.78873	.62842	.77788	.64190	.76679	4
57	.58708	.80953	.60112	.79916	.61497	.78855	.62864	.77769	.64212	.76661	3
58	.58731	.80936	.60135	.79899	.61520	.78837	.62887	.77751	.64234	.76642	2
59	.58755	.80919	.60158	.79881	.61543	.78819	.62909	.77733	.64256	.76623	1
60	.58779	.80902	.60182	.79864	.61566	.78801	.62932	.77715	.64279	.76604	0
′	Cosine	Sine	Cosine	Sine	Cosine	Sine	Cosine	Sine	Cosine	Sine	′
	54°		53°		52°		51°		50°		

TABLE 1 cont.

Natural Sines and Cosines

'	40° Sine	Cosine	41° Sine	Cosine	42° Sine	Cosine	43° Sine	Cosine	44° Sine	Cosine	'
0	.64279	.76604	.65606	.75471	.66913	.74314	.68200	.73135	.69466	.71934	60
1	.64301	.76586	.65628	.75452	.66935	.74295	.68221	.73116	.69487	.71914	59
2	.64323	.76567	.65650	.75433	.66956	.74276	.68242	.73096	.69508	.71894	58
3	.64346	.76548	.65672	.75414	.66978	.74256	.68264	.73076	.69529	.71873	57
4	.64368	.76530	.65694	.75395	.66999	.74237	.68285	.73056	.69549	.71853	56
5	.64390	.76511	.65716	.75375	.67021	.74217	.68306	.73036	.69570	.71833	55
6	.64412	.76492	.65738	.75356	.67043	.74198	.68327	.73016	.69591	.71813	54
7	.64435	.76473	.65759	.75337	.67064	.74178	.68349	.72996	.69612	.71792	53
8	.64457	.76455	.65781	.75318	.67086	.74159	.68370	.72976	.69633	.71772	52
9	.64479	.76436	.65803	.75299	.67107	.74139	.68391	.72957	.69654	.71752	51
10	.64501	.76417	.65825	.75280	.67129	.74120	.68412	.72937	.69675	.71732	50
11	.64524	.76398	.65847	.75261	.67151	.74100	.68434	.72917	.69696	.71711	49
12	.64546	.76380	.65869	.75241	.67172	.74080	.68455	.72897	.69717	.71691	48
13	.64568	.76361	.65891	.75222	.67194	.74061	.68476	.72877	.69737	.71671	47
14	.64590	.76342	.65913	.75203	.67215	.74041	.68497	.72857	.69758	.71650	46
15	.64612	.76323	.65935	.75184	.67237	.74022	.68518	.72837	.69779	.71630	45
16	.64635	.76304	.65956	.75165	.67258	.74002	.68539	.72817	.69800	.71610	44
17	.64657	.76286	.65978	.75146	.67280	.73983	.68561	.72797	.69821	.71590	43
18	.64679	.76267	.66000	.75126	.67301	.73963	.68582	.72777	.69842	.71569	42
19	.64701	.76248	.66022	.75107	.67323	.73944	.68603	.72757	.69862	.71549	41
20	.64723	.76229	.66044	.75088	.67344	.73924	.68624	.72737	.69883	.71529	40
21	.64746	.76210	.66066	.75069	.67366	.73904	.68645	.72717	.69904	.71508	39
22	.64768	.76192	.66088	.75050	.67387	.73885	.68666	.72697	.69925	.71488	38
23	.64790	.76173	.66109	.75030	.67409	.73865	.68688	.72677	.69946	.71468	37
24	.64812	.76154	.66131	.75011	.67430	.73846	.68709	.72657	.69966	.71447	36
25	.64834	.76135	.66153	.74992	.67452	.73826	.68730	.72637	.69987	.71427	35
26	.64856	.76116	.66175	.74973	.67473	.73806	.68751	.72617	.70008	.71407	34
27	.64878	.76097	.66197	.74953	.67495	.73787	.68772	.72597	.70029	.71386	33
28	.64901	.76078	.66218	.74934	.67516	.73767	.68793	.72577	.70049	.71366	32
29	.64923	.76059	.66240	.74915	.67538	.73747	.68814	.72557	.70070	.71345	31
30	.64945	.76041	.66262	.74896	.67559	.73728	.68835	.72537	.70091	.71325	30
31	.64967	.76022	.66284	.74876	.67580	.73708	.68857	.72517	.70112	.71305	29
32	.64989	.76003	.66306	.74857	.67602	.73688	.68878	.72497	.70132	.71284	28
33	.65011	.75984	.66327	.74838	.67623	.73669	.68899	.72477	.70153	.71264	27
34	.65033	.75965	.66349	.74818	.67645	.73649	.68920	.72457	.70174	.71243	26
35	.65055	.75946	.66371	.74799	.67666	.73629	.68941	.72437	.70195	.71223	25
36	.65077	.75927	.66393	.74780	.67688	.73610	.68962	.72417	.70215	.71203	24
37	.65100	.75908	.66414	.74760	.67709	.73590	.68983	.72397	.70236	.71182	23
38	.65122	.75889	.66436	.74741	.67730	.73570	.69004	.72377	.70257	.71162	22
39	.65144	.75870	.66458	.74722	.67752	.73551	.69025	.72357	.70277	.71141	21
40	.65166	.75851	.66480	.74703	.67773	.73531	.69046	.72337	.70298	.71121	20
41	.65188	.75832	.66501	.74683	.67795	.73511	.69067	.72317	.70319	.71100	19
42	.65210	.75813	.66523	.74664	.67816	.73491	.69088	.72297	.70339	.71080	18
43	.65232	.75794	.66545	.74644	.67837	.73472	.69109	.72277	.70360	.71059	17
44	.65254	.75775	.66566	.74625	.67859	.73452	.69130	.72257	.70381	.71039	16
45	.65276	.75756	.66588	.74606	.67880	.73432	.69151	.72236	.70401	.71019	15
46	.65298	.75738	.66610	.74586	.67901	.73413	.69172	.72216	.70422	.70998	14
47	.65320	.75719	.66632	.74567	.67923	.73393	.69193	.72196	.70443	.70978	13
48	.65342	.75700	.66653	.74548	.67944	.73373	.69214	.72176	.70463	.70957	12
49	.65364	.75680	.66675	.74528	.67965	.73353	.69235	.72156	.70484	.70937	11
50	.65386	.75661	.66697	.74509	.67987	.73333	.69256	.72136	.70505	.70916	10
51	.65408	.75642	.66718	.74489	.68008	.73314	.69277	.72116	.70525	.70896	9
52	.65430	.75623	.66740	.74470	.68029	.73294	.69298	.72095	.70546	.70875	8
53	.65452	.75604	.66762	.74451	.68051	.73274	.69319	.72075	.70567	.70855	7
54	.65474	.75585	.66783	.74431	.68072	.73254	.69340	.72055	.70587	.70834	6
55	.65496	.75566	.66805	.74412	.68093	.73234	.69361	.72035	.70608	.70813	5
56	.65518	.75547	.66827	.74392	.68115	.73215	.69382	.72015	.70628	.70793	4
57	.65540	.75528	.66848	.74373	.68136	.73195	.69403	.71995	.70649	.70772	3
58	.65562	.75509	.66870	.74353	.68157	.73175	.69424	.71974	.70670	.70752	2
59	.65584	.75490	.66891	.74334	.68179	.73155	.69445	.71954	.70690	.70731	1
60	.65606	.75471	.66913	.74314	.68200	.73135	.69466	.71934	.70711	.70711	0
'	Cosine	Sine	Cosine	Sine	Cosine	Sine	Cosine	Sine	Cosine	Sine	'
	49°		**48°**		**47°**		**46°**		**45°**		

TABLE II

Natural Tangents and Cotangents

′	0° Tang	0° Cotang	1° Tang	1° Cotang	2° Tang	2° Cotang	3° Tang	3° Cotang	4° Tang	4° Cotang	′
0	.00000	Infinite	.01746	57.2900	.03492	28.6363	.05241	19.0811	.06993	14.3007	60
1	.00029	3437.75	.01775	56.3506	.03521	28.3994	.05270	18.9755	.07022	14.2411	59
2	.00058	1718.87	.01804	55.4415	.03550	28.1664	.05299	18.8711	.07051	14.1821	58
3	.00087	1145.92	.01833	54.5613	.03579	27.9372	.05328	18.7678	.07080	14.1235	57
4	.00116	859.436	.01862	53.7086	.03609	27.7117	.05357	18.6656	.07110	14.0655	56
5	.00145	687.549	.01891	52.8821	.03638	27.4899	.05387	18.5645	.07139	14.0079	55
6	.00175	572.957	.01920	52.0807	.03667	27.2715	.05416	18.4645	.07168	13.9507	54
7	.00204	491.106	.01949	51.3032	.03696	27.0566	.05445	18.3655	.07197	13.8940	53
8	.00233	429.718	.01978	50.5485	.03725	26.8450	.05474	18.2677	.07227	13.8378	52
9	.00262	381.971	.02007	49.8157	.03754	26.6367	.05503	18.1708	.07256	13.7821	51
10	.00291	343.774	.02036	49.1039	.03783	26.4316	.05533	18.0750	.07285	13.7267	50
11	.00320	312.521	.02066	48.4121	.03812	26.2296	.05562	17.9802	.07314	13.6719	49
12	.00349	286.478	.02095	47.7395	.03842	26.0307	.05591	17.8863	.07344	13.6174	48
13	.00378	264.441	.02124	47.0853	.03871	25.8348	.05620	17.7934	.07373	13.5634	47
14	.00407	245.552	.02153	46.4489	.03900	25.6418	.05649	17.7015	.07402	13.5098	46
15	.00436	229.182	.02182	45.8294	.03929	25.4517	.05678	17.6106	.07431	13.4566	45
16	.00465	214.858	.02211	45.2261	.03958	25.2644	.05708	17.5205	.07461	13.4039	44
17	.00495	202.219	.02240	44.6386	.03987	25.0798	.05737	17.4314	.07490	13.3515	43
18	.00524	190.984	.02269	44.0661	.04016	24.8978	.05766	17.3432	.07519	13.2996	42
19	.00553	180.932	.02298	43.5081	.04046	24.7185	.05795	17.2558	.07548	13.2480	41
20	.00582	171.885	.02328	42.9641	.04075	24.5418	.05824	17.1693	.07578	13.1969	40
21	.00611	163.700	.02357	42.4335	.04104	24.3675	.05854	17.0837	.07607	13.1461	39
22	.00640	156.259	.02386	41.9158	.04133	24.1957	.05883	16.9990	.07636	13.0958	38
23	.00669	149.465	.02415	41.4106	.04162	24.0263	.05912	16.9150	.07665	13.0458	37
24	.00698	143.237	.02444	40.9174	.04191	23.8593	.05941	16.8319	.07695	12.9962	36
25	.00727	137.507	.02473	40.4358	.04220	23.6945	.05970	16.7496	.07724	12.9469	35
26	.00756	132.219	.02502	39.9655	.04250	23.5321	.05999	16.6681	.07753	12.8981	34
27	.00785	127.321	.02531	39.5059	.04279	23.3718	.06029	16.5874	.07782	12.8496	33
28	.00815	122.774	.02560	39.0568	.04308	23.2137	.06058	16.5075	.07812	12.8014	32
29	.00844	118.540	.02589	38.6177	.04337	23.0577	.06087	16.4283	.07841	12.7536	31
30	.00873	114.589	.02619	38.1885	.04366	22.9038	.06116	16.3499	.07870	12.7062	30
31	.00902	110.892	.02648	37.7686	.04395	22.7519	.06145	16.2722	.07899	12.6591	29
32	.00931	107.426	.02677	37.3579	.04424	22.6020	.06175	16.1952	.07929	12.6124	28
33	.00960	104.171	.02706	36.9560	.04454	22.4541	.06204	16.1190	.07958	12.5660	27
34	.00989	101.107	.02735	36.5627	.04483	22.3081	.06233	16.0435	.07987	12.5199	26
35	.01018	98.2179	.02764	36.1776	.04512	22.1640	.06262	15.9687	.08017	12.4742	25
36	.01047	95.4895	.02793	35.8006	.04541	22.0217	.06291	15.8945	.08046	12.4288	24
37	.01076	92.9085	.02822	35.4313	.04570	21.8813	.06321	15.8211	.08075	12.3838	23
38	.01105	90.4633	.02851	35.0695	.04599	21.7426	.06350	15.7483	.08104	12.3390	22
39	.01135	88.1436	.02881	34.7151	.04628	21.6056	.06379	15.6762	.08134	12.2946	21
40	.01164	85.9398	.02910	34.3678	.04658	21.4704	.06408	15.6048	.08163	12.2505	20
41	.01193	83.8435	.02939	34.0273	.04687	21.3369	.06437	15.5340	.08192	12.2067	19
42	.01222	81.8470	.02968	33.6935	.04716	21.2049	.06467	15.4638	.08221	12.1632	18
43	.01251	79.9434	.02997	33.3662	.04745	21.0747	.06496	15.3943	.08251	12.1201	17
44	.01280	78.1263	.03026	33.0452	.04774	20.9460	.06525	15.3254	.08280	12.0772	16
45	.01309	76.3900	.03055	32.7303	.04803	20.8188	.06554	15.2571	.08309	12.0346	15
46	.01338	74.7292	.03084	32.4213	.04833	20.6932	.06584	15.1893	.08339	11.9923	14
47	.01367	73.1390	.03114	32.1181	.04862	20.5691	.06613	15.1222	.08368	11.9504	13
48	.01396	71.6151	.03143	31.8205	.04891	20.4465	.06642	15.0557	.08397	11.9087	12
49	.01425	70.1533	.03172	31.5284	.04920	20.3253	.06671	14.9898	.08427	11.8673	11
50	.01455	68.7501	.03201	31.2416	.04949	20.2056	.06700	14.9244	.08456	11.8262	10
51	.01484	67.4019	.03230	30.9599	.04978	20.0872	.06730	14.8596	.08485	11.7853	9
52	.01513	66.1055	.03259	30.6833	.05007	19.9702	.06759	14.7954	.08514	11.7448	8
53	.01542	64.8580	.03288	30.4116	.05037	19.8546	.06788	14.7317	.08544	11.7045	7
54	.01571	63.6567	.03317	30.1446	.05066	19.7403	.06817	14.6685	.08573	11.6645	6
55	.01600	62.4992	.03346	29.8823	.05095	19.6273	.06847	14.6059	.08602	11.6248	5
56	.01629	61.3829	.03376	29.6245	.05124	19.5156	.06876	14.5438	.08632	11.5853	4
57	.01658	60.3058	.03405	29.3711	.05153	19.4051	.06905	14.4823	.08661	11.5461	3
58	.01687	59.2659	.03434	29.1220	.05182	19.2959	.06934	14.4212	.08690	11.5072	2
59	.01716	58.2612	.03463	28.8771	.05212	19.1879	.06963	14.3607	.08720	11.4685	1
60	.01746	57.2900	.03492	28.6363	.05241	19.0811	.06993	14.3007	.08749	11.4301	0
′	Cotang	Tang	Cotang	Tang	Cotang	Tang	Cotang	Tang	Cotang	Tang	′
	89°		88°		87°		86°		85°		

TABLE II cont.

Natural Tangents and Cotangents

′	5° Tang	Cotang	6° Tang	Cotang	7° Tang	Cotang	8° Tang	Cotang	9° Tang	Cotang	′
0	.08749	11.4301	.10510	9.51436	.12278	8.14435	.14054	7.11537	.15838	6.31375	60
1	.08778	11.3919	.10540	9.48781	.12308	8.12481	.14084	7.10038	.15868	6.30189	59
2	.08807	11.3540	.10569	9.46141	.12338	8.10536	.14113	7.08546	.15898	6.29007	58
3	.08837	11.3163	.10599	9.43515	.12367	8.08600	.14143	7.07059	.15928	6.27829	57
4	.08866	11.2789	.10628	9.40904	.12397	8.06674	.14173	7.05579	.15958	6.26655	56
5	.08895	11.2417	.10657	9.38307	.12426	8.04756	.14202	7.04105	.15988	6.25486	55
6	.08925	11.2048	.10687	9.35724	.12456	8.02848	.14232	7.02637	.16017	6.24321	54
7	.08954	11.1681	.10716	9.33155	.12485	8.00948	.14262	7.01174	.16047	6.23160	53
8	.08983	11.1316	.10746	9.30599	.12515	7.99058	.14291	6.99718	.16077	6.22003	52
9	.09013	11.0954	.10775	9.28058	.12544	7.97176	.14321	6.98268	.16107	6.20851	51
10	.09042	11.0594	.10805	9.25530	.12574	7.95302	.14351	6.96823	.16137	6.19703	50
11	.09071	11.0237	.10834	9.23016	.12603	7.93438	.14381	6.95385	.16167	6.18559	49
12	.09101	10.9882	.10863	9.20516	.12633	7.91582	.14410	6.93952	.16196	6.17419	48
13	.09130	10.9529	.10893	9.18028	.12662	7.89734	.14440	6.92525	.16226	6.16283	47
14	.09159	10.9178	.10922	9.15554	.12692	7.87895	.14470	6.91104	.16256	6.15151	46
15	.09189	10.8829	.10952	9.13093	.12722	7.86064	.14499	6.89683	.16286	6.14023	45
16	.09218	10.8483	.10981	9.10646	.12751	7.84242	.14529	6.88278	.16316	6.12899	44
17	.09247	10.8139	.11011	9.08211	.12781	7.82428	.14559	6.86874	.16346	6.11779	43
18	.09277	10.7797	.11040	9.05789	.12810	7.80622	.14588	6.85475	.16376	6.10664	42
19	.09306	10.7457	.11070	9.03379	.12840	7.78825	.14618	6.84082	.16405	6.09552	41
20	.09335	10.7119	.11099	9.00983	.12869	7.77035	.14648	6.82694	.16435	6.08444	40
21	.09365	10.6783	.11128	8.98598	.12899	7.75254	.14678	6.81312	.16465	6.07340	39
22	.09394	10.6450	.11158	8.96227	.12929	7.73480	.14707	6.79936	.16495	6.06240	38
23	.09423	10.6118	.11187	8.93867	.12958	7.71715	.14737	6.78564	.16525	6.05143	37
24	.09453	10.5789	.11217	8.91520	.12988	7.69957	.14767	6.77199	.16555	6.04051	36
25	.09482	10.5462	.11246	8.89185	.13017	7.68208	.14796	6.75838	.16585	6.02962	35
26	.09511	10.5136	.11276	8.86862	.13047	7.66466	.14826	6.74483	.16615	6.01878	34
27	.09541	10.4813	.11305	8.84551	.13076	7.64732	.14856	6.73133	.16645	6.00797	33
28	.09570	10.4491	.11335	8.82252	.13106	7.63005	.14886	6.71789	.16674	5.99720	32
29	.09600	10.4172	.11364	8.79964	.13136	7.61287	.14915	6.70450	.16704	5.98646	31
30	.09629	10.3854	.11394	8.77689	.13165	7.59575	.14945	6.69116	.16734	5.97576	30
31	.09658	10.3538	.11423	8.75425	.13195	7.57872	.14975	6.67787	.16764	5.96510	29
32	.09688	10.3224	.11452	8.73172	.13224	7.56176	.15005	6.66463	.16794	5.95448	28
33	.09717	10.2913	.11482	8.70931	.13254	7.54487	.15034	6.65144	.16824	5.94390	27
34	.09746	10.2602	.11511	8.68701	.13284	7.52806	.15064	6.63831	.16854	5.93335	26
35	.09776	10.2294	.11541	8.66482	.13313	7.51132	.15094	6.62523	.16884	5.92283	25
36	.09805	10.1988	.11570	8.64275	.13343	7.49465	.15124	6.61219	.16914	5.91236	24
37	.09834	10.1683	.11600	8.62078	.13372	7.47806	.15153	6.59921	.16944	5.90191	23
38	.09864	10.1381	.11629	8.59893	.13402	7.46154	.15183	6.58627	.16974	5.89151	22
39	.09893	10.1080	.11659	8.57718	.13432	7.44509	.15213	6.57339	.17004	5.88114	21
40	.09923	10.0780	.11688	8.55555	.13461	7.42871	.15243	6.56055	.17033	5.87080	20
41	.09952	10.0483	.11718	8.53402	.13491	7.41240	.15272	6.54777	.17063	5.86051	19
42	.09981	10.0187	.11747	8.51259	.13521	7.39616	.15302	6.53503	.17093	5.85024	18
43	.10011	9.98931	.11777	8.49128	.13550	7.37999	.15332	6.52234	.17123	5.84001	17
44	.10040	9.96007	.11806	8.47007	.13580	7.36389	.15362	6.50970	.17153	5.82982	16
45	.10069	9.93101	.11836	8.44896	.13609	7.34786	.15391	6.49710	.17183	5.81966	15
46	.10099	9.90211	.11865	8.42795	.13639	7.33190	.15421	6.48456	.17213	5.80953	14
47	.10128	9.87338	.11895	8.40705	.13669	7.31600	.15451	6.47206	.17243	5.79944	13
48	.10158	9.84482	.11924	8.38625	.13698	7.30018	.15481	6.45961	.17273	5.78938	12
49	.10187	9.81641	.11954	8.36555	.13728	7.28442	.15511	6.44720	.17303	5.77936	11
50	.10216	9.78817	.11983	8.34496	.13758	7.26873	.15540	6.43484	.17333	5.76937	10
51	.10246	9.76009	.12013	8.32446	.13787	7.25310	.15570	6.42253	.17363	5.75941	9
52	.10275	9.73217	.12042	8.30406	.13817	7.23754	.15600	6.41026	.17393	5.74949	8
53	.10305	9.70441	.12072	8.28376	.13846	7.22204	.15630	6.39804	.17423	5.73960	7
54	.10334	9.67680	.12101	8.26355	.13876	7.20661	.15660	6.38587	.17453	5.72974	6
55	.10363	9.64935	.12131	8.24345	.13906	7.19125	.15689	6.37374	.17483	5.71992	5
56	.10393	9.62205	.12160	8.22344	.13935	7.17594	.15719	6.36165	.17513	5.71013	4
57	.10422	9.59490	.12190	8.20352	.13965	7.16071	.15749	6.34961	.17543	5.70037	3
58	.10452	9.56791	.12219	8.18370	.13995	7.14553	.15779	6.33761	.17573	5.69064	2
59	.10481	9.54106	.12249	8.16398	.14024	7.13042	.15809	6.32566	.17603	5.68094	1
60	.10510	9.51436	.12278	8.14435	.14054	7.11537	.15838	6.31375	.17633	5.67128	0
′	Cotang	Tang	Cotang	Tang	Cotang	Tang	Cotang	Tang	Cotang	Tang	′
	84°		83°		82°		81°		80°		

TABLE II cont.

Natural Tangents and Cotangents

′	10°		11°		12°		13°		14°		′
	Tang	Cotang	Tang	Cotang	Tang	Cotang	Tang	Cotang	Tang	Cotang	
0	.17633	5.67128	.19438	5.14455	.21256	4.70463	.23087	4.33148	.24933	4.01078	60
1	.17663	5.66165	.19468	5.13658	.21286	4.69791	.23117	4.32573	.24964	4.00582	59
2	.17693	5.65205	.19498	5.12862	.21316	4.69121	.23148	4.32001	.24995	4.00086	58
3	.17723	5.64248	.19529	5.12069	.21347	4.68452	.23179	4.31430	.25026	3.99592	57
4	.17753	5.63295	.19559	5.11279	.21377	4.67786	.23209	4.30860	.25056	3.99099	56
5	.17783	5.62344	.19589	5.10490	.21408	4.67121	.23240	4.30291	.25087	3.98607	55
6	.17813	5.61397	.19619	5.09704	.21438	4.66458	.23271	4.29724	.25118	3.98117	54
7	.17843	5.60452	.19649	5.08921	.21469	4.65797	.23301	4.29159	.25149	3.97627	53
8	.17873	5.59511	.19680	5.08139	.21499	4.65138	.23332	4.28595	.25180	3.97139	52
9	.17903	5.58573	.19710	5.07360	.21529	4.64480	.23363	4.28032	.25211	3.96651	51
10	.17933	5.57638	.19740	5.06584	.21560	4.63825	.23393	4.27471	.25242	3.96165	50
11	.17963	5.56706	.19770	5.05809	.21590	4.63171	.23424	4.26911	.25273	3.95680	49
12	.17993	5.55777	.19801	5.05037	.21621	4.62518	.23455	4.26352	.25304	3.95196	48
13	.18023	5.54851	.19831	5.04267	.21651	4.61868	.23485	4.25795	.25335	3.94713	47
14	.18053	5.53927	.19861	5.03499	.21682	4.61219	.23516	4.25239	.25366	3.94232	46
15	.18083	5.53007	.19891	5.02734	.21712	4.60572	.23547	4.24685	.25397	3.93751	45
16	.18113	5.52090	.19921	5.01971	.21743	4.59927	.23578	4.24132	.25428	3.93271	44
17	.18143	5.51176	.19952	5.01210	.21773	4.59283	.23608	4.23580	.25459	3.92793	43
18	.18173	5.50264	.19982	5.00451	.21804	4.58641	.23639	4.23030	.25490	3.92316	42
19	.18203	5.49356	.20012	4.99695	.21834	4.58001	.23670	4.22481	.25521	3.91839	41
20	.18233	5.48451	.20042	4.98940	.21864	4.57363	.23700	4.21933	.25552	3.91364	40
21	.18263	5.47548	.20073	4.98188	.21895	4.56726	.23731	4.21387	.25583	3.90890	39
22	.18293	5.46648	.20103	4.97438	.21925	4.56091	.23762	4.20842	.25614	3.90417	38
23	.18323	5.45751	.20133	4.96690	.21956	4.55458	.23793	4.20298	.25645	3.89945	37
24	.18353	5.44857	.20164	4.95945	.21986	4.54826	.23823	4.19756	.25676	3.89474	36
25	.18384	5.43966	.20194	4.95201	.22017	4.54196	.23854	4.19215	.25707	3.89004	35
26	.18414	5.43077	.20224	4.94460	.22047	4.53568	.23885	4.18675	.25738	3.88536	34
27	.18444	5.42192	.20254	4.93721	.22078	4.52941	.23916	4.18137	.25769	3.88068	33
28	.18474	5.41309	.20285	4.92984	.22108	4.52316	.23946	4.17600	.25800	3.87601	32
29	.18504	5.40429	.20315	4.92249	.22139	4.51693	.23977	4.17064	.25831	3.87136	31
30	.18534	5.39552	.20345	4.91516	.22169	4.51071	.24008	4.16530	.25862	3.86671	30
31	.18564	5.38677	.20376	4.90785	.22200	4.50451	.24039	4.15997	.25893	3.86208	29
32	.18594	5.37805	.20406	4.90056	.22231	4.49832	.24069	4.15465	.25924	3.85745	28
33	.18624	5.36936	.20436	4.89330	.22261	4.49215	.24100	4.14934	.25955	3.85284	27
34	.18654	5.36070	.20466	4.88605	.22292	4.48600	.24131	4.14405	.25986	3.84824	26
35	.18684	5.35206	.20497	4.87882	.22322	4.47986	.24162	4.13877	.26017	3.84364	25
36	.18714	5.34345	.20527	4.87162	.22353	4.47374	.24193	4.13350	.26048	3.83906	24
37	.18745	5.33487	.20557	4.86444	.22383	4.46764	.24223	4.12825	.26079	3.83449	23
38	.18775	5.32631	.20588	4.85727	.22414	4.46155	.24254	4.12301	.26110	3.82992	22
39	.18805	5.31778	.20618	4.85013	.22444	4.45543	.24285	4.11778	.26141	3.82537	21
40	.18835	5.30928	.20648	4.84300	.22475	4.44942	.24316	4.11256	.26172	3.82083	20
41	.18865	5.30080	.20679	4.83590	.22505	4.44338	.24347	4.10736	.26203	3.81630	19
42	.18895	5.29235	.20709	4.82882	.22536	4.43735	.24377	4.10216	.26235	3.81177	18
43	.18925	5.28393	.20739	4.82175	.22567	4.43134	.24408	4.09699	.26266	3.80726	17
44	.18955	5.27553	.20770	4.81471	.22597	4.42534	.24439	4.09182	.26297	3.80276	16
45	.18986	5.26715	.20800	4.80769	.22628	4.41936	.24470	4.08666	.26328	3.79827	15
46	.19016	5.25880	.20830	4.80068	.22658	4.41340	.24501	4.08152	.26359	3.79378	14
47	.19046	5.25048	.20861	4.79370	.22689	4.40745	.24532	4.07639	.26390	3.78931	13
48	.19076	5.24218	.20891	4.78673	.22719	4.40152	.24562	4.07127	.26421	3.78485	12
49	.19106	5.23391	.20921	4.77978	.22750	4.39560	.24593	4.06616	.26452	3.78040	11
50	.19136	5.22566	.20952	4.77286	.22781	4.38969	.24624	4.06107	.26483	3.77595	10
51	.19166	5.21744	.20982	4.76595	.22811	4.38381	.24655	4.05599	.26515	3.77152	9
52	.19197	5.20925	.21013	4.75906	.22842	4.37793	.24686	4.05092	.26546	3.76709	8
53	.19227	5.20107	.21043	4.75219	.22872	4.37207	.24717	4.04586	.26577	3.76268	7
54	.19257	5.19293	.21073	4.74534	.22903	4.36623	.24747	4.04081	.26608	3.75828	6
55	.19287	5.18480	.21104	4.73851	.22934	4.36040	.24778	4.03578	.26639	3.75388	5
56	.19317	5.17671	.21134	4.73170	.22964	4.35459	.24809	4.03076	.26670	3.74950	4
57	.19347	5.16863	.21164	4.72490	.22995	4.34879	.24840	4.02574	.26701	3.74512	3
58	.19378	5.16058	.21195	4.71813	.23026	4.34300	.24871	4.02074	.26733	3.74075	2
59	.19408	5.15256	.21225	4.71137	.23056	4.33723	.24902	4.01576	.26764	3.73640	1
60	.19438	5.14455	.21256	4.70463	.23087	4.33148	.24933	4.01078	.26795	3.73205	0
′	Cotang	Tang	Cotang	Tang	Cotang	Tang	Cotang	Tang	Cotang	Tang	′
	79°		78°		77°		76°		75°		

TABLE II cont.

Natural Tangents and Cotangents

′	15°		16°		17°		18°		19°		′
	Tang	Cotang	Tang	Cotang	Tang	Cotang	Tang	Cotang	Tang	Cotang	
0	.26795	3.73205	.28675	3.48741	.30573	3.27085	.32492	3.07768	.34433	2.90421	60
1	.26826	3.72771	.28706	3.48359	.30605	3.26745	.32524	3.07464	.34465	2.90147	59
2	.26857	3.72338	.28738	3.47977	.30637	3.26406	.32556	3.07160	.34498	2.89873	58
3	.26888	3.71907	.28769	3.47596	.30669	3.26067	.32588	3.06857	.34530	2.89600	57
4	.26920	3.71476	.28800	3.47216	.30700	3.25729	.32621	3.06554	.34563	2.89327	56
5	.26951	3.71046	.28832	3.46837	.30732	3.25392	.32653	3.06252	.34596	2.89055	55
6	.26982	3.70616	.28864	3.46458	.30764	3.25055	.32685	3.05950	.34628	2.88783	54
7	.27013	3.70188	.28895	3.46080	.30796	3.24719	.32717	3.05649	.34661	2.88511	53
8	.27044	3.69761	.28927	3.45703	.30828	3.24383	.32749	3.05349	.34693	2.88240	52
9	.27076	3.69335	.28958	3.45327	.30860	3.24049	.32782	3.05049	.34726	2.87970	51
10	.27107	3.68909	.28990	3.44951	.30891	3.23714	.32814	3.04749	.34758	2.87700	50
11	.27138	3.68485	.29021	3.44576	.30923	3.23381	.32846	3.04450	.34791	2.87430	49
12	.27169	3.68061	.29053	3.44202	.30955	3.23048	.32878	3.04152	.34824	2.87161	48
13	.27201	3.67638	.29084	3.43829	.30987	3.22715	.32911	3.03854	.34856	2.86892	47
14	.27232	3.67217	.29116	3.43456	.31019	3.22384	.32943	3.03556	.34889	2.86624	46
15	.27263	3.66796	.29147	3.43084	.31051	3.22053	.32975	3.03260	.34922	2.86356	45
16	.27294	3.66376	.29179	3.42713	.31083	3.21722	.33007	3.02963	.34954	2.86089	44
17	.27326	3.65957	.29210	3.42343	.31115	3.21392	.33040	3.02667	.34987	2.85822	43
18	.27357	3.65538	.29242	3.41973	.31147	3.21063	.33072	3.02372	.35020	2.85555	42
19	.27388	3.65121	.29274	3.41604	.31178	3.20734	.33104	3.02077	.35052	2.85289	41
20	.27419	3.64705	.29305	3.41236	.31210	3.20406	.33136	3.01783	.35085	2.85023	40
21	.27451	3.64289	.29337	3.40869	.31242	3.20079	.33169	3.01489	.35118	2.84758	39
22	.27482	3.63874	.29368	3.40502	.31274	3.19752	.33201	3.01196	.35150	2.84494	38
23	.27513	3.63461	.29400	3.40136	.31306	3.19426	.33233	3.00903	.35183	2.84229	37
24	.27545	3.63048	.29432	3.39771	.31338	3.19100	.33266	3.00611	.35216	2.83965	36
25	.27576	3.62636	.29463	3.39406	.31370	3.18775	.33298	3.00319	.35248	2.83702	35
26	.27607	3.62224	.29495	3.39042	.31402	3.18451	.33330	3.00028	.35281	2.83439	34
27	.27638	3.61814	.29526	3.38679	.31434	3.18127	.33363	2.99738	.35314	2.83176	33
28	.27670	3.61405	.29558	3.38317	.31466	3.17804	.33395	2.99447	.35346	2.82914	32
29	.27701	3.60996	.29590	3.37955	.31498	3.17481	.33427	2.99158	.25379	2.82653	31
30	.27732	3.60588	.29621	3.37594	.31530	3.17159	.33460	2.98868	.35412	2.82391	30
31	.27764	3.60181	.29653	3.37234	.31562	3.16838	.33492	2.98580	.35445	2.82130	29
32	.27795	3.59775	.29685	3.36875	.31594	3.16517	.33524	2.98292	.35477	2.81870	28
33	.27826	3.59370	.29716	3.36516	.31626	3.16197	.33557	2.98004	.35510	2.81610	27
34	.27858	3.58966	.29748	3.36158	.31658	3.15877	.33589	2.97717	.35543	2.81350	26
35	.27889	3.58562	.29780	3.35800	.31690	3.15558	.33621	2.97430	.35576	2.81091	25
36	.27921	3.58160	.29811	3.35443	.31722	3.15240	.33654	2.97144	.35608	2.80833	24
37	.27952	3.57758	.29843	3.35087	.31754	3.14922	.33686	2.96858	.35641	2.80574	23
38	.27983	3.57357	.29875	3.34732	.31786	3.14605	.33718	2.96573	.35674	2.80316	22
39	.28015	3.56957	.29906	3.34377	.31818	3.14288	.33751	2.96288	.35707	2.80059	21
40	.28046	3.56557	.29938	3.34023	.31850	3.13972	.33783	2.96004	.35740	2:79802	20
41	.28077	3.56159	.29970	3.33670	.31882	3.13656	.33816	2.95721	.35772	2.79545	19
42	.28109	3.55761	.30001	3.33317	.31914	3.13341	.33848	2.95437	.35805	2.79289	18
43	.28140	3.55364	.30033	3.32965	.31946	3.13027	.33881	2.95155	.35838	2.79033	17
44	.28172	3.54968	.30065	3.32614	.31978	3.12713	.33913	2.94872	.35871	2.78778	16
45	.28203	3.54573	.30097	3.32264	.32010	3.12400	.33945	2.94591	.35904	2.78523	15
46	.28234	3.54179	.30128	3.31914	.32042	3.12087	.33978	2.94309	.35937	2.78269	14
47	.28266	3.53785	.30160	3.31565	.32074	3.11775	.34010	2.94028	.35969	2.78014	13
48	.28297	3.53393	.30192	3.31216	.32106	3.11464	.34043	2.93748	.36002	2.77761	12
49	.28329	3.53001	.30224	3.30868	.32139	3.11153	.34075	2.93468	.36035	2.77507	11
50	.28360	3.52609	.30255	3.30521	.32171	3.10842	.34108	2.93189	.36068	2.77254	10
51	.28391	3.52219	.30287	3.30174	.32203	3.10532	.34140	2.92910	.36101	2.77002	9
52	.28423	3.51829	.30319	3.29829	.32235	3.10223	.34173	2.92632	.36134	2.76750	8
53	.28454	3.51441	.30351	3.29483	.32267	3.09914	.34205	2.92354	.36167	2.76498	7
54	.28486	3.51053	.30382	3.29139	.32299	3.09606	.34238	2.92076	.36199	2.76247	6
55	.28517	3.50666	.30414	3.28795	.32331	3.09298	.34270	2.91799	.36232	2.75996	5
56	.28549	3.50279	.30446	3.28452	.32363	3.08991	.34303	2.91523	.36265	2.75746	4
57	.28580	3.49894	.30478	3.28109	.32396	3.08685	.34335	2.91246	.36298	2.75496	3
58	.28612	3.49509	.30509	3.27767	.32428	3.08379	.34368	2.90971	.36331	2.75246	2
59	.28643	3.49125	.30541	3.27426	.32460	3.08073	.34400	2.90696	.36364	2.74997	1
60	.28675	3.48741	.30573	3.27085	.32492	3.07768	.34433	2.90421	.36397	2.74748	0
′	Cotang	Tang	Cotang	Tang	Cotang	Tang	Cotang	Tang	Cotang	Tang	′
	74°		73°		72°		71°		70°		

TABLE II cont.

Natural Tangents and Cotangents

′	20° Tang	Cotang	21° Tang	Cotang	22° Tang	Cotang	23° Tang	Cotang	24° Tang	Cotang	′
0	.36397	2.74748	.38386	2.60509	.40403	2.47509	.42447	2.35585	.44523	2.24604	60
1	.36430	2.74499	.38420	2.60283	.40436	2.47302	.42482	2.35395	.44558	2.24428	59
2	.36463	2.74251	.38453	2.60057	.40470	2.47095	.42516	2.35205	.44593	2.24252	58
3	.36496	2.74004	.38487	2.59831	.40504	2.46888	.42551	2.35015	.44627	2.24077	57
4	.36529	2.73756	.38520	2.59606	.40538	2.46682	.42585	2.34825	.44662	2.23902	56
5	.36562	2.73509	.38553	2.59381	.40572	2.46476	.42619	2.34636	.44697	2.23727	55
6	.36595	2.73263	.38587	2.59156	.40606	2.46270	.42654	2.34447	.44732	2.23553	54
7	.36628	2.73017	.38620	2.58932	.40640	2.46065	.42688	2.34258	.44767	2.23378	53
8	.36661	2.72771	.38654	2.58708	.40674	2.45860	.42722	2.34069	.44802	2.23204	52
9	.36694	2.72526	.38687	2.58484	.40707	2.45655	.42757	2.33881	.44837	2.23030	51
10	.36727	2.72281	.38721	2.58261	.40741	2.45451	.42791	2.33693	.44872	2.22857	50
11	.36760	2.72036	.38754	2.58038	.40775	2.45246	.42826	2.33505	.44907	2.22683	49
12	.36793	2.71792	.38787	2.57815	.40809	2.45043	.42860	2.33317	.44942	2.22510	48
13	.36826	2.71548	.38821	2.57593	.40843	2.44839	.42894	2.33130	.44977	2.22337	47
14	.36859	2.71305	.38854	2.57371	.40877	2.44636	.42929	2.32943	.45012	2.22164	46
15	.36892	2.71062	.38888	2.57150	.40911	2.44433	.42963	2.32756	.45047	2.21992	45
16	.36925	2.70819	.38921	2.56928	.40945	2.44230	.42998	2.32570	.45082	2.21819	44
17	.36958	2.70577	.38955	2.56707	.40979	2.44027	.43032	2.32383	.45117	2.21647	43
18	.36991	2.70335	.38988	2.56487	.41013	2.43825	.43067	2.32197	.45152	2.21475	42
19	.37024	2.70094	.39022	2.56266	.41047	2.43623	.43101	2.32012	.45187	2.21304	41
20	.37057	2.69853	.39055	2.56046	.41081	2.43422	.43136	2.31826	.45222	2.21132	40
21	.37090	2.69612	.39089	2.55827	.41115	2.43220	.43170	2.31641	.45257	2.20961	39
22	.37123	2.69371	.39122	2.55608	.41149	2.43019	.43205	2.31456	.45292	2.20790	38
23	.37157	2.69131	.39156	2.55389	.41183	2.42819	.43230	2.31271	.45327	2.20619	37
24	.37190	2.68892	.39190	2.55170	.41217	2.42618	.43274	2.31086	.45362	2.20449	36
25	.37223	2.68653	.39223	2.54952	.41251	2.42418	.43308	2.30902	.45397	2.20278	35
26	.37256	2.68414	.39257	2.54734	.41285	2.42218	.43343	2.30718	.45432	2.20108	34
27	.37289	2.68175	.39290	2.54516	.41319	2.42019	.43378	2.30534	.45467	2.19938	33
28	.37322	2.67937	.39324	2.54299	.41353	2.41819	.43412	2.30351	.45502	2.19769	32
29	.37355	2.67700	.39357	2.54082	.41387	2.41620	.43447	2.30167	.45538	2.19599	31
30	.37388	2.67462	.39391	2.53865	.41421	2.41421	.43481	2.29984	.45573	2.19430	30
31	.37422	2.67225	.39425	2.53648	.41455	2.41223	.43516	2.29801	.45608	2.19261	29
32	.37455	2.66989	.39458	2.53432	.41490	2.41025	.43550	2.29619	.45643	2.19092	28
33	.37488	2.66752	.39492	2.53217	.41524	2.40827	.43585	2.29437	.45678	2.18923	27
34	.37521	2.66516	.39526	2.53001	.41558	2.40629	.43620	2.29254	.45713	2.18755	26
35	.37554	2.66281	.39559	2.52786	.41592	2.40432	.43654	2.29073	.45748	2.18587	25
36	.37588	2.66046	.39593	2.52571	.41626	2.40235	.43689	2.28891	.45784	2.18419	24
37	.37621	2.65811	.39626	2.52357	.41660	2.40038	.43724	2.28710	.45819	2.18251	23
38	.37654	2.65576	.39660	2.52142	.41694	2.39841	.43758	2.28528	.45854	2.18084	22
39	.37687	2.65342	.39694	2.51929	.41728	2.39645	.43793	2.28348	.45889	2.17916	21
40	.37720	2.65109	.39727	2.51715	.41763	2.39449	.43828	2.28167	.45924	2.17749	20
41	.37754	2.64875	.39761	2.51502	.41797	2.39253	.43862	2.27987	.45960	2.17582	19
42	.37787	2.64642	.39795	2.51289	.41831	2.39058	.43897	2.27806	.45995	2.17416	18
43	.37820	2.64410	.39829	2.51076	.41865	2.38863	.43932	2.27626	.46030	2.17249	17
44	.37853	2.64177	.39862	2.50864	.41899	2.38668	.43966	2.27447	.46065	2.17083	16
45	.37887	2.63945	.39896	2.50652	.41933	2.38473	.44001	2.27267	.46101	2.16917	15
46	.37920	2.63714	.39930	2.50440	.41968	2.38279	.44036	2.27088	.46136	2.16751	14
47	.37953	2.63483	.39963	2.50229	.42002	2.38084	.44071	2.26909	.46171	2.16585	13
48	.37986	2.63252	.39997	2.50018	.42036	2.37891	.44105	2.26730	.46206	2.16420	12
49	.38020	2.63021	.40031	2.49807	.42070	2.37697	.44140	2.26552	.46242	2.16255	11
50	.38053	2.62791	.40065	2.49597	.42105	2.37504	.44175	2.26374	.46277	2.16090	10
51	.38086	2.62561	.40098	2.49386	.42139	2.37311	.44210	2.26196	.46312	2.15925	9
52	.38120	2.62332	.40132	2.49177	.42173	2.37118	.44244	2.26018	.46348	2.15760	8
53	.38153	2.62103	.40166	2.48967	.42207	2.36925	.44279	2.25840	.46383	2.15596	7
54	.38186	2.61874	.40200	2.48758	.42242	2.36733	.44314	2.25663	.46418	2.15432	6
55	.38220	2.61646	.40234	2.48549	.42276	2.36541	.44349	2.25486	.46454	2.15268	5
56	.38253	2.61418	.40267	2.48340	.42310	2.36349	.44384	2.25309	.46489	2.15104	4
57	.38286	2.61190	.40301	2.48132	.42345	2.36158	.44418	2.25132	.46525	2.14940	3
58	.38320	2.60963	.40335	2.47924	.42379	2.35967	.44453	2.24956	.46560	2.14777	2
59	.38353	2.60736	.40369	2.47716	.42413	2.35776	.44488	2.24780	.46595	2.14614	1
60	.38386	2.60509	.40403	2.47509	.42447	2.35585	.44523	2.24604	.46631	2.14451	0
′	Cotang	Tang	Cotang	Tang	Cotang	Tang	Cotang	Tang	Cotang	Tang	′
	69°		68°		67°		66°		65°		

TABLE II cont.

Natural Tangents and Cotangents

′	25° Tang	25° Cotang	26° Tang	26° Cotang	27° Tang	27° Cotang	28° Tang	28° Cotang	29° Tang	29° Cotang	′
0	.46631	2.14451	.48773	2.05030	.50953	1.96261	.53171	1.88073	.55431	1.80405	60
1	.46666	2.14288	.48809	2.04879	.50989	1.96120	.53208	1.87941	.55469	1.80281	59
2	.46702	2.14125	.48845	2.04728	.51026	1.95979	.53246	1.87809	.55507	1.80158	58
3	.46737	2.13963	.48881	2.04577	.51063	1.95838	.53283	1.87677	.55545	1.80034	57
4	.46772	2.13801	.48917	2.04426	.51099	1.95698	.53320	1.87546	.55583	1.79911	56
5	.46808	2.13639	.48953	2.04276	.51136	1.95557	.53258	1.87415	.55621	1.79788	55
6	.46843	2.13477	.48989	2.04125	.51173	1.95417	.53395	1.87283	.55659	1.79665	54
7	.46879	2.13316	.49026	2.03975	.51209	1.95277	.53432	1.87152	.55697	1.79542	53
8	.46914	2.13154	.49062	2.03825	.51246	1.95137	.53470	1.87021	.55736	1.79419	52
9	.46950	2.12993	.49098	2.03675	.51283	1.94997	.53507	1.86891	.55774	1.79296	51
10	.46985	2.12832	.49134	2.03526	.51319	1.94858	.53545	1.86760	.55812	1.79174	50
11	.47021	2.12671	.49170	2.03376	.51356	1.94718	.53582	1.86630	.55850	1.79051	49
12	.47056	2.12511	.49206	2.03227	.51393	1.94579	.53620	1.86499	.55888	1.78929	48
13	.47092	2.12350	.49242	2.03078	.51430	1.94440	.53657	1.86369	.55926	1.78807	47
14	.47128	2.12190	.49278	2.02929	.51467	1.94301	.53694	1.86239	.55964	1.78685	46
15	.47163	2.12030	.49315	2.02780	.51503	1.94162	.53732	1.86109	.56003	1.78563	45
16	.47199	2.11871	.49351	2.02631	.51540	1.94023	.53769	1.85979	.56041	1.78441	44
17	.47234	2.11711	.49387	2.02483	.51577	1.93885	.53807	1.85850	.56079	1.78319	43
18	.47270	2.11552	.49423	2.02335	.51614	1.93746	.53844	1.85720	.56117	1.78198	42
19	.47305	2.11392	.49459	2.02187	.51651	1.93608	.53882	1.85591	.56156	1.78077	41
20	.47341	2.11233	.49495	2.02039	.51688	1.93470	.53920	1.85462	.56194	1.77955	40
21	.47377	2.11075	.49532	2.01891	.51724	1.93332	.53957	1.85333	.56232	1.77834	39
22	.47412	2.10916	.49568	2.01743	.51761	1.93195	.53995	1.85204	.56270	1.77713	38
23	.47448	2.10758	.49604	2.01596	.51798	1.93057	.54032	1.85075	.56309	1.77592	37
24	.47483	2.10600	.49640	2.01449	.51835	1.92920	.54070	1.84946	.56347	1.77471	36
25	.47519	2.10442	.49677	2.01302	.51872	1.92782	.54107	1.84818	.56385	1.77351	35
26	.47555	2.10284	.49713	2.01155	.51909	1.92645	.54145	1.84689	.56424	1.77230	34
27	.47590	2.10126	.49749	2.01008	.51946	1.92508	.54183	1.84561	.56462	1.77110	33
28	.47626	2.09969	.49786	2.00862	.51983	1.92371	.54220	1.84433	.56501	1.76990	32
29	.47662	2.09811	.49822	2.00715	.52020	1.92235	.54258	1.84305	.56539	1.76869	31
30	.47698	2.09654	.49858	2.00569	.52057	1.92098	.54296	1.84177	.56577	1.76749	30
31	.47733	2.09498	.49894	2.00423	.52094	1.91962	.54333	1.84049	.56616	1.76629	29
32	.47769	2.09341	.49931	2.00277	.52131	1.91826	.54371	1.83922	.56654	1.76510	28
33	.47805	2.09184	.49967	2.00131	.52168	1.91690	.54409	1.83794	.56693	1.76390	27
34	.47840	2.09028	.50004	1.99986	.52205	1.91554	.54446	1.83667	.56731	1.76271	26
35	.47876	2.08872	.50040	1.99841	.52242	1.91418	.54484	1.83540	.56769	1.76151	25
36	.47912	2.08716	.50076	1.99695	.52279	1.91282	.54522	1.83413	.56808	1.76032	24
37	.47948	2.08560	.50113	1.99550	.52316	1.91147	.54560	1.83286	.56846	1.75913	23
38	.47984	2.08405	.50149	1.99406	.52353	1.91012	.54597	1.83159	.56885	1.75794	22
39	.48019	2.08250	.50185	1.99261	.52390	1.90876	.54635	1.83033	.56923	1.75675	21
40	.48055	2.08094	.50222	1.99116	.52427	1.90741	.54673	1.82906	.56962	1.75556	20
41	.48091	2.07939	.50258	1.98972	.52464	1.90607	.54711	1.82780	.57000	1.75437	19
42	.48127	2.07785	.50295	1.98828	.52501	1.90472	.54748	1.82654	.57039	1.75319	18
43	.48163	2.07630	.50331	1.98684	.52538	1.90337	.54786	1.82528	.57078	1.75200	17
44	.48198	2.07476	.50368	1.98540	.52575	1.90203	.54824	1.82402	.57116	1.75082	16
45	.48234	2.07321	.50404	1.98396	.52613	1.90069	.54862	1.82276	.57155	1.74964	15
46	.48270	2.07167	.50441	1.98253	.52650	1.89935	.54900	1.82150	.57193	1.74846	14
47	.48306	2.07014	.50477	1.98110	.52687	1.89801	.54938	1.82025	.57232	1.74728	13
48	.48342	2.06860	.50514	1.97966	.52724	1.89667	.54975	1.81899	.57271	1.74610	12
49	.48378	2.06706	.50550	1.97823	.52761	1.89533	.55013	1.81774	.57309	1.74492	11
50	.48414	2.06553	.50587	1.97681	.52798	1.89400	.55051	1.81649	.57348	1.74375	10
51	.48450	2.06400	.50623	1.97538	.52836	1.89266	.55089	1.81524	.57386	1.74257	9
52	.48486	2.06247	.50660	1.97395	.52873	1.89133	.55127	1.81399	.57425	1.74140	8
53	.48521	2.06094	.50696	1.97253	.52910	1.89000	.55165	1.81274	.57464	1.74022	7
54	.48557	2.05942	.50733	1.97111	.52947	1.88867	.55203	1.81150	.57503	1.73905	6
55	.48593	2.05790	.50769	1.96969	.52985	1.88734	.55241	1.81025	.57541	1.73788	5
56	.48629	2.05637	.50806	1.96827	.53022	1.88602	.55279	1.80901	.57580	1.73671	4
57	.48665	2.05485	.50843	1.96685	.53059	1.88469	.55317	1.80777	.57619	1.73555	3
58	.48701	2.05333	.50879	1.96544	.53096	1.88337	.55355	1.80653	.57657	1.73438	2
59	.48737	2.05182	.50916	1.96402	.53134	1.88205	.55393	1.80529	.57696	1.73321	1
60	.48773	2.05030	.50953	1.96261	.53171	1.88073	.55431	1.80405	.57735	1.73205	0
′	Cotang	Tang	Cotang	Tang	Cotang	Tang	Cotang	Tang	Cotang	Tang	′
	64°		63°		62°		61°		60°		

TABLE II cont.

Natural Tangents and Cotangents

′	30° Tang	Cotang	31° Tang	Cotang	32° Tang	Cotang	33° Tang	Cotang	34° Tang	Cotang	′
0	.57735	1.73205	.60086	1.66428	.62487	1.60033	.64941	1.53986	.67451	1.48256	60
1	.57774	1.73089	.60126	1.66318	.62527	1.59930	.64982	1.53888	.67493	1.48163	59
2	.57813	1.72973	.60165	1.66209	.62568	1.59826	.65024	1.53791	.67536	1.48070	58
3	.57851	1.72857	.60205	1.66099	.62608	1.59723	.65065	1.53693	.67578	1.47977	57
4	.57890	1.72741	.60245	1.65990	.62649	1.59620	.65106	1.53595	.67620	1.47885	56
5	.57929	1.72625	.60284	1.65881	.62689	1.59517	.65148	1.53497	.67663	1.47792	55
6	.57968	1.72509	.60324	1.65772	.62730	1.59414	.65189	1.53400	.67705	1.47699	54
7	.58007	1.72393	.60364	1.65663	.62770	1.59311	.65231	1.53302	.67748	1.47607	53
8	.58046	1.72278	.60403	1.65554	.62811	1.59208	.65272	1.53205	.67790	1.47514	52
9	.58085	1.72163	.60443	1.65445	.62852	1.59105	.65314	1.53107	.67832	1.47422	51
10	.58124	1.72047	.60483	1.65337	.62892	1.59002	.65355	1.53010	.67875	1.47330	50
11	.58162	1.71932	.60522	1.65228	.62933	1.58900	.65397	1.52913	.67917	1.47238	49
12	.58201	1.71817	.60562	1.65120	.62973	1.58797	.65438	1.52816	.67960	1.47146	48
13	.58240	1.71702	.60602	1.65011	.63014	1.58695	.65480	1.52719	.68002	1.47053	47
14	.58279	1.71588	.60642	1.64903	.63055	1.58593	.65521	1.52622	.68045	1.46962	46
15	.58318	1.71473	.60681	1.64795	.63095	1.58490	.65563	1.52525	.68088	1.46870	45
16	.58357	1.71358	.60721	1.64687	.63136	1.58388	.65604	1.52429	.68130	1.46778	44
17	.58396	1.71244	.60761	1.64579	.63177	1.58286	.65646	1.52332	.68173	1.46686	43
18	.58435	1.71129	.60801	1.64471	.63217	1.58184	.65688	1.52235	.68215	1.46595	42
19	.58474	1.71015	.60841	1.64363	.63258	1.58083	.65729	1.52139	.68258	1.46503	41
20	.58513	1.70901	.60881	1.64256	.63299	1.57981	.65771	1.52043	.68301	1.46411	40
21	.58552	1.70787	.60921	1.64148	.63340	1.57879	.65813	1.51946	.68343	1.46320	39
22	.58591	1.70673	.60960	1.64041	.63380	1.57778	.65854	1.51850	.68386	1.46229	38
23	.58631	1.70560	.61000	1.63934	.63421	1.57676	.65896	1.51754	.68429	1.46137	37
24	.58670	1.70446	.61040	1.63826	.63462	1.57575	.65938	1.51658	.68471	1.46046	36
25	.58709	1.70332	.61080	1.63719	.63503	1.57474	.65980	1.51562	.68514	1.45955	35
26	.58748	1.70219	.61120	1.63612	.63544	1.57372	.66021	1.51466	.68557	1.45864	34
27	.58787	1.70106	.61160	1.63505	.63584	1.57271	.66063	1.51370	.68600	1.45773	33
28	.58826	1.69992	.61200	1.63398	.63625	1.57170	.66105	1.51275	.68642	1.45682	32
29	.58865	1.69879	.61240	1.63292	.63666	1.57069	.66147	1.51179	.68685	1.45592	31
30	.58905	1.69766	.61280	1.63185	.63707	1.56969	.66189	1.51084	.68728	1.45501	30
31	.58944	1.69653	.61320	1.63079	.63748	1.56868	.66230	1.50988	.68771	1.45410	29
32	.58983	1.69541	.61360	1.62972	.63789	1.56767	.66272	1.50893	.68814	1.45320	28
33	.59022	1.69428	.61400	1.62866	.63830	1.56667	.66314	1.50797	.68857	1.45229	27
34	.59061	1.69316	.61440	1.62760	.63871	1.56566	.66356	1.50702	.68900	1.45139	26
35	.59101	1.69203	.61480	1.62654	.63912	1.56466	.66398	1.50607	.68942	1.45049	25
36	.59140	1.69091	.61520	1.62548	.63953	1.56366	.66440	1.50512	.68985	1.44958	24
37	.59179	1.68979	.61561	1.62442	.63994	1.56265	.66482	1.50417	.69028	1.44868	23
38	.59218	1.68866	.61601	1.62336	.64035	1.56165	.66524	1.50322	.69071	1.44778	22
39	.59258	1.68754	.61641	1.62230	.64076	1.56065	.66566	1.50228	.69114	1.44688	21
49	.59297	1.68643	.61681	1.62125	.64117	1.55966	.66608	1.50133	.69157	1.44598	20
41	.59336	1.68531	.61721	1.62019	.64158	1.55866	.66650	1.50038	.69200	1.44508	19
42	.59376	1.68419	.61761	1.61914	.64199	1.55766	.66692	1.49944	.69243	1.44418	18
43	.59415	1.68308	.61801	1.61808	.64240	1.55666	.66734	1.49849	.69286	1.44329	17
44	.59454	1.68196	.61842	1.61703	.64281	1.55567	.66776	1.49755	.69329	1.44239	16
45	.59494	1.68085	.61882	1.61598	.64322	1.55467	.66818	1.49661	.69372	1.44149	15
46	.59533	1.67974	.61922	1.61493	.64363	1.55368	.66860	1.49566	.69416	1.44060	14
47	.59573	1.67863	.61962	1.61388	.64404	1.55269	.66902	1.49472	.69459	1.43970	13
48	.59612	1.67752	.62003	1.61283	.64446	1.55170	.66944	1.49378	.69502	1.43881	12
49	.59651	1.67641	.62043	1.61179	.64487	1.55071	.66986	1.49284	.69545	1.43792	11
50	.59691	1.67530	.62083	1.61074	.64528	1.54972	.67028	1.49190	.69588	1.43703	10
51	.59730	1.67419	.62124	1.60970	.64569	1.54873	.67071	1.49097	.69631	1.43614	9
52	.59770	1.67309	.62164	1.60865	.64610	1.54774	.67113	1.49003	.69675	1.43525	8
53	.59809	1.67198	.62204	1.60761	.64652	1.54675	.67155	1.48909	.69718	1.43436	7
54	.59849	1.67088	.62245	1.60657	.64693	1.54576	.67197	1.48816	.69761	1.43347	6
55	.59888	1.66978	.62285	1.60553	.64734	1.54478	.67239	1.48722	.69804	1.43258	5
56	.59928	1.66867	.62325	1.60449	.64775	1.54379	.67282	1.48629	.69847	1.43169	4
57	.59967	1.66757	.62366	1.60345	.64817	1.54281	.67324	1.48536	.69891	1.43080	3
58	.60007	1.66647	.62406	1.60241	.64858	1.54183	.67366	1.48442	.69934	1.42992	2
59	.60046	1.66538	.62446	1.60137	.64899	1.54085	.67409	1.48349	.69977	1.42903	1
60	.60086	1.66428	.62487	1.60033	.64941	1.53986	.67451	1.48256	.70021	1.42815	0
′	Cotang	Tang	Cotang	Tang	Cotang	Tang	Cotang	Tang	Cotang	Tang	′
	59°		58°		57°		56°		55°		

TABLE II cont.

Natural Tangents and Cotangents

′	35° Tang	35° Cotang	36° Tang	36° Cotang	37° Tang	37° Cotang	38° Tang	38° Cotang	39° Tang	39° Cotang	′
0	.70021	1.42815	.72654	1.37638	.75355	1.32704	.78129	1.27994	.80978	1.23490	60
1	.70064	1.42726	.72699	1.37554	.75401	1.32624	.78175	1.27917	.81027	1.23416	59
2	.70107	1.42638	.72743	1.37470	.75447	1.32544	.78222	1.27841	.81075	1.23343	58
3	.70151	1.42550	.72788	1.37386	.75492	1.32464	.78269	1.27764	.81123	1.23270	57
4	.70194	1.42462	.72832	1.37302	.75538	1.32384	.78316	1.27688	.81171	1.23196	56
5	.70238	1.42374	.72877	1.37218	.75584	1.32304	.78363	1.27611	.81220	1.23123	55
6	.70281	1.42286	.72921	1.37134	.75629	1.32224	.78410	1.27535	.81268	1.23050	54
7	.70325	1.42198	.72966	1.37050	.75675	1.32144	.78457	1.27458	.81316	1.22977	53
8	.70368	1.42110	.73010	1.36967	.75721	1.32064	.78504	1.27382	.81364	1.22904	52
9	.70412	1.42022	.73055	1.36883	.75767	1.31984	.78551	1.27306	.81413	1.22831	51
10	.70455	1.41934	.73100	1.36800	.75812	1.31904	.78598	1.27230	.81461	1.22758	50
11	.70499	1.41847	.73144	1.36716	.75858	1.31825	.78645	1.27153	.81510	1.22685	49
12	.70542	1.41759	.73189	1.36633	.75904	1.31745	.78692	1.27077	.81558	1.22612	48
13	.70586	1.41672	.73234	1.36549	.75950	1.31666	.78739	1.27001	.81606	1.22539	47
14	.70629	1.41584	.73278	1.36466	.75996	1.31586	.78786	1.26925	.81655	1.22467	46
15	.70673	1.41497	.73323	1.36383	.76042	1.31507	.78834	1.26849	.81703	1.22394	45
16	.70717	1.41409	.73368	1.36300	.76088	1.31427	.78881	1.26774	.81752	1.22321	44
17	.70760	1.41322	.73413	1.36217	.76134	1.31348	.78928	1.26698	.81800	1.22249	43
18	.70804	1.41235	.73457	1.36134	.76180	1.31269	.78975	1.26622	.81849	1.22176	42
19	.70848	1.41148	.73502	1.36051	.76226	1.31190	.79022	1.26546	.81898	1.22104	41
20	.70891	1.41061	.73547	1.35968	.76272	1.31110	.79070	1.26471	.81946	1.22031	40
21	.70935	1.40974	.73592	1.35885	.76318	1.31031	.79117	1.26395	.81995	1.21959	39
22	.70979	1.40887	.73637	1.35802	.76364	1.30952	.79164	1.26319	.82044	1.21886	38
23	.71023	1.40800	.73681	1.35719	.76410	1.30873	.79212	1.26244	.82092	1.21814	37
24	.71066	1.40714	.73726	1.35637	.76456	1.30795	.79259	1.26169	.82141	1.21742	36
25	.71110	1.40627	.73771	1.35554	.76502	1.30716	.79306	1.26093	.82190	1.21670	35
26	.71154	1.40540	.73816	1.35472	.76548	1.30637	.79354	1.26018	.82238	1.21598	34
27	.71198	1.40454	.73861	1.35389	.76594	1.30558	.79401	1.25943	.82287	1.21526	33
28	.71242	1.40367	.73906	1.35307	.76640	1.30480	.79449	1.25867	.82336	1.21454	32
29	.71285	1.40281	.73951	1.35224	.76686	1.30401	.79496	1.25792	.82385	1.21382	31
30	.71329	1.40195	.73996	1.35142	.76733	1.30323	.79544	1.25717	.82434	1.21310	30
31	.71373	1.40109	.74041	1.35060	.76779	1.30244	.79591	1.25642	.82483	1.21238	29
32	.71417	1.40022	.74086	1.34978	.76825	1.30166	.79639	1.25567	.82531	1.21166	28
33	.71461	1.39936	.74131	1.34896	.76871	1.30087	.79686	1.25492	.82580	1.21094	27
34	.71505	1.39850	.74176	1.34814	.76918	1.30009	.79734	1.25417	.82629	1.21023	26
35	.71549	1.39764	.74221	1.34732	.76964	1.29931	.79781	1.25343	.82678	1.20951	25
36	.71593	1.39679	.74257	1.34650	.77010	1.29853	.79829	1.25268	.82727	1.20879	24
37	.71637	1.39593	.74312	1.34568	.77057	1.29775	.79877	1.25193	.82776	1.20808	23
38	.71681	1.39507	.74357	1.34487	.77103	1.29696	.79924	1.25118	.82825	1.20736	22
39	.71725	1.39421	.74402	1.34405	.77149	1.29618	.79972	1.25044	.82874	1.20665	21
40	.71769	1.39336	.74447	1.34323	.77196	1.29541	.80020	1.24969	.82923	1.20593	20
41	.71813	1.39250	.74492	1.34242	.77242	1.29463	.80067	1.24895	.82972	1.20522	19
42	.71857	1.39165	.74538	1.34160	.77289	1.29385	.80115	1.24820	.83022	1.20451	18
43	.71901	1.39079	.74583	1.34079	.77335	1.29307	.80163	1.24746	.83071	1.20379	17
44	.71946	1.38994	.74628	1.33998	.77382	1.29229	.80211	1.24672	.83120	1.20308	16
45	.71990	1.38909	.74674	1.33916	.77428	1.29152	.80258	1.24597	.83169	1.20237	15
46	.72034	1.38824	.74719	1.33835	.77475	1.29074	.80306	1.24523	.83218	1.20166	14
47	.72078	1.38738	.74764	1.33754	.77521	1.28997	.80354	1.24449	.83268	1.20095	13
48	.72122	1.38653	.74810	1.33673	.77568	1.28919	.80402	1.24375	.83317	1.20024	12
49	.72167	1.38568	.74855	1.33592	.77615	1.28842	.80450	1.24301	.83366	1.19953	11
50	.72211	1.38484	.74900	1.33511	.77661	1.28764	.80498	1.24227	.83415	1.19882	10
51	.72255	1.38399	.74946	1.33430	.77708	1.28687	.80546	1.24153	.83465	1.19811	9
52	.72299	1.38314	.74991	1.33349	.77754	1.28610	.80594	1.24079	.83514	1.19740	8
53	.72344	1.38229	.75037	1.33268	.77801	1.28533	.80642	1.24005	.83564	1.19669	7
54	.72388	1.38145	.75082	1.33187	.77848	1.28456	.80690	1.23931	.83613	1.19599	6
55	.72432	1.38060	.75128	1.33107	.77895	1.28379	.80738	1.23858	.83662	1.19528	5
56	.72477	1.37976	.75173	1.33026	.77941	1.28302	.80786	1.23784	.83712	1.19457	4
57	.72521	1.37891	.75219	1.32946	.77988	1.28225	.80834	1.23710	.83761	1.19387	3
58	.72565	1.37807	.75264	1.32865	.78035	1.28148	.80882	1.23637	.83811	1.19316	2
59	.72610	1.37722	.75310	1.32785	.78082	1.28071	.80930	1.23563	.83860	1.19246	1
60	.72654	1.37638	.75355	1.32704	.78129	1.27994	.80978	1.23490	.83910	1.19175	0
′	Cotang	Tang	Cotang	Tang	Cotang	Tang	Cotang	Tang	Cotang	Tang	′
	54°		53°		52°		51°		50°		

TABLE II cont.

Natural Tangents and Cotangents

′	40°		41°		42°		43°		44°		′
	Tang	Cotang	Tang	Cotang	Tang	Cotang	Tang	Cotang	Tang	Cotang	
0	.83910	1.19175	.86929	1.15037	.90040	1.11061	.93252	1.07237	.96569	1.03553	60
1	.83960	1.19105	.86980	1.14969	.90093	1.10996	.93306	1.07174	.96625	1.03493	59
2	.84009	1.19035	.87031	1.14902	.90146	1.10931	.93360	1.07112	.96681	1.03433	58
3	.84059	1.18964	.87082	1.14834	.90199	1.10867	.93415	1.07049	.96738	1.03372	57
4	.84108	1.18894	.87133	1.14767	.90251	1.10802	.93469	1.06987	.96794	1.03312	56
5	.84158	1.18824	.87184	1.14699	.90304	1.10737	.93524	1.06925	.96850	1.03252	55
6	.84208	1.18754	.87236	1.14632	.90357	1.10672	.93578	1.06862	.96907	1.03192	54
7	.84258	1.18684	.87287	1.14565	.90410	1.10607	.93633	1.06800	.96963	1.03132	53
8	.84307	1.18614	.87338	1.14498	.90463	1.10543	.93688	1.06738	.97020	1.03072	52
9	.84357	1.18544	.87389	1.14430	.90516	1.10478	.93742	1.06676	.97076	1.03012	51
10	.84407	1.18474	.87441	1.14363	.90569	1.10414	.93797	1.06613	.97133	1.02952	50
11	.84457	1.18404	.87492	1.14296	.90621	1.10349	.93852	1.06551	.97189	1.02892	49
12	.84507	1.18334	.87543	1.14229	.90674	1.10285	.93906	1.06489	.97246	1.02832	48
13	.84556	1.18264	.87595	1.14162	.90727	1.10220	.93961	1.06427	.97302	1.02772	47
14	.84606	1.18194	.87646	1.14095	.90781	1.10156	.94016	1.06365	.97359	1.02713	46
15	.84656	1.18125	.87698	1.14028	.90834	1.10091	.94071	1.06303	.97416	1.02653	45
16	.84706	1.18055	.87749	1.13961	.90887	1.10027	.94125	1.06241	.97472	1.02593	44
17	.84756	1.17986	.87801	1.13894	.90940	1.09963	.94180	1.06179	.97529	1.02533	43
18	.84806	1.17916	.87852	1.13828	.90993	1.09399	.94235	1.06117	.97586	1.02474	42
19	.84856	1.17846	.87904	1.13761	.91046	1.09834	.94290	1.06056	.97643	1.02414	41
20	.84906	1.17777	.87955	1.13694	.91099	1.09770	.94345	1.05994	.97700	1.02355	40
21	.84956	1.17708	.88007	1.13627	.91153	1.09706	.94400	1.05932	.97756	1.02295	39
22	.85006	1.17638	.88059	1.13561	.91206	1.09642	.94455	1.05870	.97813	1.02236	38
23	.85057	1.17569	.88110	1.13494	.91259	1.09578	.94510	1.05809	.97870	1.02176	37
24	.85107	1.17500	.88162	1.13428	.91313	1.09514	.94565	1.05747	.97927	1.02117	36
25	.85157	1.17430	.88214	1.13361	.91366	1.09450	.94620	1.05685	.97984	1.02057	35
26	.85207	1.17361	.88265	1.13295	.91419	1.09386	.94676	1.05624	.98041	1.01998	34
27	.85257	1.17292	.88317	1.13228	.91473	1.09322	.94731	1.05562	.98098	1.01939	33
28	.85308	1.17223	.88369	1.13162	.91526	1.09258	.94786	1.05501	.98155	1.01879	32
29	.85358	1.17154	.88421	1.13096	.91580	1.09195	.94841	1.05439	.98213	1.01820	31
30	.85408	1.17085	.88473	1.13029	.91633	1.09131	.94896	1.05378	.98270	1.01761	30
31	.85458	1.17016	.88524	1.12963	.91687	1.09067	.94952	1.05317	.98327	1.01702	29
32	.85509	1.16947	.88576	1.12897	.91740	1.09003	.95007	1.05255	.98384	1.01642	28
33	.85559	1.16878	.88628	1.12831	.91794	1.08940	.95062	1.05194	.98441	1.01583	27
34	.85609	1.16809	.88680	1.12765	.91847	1.08876	.95118	1.05133	.98499	1.01524	26
35	.85660	1.16741	.88732	1.12699	.91901	1.08813	.95173	1.05072	.98556	1.01465	25
36	.85710	1.16672	.88784	1.12633	.91955	1.08749	.95229	1.05010	.98613	1.01406	24
37	.85761	1.16603	.88836	1.12567	.92008	1.08686	.95284	1.04949	.98671	1.01347	23
38	.85811	1.16535	.88888	1.12501	.92062	1.08622	.95340	1.04888	.98728	1.01288	22
39	.85862	1.16466	.88940	1.12435	.92116	1.08559	.95395	1.04827	.98786	1.01229	21
40	.85912	1.16398	.88992	1.12369	.92170	1.08496	.95451	1.04766	.98843	1.01170	20
41	.85963	1.16329	.89045	1.12303	92224	1.08432	.95506	1.04705	.98901	1.01112	19
42	.86014	1.16261	.89097	1.12238	.92277	1.08369	.95562	1.04644	.98958	1.01053	18
43	.86064	1.16192	.89149	1.12172	.92331	1.08306	.95618	1.04583	.99016	1.00994	17
44	.86115	1.16124	.89201	1.12106	.92385	1.08243	.95673	1.04522	.99073	1.00935	16
45	.86166	1.16056	.89253	1.12041	.92439	1.08179	.95729	1.04461	.99131	1.00876	15
46	.86216	1.15987	.89306	1.11975	.92493	1.08116	.95785	1.04401	.99189	1.00818	14
47	.86267	1.15919	.89358	1.11909	.92547	1.08053	.95841	1.04340	.99247	1.00759	13
48	.86318	1.15851	.89410	1.11844	.92601	1.07990	.95897	1.04279	.99304	1.00701	12
49	.86368	1.15783	.89463	1.11778	.92655	1.07927	.95952	1.04218	.99362	1.00642	11
50	.86419	1.15715	.89515	1.11713	.92709	1.07864	.96008	1.04158	.99420	1.00583	10
51	.86470	1.15647	.89567	1.11648	.92763	1.07801	.96064	1.04097	.99478	1.00525	9
52	.86521	1.15579	.89620	1.11582	.92817	1.07738	.96120	1.04036	.99536	1.00467	8
53	.86572	1.15511	.89672	1.11517	.92872	1.07676	.96176	1.03976	.99594	1.00408	7
54	.86623	1.15443	.89725	1.11452	.92926	1.07613	.96232	1.03915	.99652	1.00350	6
55	.86674	1.15375	.89777	1.11387	.92980	1.07550	.96288	1.03855	.99710	1.00291	5
56	.86725	1.15308	.89830	1.11321	.93034	1.07487	.96344	1.03794	.99768	1.00233	4
57	.86776	1.15240	.89883	1.11256	.93088	1.07425	.96400	1.03734	.99826	1.00175	3
58	.86827	1.15172	.89935	1.11191	.93143	1.07362	.96457	1.03674	.99884	1.00116	2
59	.86878	1.15104	.89988	1.11126	.93197	1.07299	.96513	1.03613	.99942	1.00058	1
60	.86929	1.15037	.90040	1.11061	.93252	1.07237	.96569	1.03553	1.00000	1.00000	0
′	Cotang	Tang	Cotang	Tang	Cotang	Tang	Cotang	Tang	Cotang	Tang	′
	49°		48°		47°		46°		45°		

TABLE III

Temperature Corrections for Steel Tapes
per 100-Ft. Length

Temp. °F.	Correction	Temp. °F.	Correction	Temp. °F.	Correction
0	0	34	.021930	68	0
1	.043215	35	.021285	69	.000645
2	.042570	36	.020640	70	.001290
3	.041925	37	.019995	71	.001935
4	.041280	38	.019350	72	.002580
5	.040635	39	.018705	73	.003225
6	.039990	40	.018060	74	.003870
7	.039345	41	.017415	75	.004515
8	.038700	42	.016770	76	.005160
9	.038055	43	.016125	77	.005805
10	.037410	44	.015480	78	.006450
11	.036765	45	.014835	79	.007095
12	.036120	46	.014190	80	.007740
13	.035475	47	.013545	81	.008385
14	.034830	48	.012900	82	.009030
15	.034185	49	.012255	83	.009675
16	.033540	50	.011610	84	.010320
17	.032895	51	.010965	85	.010965
18	.032250	52	.010320	86	.011610
19	.031605	53	.009675	87	.012255
20	.030960	54	.009030	88	.012900
21	.030315	55	.008385	89	.013545
22	.029670	56	.007740	90	.014190
23	.029025	57	.007095	91	.014835
24	.028380	58	.006450	92	.015480
25	.027735	59	.005805	93	.016125
26	.027090	60	.005160	94	.016770
27	.026445	61	.004515	95	.017415
28	.025800	62	.003870	96	.018060
29	.025155	63	.003225	97	.018705
30	.024510	64	.002580	98	.019350
31	.023865	65	.001935	99	.019995
32	.023220	66	.001290	100	.020640
33	.022575	67	.000645		

Corrections are based on a coefficient of expansion of 0.00000645.

When correcting a distance measured between two points:
    Above 68° F.—add correction
    Below 68° F.—subtract correction

When preparing to set a point at a predetermined distance:
    Above .68° F.—subtract correction
    Below 68° F.—add correction

TABLE IV

Slope Corrections—Slope Angle Given
(Subtract Correction per 100 Ft. of Slope Distance)

Slope Angle	Corr.	Slope Angle	Corr.	Slope Angle	Corr.	Slope Angle	Corr.
0°00′	.00	3°35′	.20	5°06′	.40	6°16′	.60
0°34′	.00	3°39′	.20	5°09′	.40	6°18′	.60
0°35′	.01	3°40′	.21	5°10′	.41	6°19′	.61
0°59′	.01	3°45′	.21	5°13′	.41	6°21′	.61
1°00′	.02	3°46′	.22	5°14′	.42	6°22′	.62
1°16′	.02	3°50′	.22	5°17′	.42	6°24′	.62
1°17′	.03	3°51′	.23	5°18′	.43	6°25′	.63
1°31′	.03	3°55′	.23	5°20′	.43	6°27′	.63
1°32′	.04	3°56′	.24	5°21′	.44	6°28′	.64
1°42′	.04	4°00′	.24	5°24′	.44	6°30′	.64
1°43′	.05	4°01′	.25	5°25′	.45	6°31′	.65
1°53′	.05	4°05′	.25	5°28′	.45	6°33′	.65
1°54′	.06	4°06′	.26	5°29′	.46	6°34′	.66
2°03′	.06	4°10′	.26	5°31′	.46	6°36′	.66
2°04′	.07	4°11′	.27	5°32′	.47	6°37′	.67
2°12′	.07	4°14′	.27	5°35′	.47	6°39′	.67
2°13′	.08	4°15′	.28	5°36′	.48	6°40′	.68
2°21′	.08	4°19′	.28	5°38′	.48	6°42′	.68
2°22′	.09	4°20′	.29	5°39′	.49	6°43′	.69
2°29′	.09	4°24′	.29	5°42′	.49	6°45′	.69
2°30′	.10	4°25′	.30	5°43′	.50	6°46′	.70
2°37′	.10	4°28′	.30	5°45′	.50	6°48′	.70
2°38′	.11	4°29′	.31	5°46′	.51	6°49′	.71
2°44′	.11	4°32′	.31	5°48′	.51	6°51′	.71
2°45′	.12	4°33′	.32	5°49′	.52	6°52′	.72
2°51′	.12	4°37′	.32	5°52′	.52	6°54′	.72
2°52′	.13	4°38′	.33	5°53′	.53	6°55′	.73
2°58′	.13	4°41′	.33	5°55′	.53	6°57′	.73
2°59′	.14	4°42′	.34	5°56′	.54	6°58′	.74
3°05′	.14	4°45′	.34	5°58′	.54	6°59′	.74
3°06′	.15	4°46′	.35	5°59′	.55	7°00′	.75
3°11′	.15	4°49′	.35	6°02′	.55	7°02′	.75
3°12′	.16	4°50′	.36	6°03′	.56	7°03′	.76
3°17′	.16	4°53′	.36	6°05′	.56	7°05′	.76
3°18′	.17	4°54′	.37	6°06′	.57	7°06′	.77
3°23′	.17	4°57′	.37	6°08′	.57	7°08′	.77
3°24′	.18	4°58′	.38	6°09′	.58	7°09′	.78
3°29′	.18	5°01′	.38	6°11′	.58	7°11′	.78
3°30′	.19	5°02′	.39	6°12′	.59	7°12′	.79
3°34′	.19	5°05′	.39	6°15′	.59	7°13′	.79

TABLE IV cont.

Slope Angle	Corr.	Slope Angle	Corr.	Slope Angle	Corr.	Slope Angle	Corr.
7°14′	.80	8°02′	.98	8°46′	1.17	9°26′	1.35
7°16′	.80	8°03′	.99	8°47′	1.17	9°27′	1.36
7°17′	.81	8°05′	.99	8°48′	1.18	9°28′	1.36
7°19′	.81	8°06′	1.00	8°49′	1.18	9°29′	1.37
7°20′	.82	8°07′	1.00	8°50′	1.19	9°30′	1.37
7°21′	.82	8°08′	1.01	8°51′	1.19	9°31′	1.38
7°22′	.83	8°10′	1.01	8°52′	1.20	9°32′	1.38
7°24′	.83	8°11′	1.02	8°54′	1.20	9°33′	1.39
7°25′	.84	8°12′	1.02	8°55′	1.21	9°34′	1.39
7°27′	.84	8°13′	1.03	8°56′	1.21	9°35′	1.40
7°28′	.85	8°15′	1.03	8°57′	1.22	9°36′	1.40
7°29′	.85	8°16′	1.04	8°58′	1.22	9°37′	1.41
7°30′	.86	8°17′	1.04	8°59′	1.23	9°38′	1.41
7°32′	.86	8°18′	1.05	9°00′	1.23	9°39′	1.42
7°33′	.87	8°19′	1.05	9°01′	1.24	9°40′	1.42
7°35′	.87	8°20′	1.06	9°03′	1.24	9°41′	1.43
7°36′	.88	8°22′	1.06	9°04′	1.25	9°42′	1.43
7°37′	.88	8°23′	1.07	9°05′	1.25	9°43′	1.44
7°38′	.89	8°24′	1.07	9°06′	1.26	9°45′	1.44
7°40′	.89	8°25′	1.08	9°07′	1.26	9°46′	1.45
7°41′	.90	8°26′	1.08	9°08′	1.27	9°47′	1.45
7°42′	.90	8°27′	1.09	9°09′	1.27	9°48′	1.46
7°43′	.91	8°29′	1.09	9°10′	1.28	9°49′	1.46
7°45′	.91	8°30′	1.10	9°11′	1.28	9°50′	1.47
7°46′	.92	8°31′	1.10	9°12′	1.29	9°51′	1.47
7°47′	.92	8°32′	1.11	9°13′	1.29	9°52′	1.48
7°48′	.93	8°33′	1.11	9°14′	1.30	9°53′	1.48
7°50′	.93	8°34′	1.12	9°15′	1.30	9°54′	1.49
7°51′	.94	8°36′	1.12	9°16′	1.31	9°55′	1.49
7°52′	.94	8°37′	1.13	9°18′	1.31	9°56′	1.50
7°53′	.95	8°38′	1.13	9°19′	1.32	9°57′	1.50
7°55′	.95	8°39′	1.14	9°20′	1.32	9°58′	1.51
7°56′	.96	8°40′	1.14	9°21′	1.33	9°59′	1.51
7°57′	.96	8°41′	1.15	9°22′	1.33	10°00′	1.52
7°58′	.97	8°42′	1.15	9°23′	1.34		
8°00′	.97	8°43′	1.16	9°24′	1.34		
8°01′	.98	8°45′	1.16	9°25′	1.35		

Multiply correction by slope distance/100 and subtract the result from the slope distance.

Example: Find horizontal distance for 230.50 ft. measured on a slope of 7°36′.

Answer: correction $= .88 \times \dfrac{230.50}{100} = 2.03$ ft.

horizontal distance $= 230.50 - 2.03 = 228.47$ ft.

TABLE V
Stadia Reduction

Stadia reduction involves determining H, V, and Elevation from the stadia intercept and the vertical angle as read and recorded in the field. The table contains horizontal distances and differences in elevation for a stadia intercept of 1.00 and vertical angles from 0° to 15°. Each value in the table must be multiplied by the stadia intercept to obtain the appropriate distance and difference in elevation. The values thus determined are H and V as shown in Figures 7-4 and 7-5. H is the horizontal distance and V is used to determine elevation.

Minutes	0°		1°		2°		3°	
	Hor. dist.	Diff. elev.	Hor. dist.	Diff. elev.	Hor. dist.	Diff. elev.	Hor. dist.	Diff. elev.
0.........	100.00	0.00	99.97	1.74	99.88	3.49	99.73	5.23
2.........	100.00	0.06	99.97	1.80	99.87	3.55	99.72	5.28
4.........	100.00	0.12	99.97	1.86	99.87	3.60	99.71	5.34
6.........	100.00	0.17	99.96	1.92	99.87	3.66	99.71	5.40
8.........	100.00	0.23	99.96	1.98	99.86	3.72	99.70	5.46
10.........	100.00	0.29	99.96	2.04	99.86	3.78	99.69	5.52
12.........	100.00	0.35	99.96	2.09	99.85	3.84	99.69	5.57
14.........	100.00	0.41	99.95	2.15	99.85	3.90	99.68	5.63
16.........	100.00	0.47	99.95	2.21	99.84	3.95	99.68	5.69
18.........	100.00	0.52	99.95	2.27	99.84	4.01	99.67	5.75
20.........	100.00	0.58	99.95	2.33	99.83	4.07	99.66	5.80
22.........	100.00	0.64	99.94	2.38	99.83	4.13	99.66	5.86
24.........	100.00	0.70	99.94	2.44	99.82	4.18	99.65	5.92
26.........	99.99	0.76	99.94	2.50	99.82	4.24	99.64	5.98
28.........	99.99	0.81	99.93	2.56	99.81	4.30	99.63	6.04
30.........	99.99	0.87	99.93	2.62	99.81	4.36	99.63	6.09
32.........	99.99	0.93	99.93	2.67	99.80	4.42	99.62	6.15
34.........	99.99	0.99	99.93	2.73	99.80	4.48	99.62	6.21
36.........	99.99	1.05	99.92	2.79	99.79	4.53	99.61	6.27
38.........	99.99	1.11	99.92	2.85	99.79	4.59	99.60	6.33
40.........	99.99	1.16	99.92	2.91	99.78	4.65	99.59	6.38
42.........	99.99	1.22	99.91	2.97	99.78	4.71	99.59	6.44
44.........	99.98	1.28	99.91	3.02	99.77	4.76	99.58	6.50
46.........	99.98	1.34	99.90	3.08	99.77	4.82	99.57	6.56
48.........	99.98	1.40	99.90	3.14	99.76	4.88	'99.56	6.61
50.........	99.98	1.45	99.90	3.20	99.76	4.94	99.56	6.67
52.........	99.98	1.51	99.89	3.26	99.75	4.99	99.55	6.73
54.........	99.98	1.57	99.89	3.31	99.74	5.05	99.54	6.78
56.........	99.97	1.63	99.89	3.37	99.74	5.11	99.53	6.84
58.........	99.97	1.69	99.88	3.43	99.73	5.17	99.52	6.90
60.........	99.97	1.74	99.88	3.49	99.73	5.23	99.51	6.96

TABLE V cont.

Stadia Reduction

Minutes	4°		5°		6°		7°	
	Hor. dist.	Diff. elev.	Hor. dist.	Diff. elev.	Hor. dist.	Diff. elev.	Hor. dist.	Diff. elev.
0.........	99.51	6.96	99.24	8.68	98.91	10.40	98.51	12.10
2.........	99.51	7.02	99.23	8.74	98.90	10.45	98.50	12.15
4.........	99.50	7.07	99.22	8.80	98.88	10.51	98.48	12.21
6.........	99.49	7.13	99.21	8.85	98.87	10.57	98.47	12.26
8.........	99.48	7.19	99.20	8.91	98.86	10.62	98.46	12.32
10.........	99.47	7.25	99.19	8.97	98.85	10.68	98.44	12.38
12.........	99.46	7.30	99.18	9.03	98.83	10.74	98.43	12.43
14.........	99.46	7.36	99.17	9.08	98.82	10.79	98.41	12.49
16.........	99.45	7.42	99.16	9.14	98.81	10.85	98.40	12.55
18.........	99.44	7.48	99.15	9.20	98.80	10.91	98.39	12.60
20.........	99.43	7.53	99.14	9.25	98.78	10.96	98.37	12.66
22.........	99.42	7.59	99.13	9.31	98.77	11.02	98.36	12.72
24.........	99.41	7.65	99.11	9.37	98.76	11.08	98.34	12.77
26.........	99.40	7.71	99.10	9.43	98.74	11.13	98.33	12.83
28.........	99.39	7.76	99.09	9.48	98.73	11.19	98.31	12.88
30.........	99.38	7.82	99.08	9.54	98.72	11.25	98.29	12.94
32.........	99.38	7.88	99.07	9.60	98.71	11.30	98.28	13.00
34.........	99.37	7.94	99.06	9.65	98.69	11.36	98.27	13.05
36.........	99.36	7.99	99.05	9.71	98.68	11.42	98.25	13.11
38.........	99.35	8.05	99.04	9.77	98.67	11.47	98.24	13.17
40.........	99.34	8.11	99.03	9.83	98.65	11.53	98.22	13.22
42.........	99.33	8.17	99.01	9.88	98.64	11.59	98.20	13.28
44.........	99.32	8.22	99.00	9.94	98.63	11.64	98.19	13.33
46.........	99.31	8.28	98.99	10.00	98.61	11.70	98.17	13.39
48.........	99.30	8.34	98.98	10.05	98.60	11.76	98.16	13.45
50.........	99.29	8.40	98.97	10.11	98.58	11.81	98.14	13.50
52.........	99.28	8.45	98.96	10.17	98.57	11.87	98.13	13.56
54.........	99.27	8.51	98.94	10.22	98.56	11.93	98.11	13.61
56.........	99.26	8.57	98.93	10.28	98.54	11.98	98.10	13.67
58.........	99.25	8.63	98.92	10.34	98.53	12.04	98.08	13.73
60.........	99.24	8.68	98.91	10.40	98.51	12.10	98.06	13.78

TABLE V cont.

Stadia Reduction

Minutes	8° Hor. dist.	8° Diff. elev.	9° Hor. dist.	9° Diff. elev.	10° Hor. dist.	10° Diff. elev.	11° Hor. dist.	11° Diff. elev.
0.........	98.06	13.78	97.55	15.45	96.98	17.10	96.36	18.73
2.........	98.05	13.84	97.53	15.51	96.96	17.16	96.34	18.78
4.........	98.03	13.89	97.52	15.56	96.94	17.21	96.32	18.84
6.........	98.01	13.95	97.50	15.62	96.92	17.26	96.29	18.89
8.........	98.00	14.01	97.48	15.67	96.90	17.32	96.27	18.95
10.........	97.98	14.06	97.46	15.73	96.88	17.37	96.25	19.00
12.........	97.97	14.12	97.44	15.78	96.86	17.43	96.23	19.05
14.........	97.95	14.17	97.43	15.84	96.84	17.48	96.21	19.11
16.........	97.93	14.23	97.41	15.89	96.82	17.54	96.18	19.16
18.........	97.92	14.28	97.39	15.95	96.80	17.59	96.16	19.21
20.........	97.90	14.34	97.37	16.00	96.78	17.65	96.14	19.27
22.........	97.88	14.40	97.35	16.06	96.76	17.70	96.12	19.32
24.........	97.87	14.45	97.33	16.11	96.74	17.76	96.09	19.38
26.........	97.85	14.51	97.31	16.17	96.72	17.81	96.07	19.43
28.........	97.83	14.56	97.29	16.22	96.70	17.86	96.05	19.48
30.........	97.82	14.62	97.28	16.28	96.68	17.92	96.03	19.54
32.........	97.80	14.67	97.26	16.33	96.66	17.97	96.00	19.59
34.........	97.78	14.73	97.24	16.39	96.64	18.03	95.98	19.64
36.........	97.76	14.79	97.22	16.44	96.62	18.08	95.96	19.70
38.........	97.75	14.84	97.20	16.50	96.60	18.14	95.93	19.75
40.........	97.73	14.90	97.18	16.55	96.57	18.19	95.91	19.80
42.........	97.71	14.95	97.16	16.61	96.55	18.24	95.89	19.86
44.........	97.69	15.01	97.14	16.66	96.53	18.30	95.86	19.91
46.........	97.68	15.06	97.12	16.72	96.51	18.35	95.84	19.96
48.........	97.66	15.12	97.10	16.77	96.49	18.41	95.82	20.02
50.........	97.64	15.17	97.08	16.83	96.47	18.46	95.79	20.07
52.........	97.62	15.23	97.06	16.88	96.45	18.51	95.77	20.12
54.........	97.61	15.28	97.04	16.94	96.42	18.57	95.75	20.18
56.........	97.59	15.34	97.02	16.99	96.40	18.62	95.72	20.23
58.........	97.57	15.40	97.00	17.05	96.38	18.68	95.70	20.28
60.........	97.55	15.45	96.98	17.10	96.36	18.73	95.68	20.34

TABLE V cont.

Stadia Reduction

Minutes	12°		13°		14°		15°	
	Hor. dist.	Diff. elev.	Hor. dist.	Diff. elev.	Hor. dist.	Diff. elev.	Hor. dist.	Diff. elev.
0.........	95.68	20.34	94.94	21.92	94.15	23.47	93.30	25.00
2.........	95.65	20.39	94.91	21.97	94.12	23.52	93.27	25.05
4.........	95.63	20.44	94.89	22.02	94.09	23.58	93.24	25.10
6.........	95.61	20.50	94.86	22.08	94.07	23.63	93.21	25.15
8.........	95.58	20.55	94.84	22.13	94.04	23.68	93.18	25.20
10.........	95.56	20.60	94.81	22.18	94.01	23.73	93.16	25.25
12.........	95.53	20.66	94.79	22.23	93.98	23.78	93.13	25.30
14.........	95.51	20.71	94.76	22.28	93.95	23.83	93.10	25.35
16.........	95.49	20.76	94.73	22.34	93.93	23.88	93.07	25.40
18.........	95.46	20.81	94.71	22.39	93.90	23.93	93.04	25.45
20.........	95.44	20.87	94.68	22.44	93.87	23.99	93.01	25.50
22.........	95.41	20.92	94.66	22.49	93.84	24.04	92.98	25.55
24.........	95.39	20.97	94.63	22.54	93.81	24.09	92.95	25.60
26.........	95.36	21.03	94.60	22.60	93.79	24.14	92.92	25.65
28.........	95.34	21.08	94.58	22.65	93.76	24.19	92.89	25.70
30.........	95.32	21.13	94.55	22.70	93.73	24.24	92.86	25.75
32.........	95.29	21.18	94.52	22.75	93.70	24.29	92.83	25.80
34.........	95.27	21.24	94.50	22.80	93.67	24.34	92.80	25.85
36.........	95.24	21.29	94.47	22.85	93.65	24.39	92.77	25.90
38.........	95.22	21.34	94.44	22.91	93.62	24.44	92.74	25.95
40.........	95.19	21.39	94.42	22.96	93.59	24.49	92.71	26.00
42.........	95.17	21.45	94.39	23.01	93.56	24.55	92.68	26.05
44.........	95.14	21.50	94.36	23.06	93.53	24.60	92.65	26.10
46.........	95.12	21.55	94.34	23.11	93.50	24.65	92.62	26.15
48.........	95.09	21.60	94.31	23.16	93.47	24.70	92.59	26.20
50.........	95.07	21.66	94.28	23.22	93.45	24.75	92.56	26.25
52.........	95.04	21.71	94.26	23.27	93.42	24.80	92.53	26.30
54.........	95.02	21.76	94.23	23.32	93.39	24.85	92.49	26.35
56.........	94.99	21.81	94.20	23.37	93.36	24.90	92.46	26.40
58.........	94.97	21.87	94.17	23.42	93.33	24.95	92.43	26.45
60.........	94.94	21.92	94.15	23.47	93.90	25.00	92.40	26.50

TABLE VI

Conversion from Hundredths of a Foot to Inches and Fractions

Ft	In.	Ft	In.	Ft	In.	Ft	In.
.01	$\frac{1}{8}$	.26	$3\frac{1}{8}$	.51	$6\frac{1}{8}$	.76	$9\frac{1}{8}$
.02	$\frac{1}{4}$	.27	$\frac{1}{4}$	.52	$\frac{1}{4}$	.77	$\frac{1}{4}$
.03	$\frac{3}{8}$	.28	$\frac{3}{8}$	.53	$\frac{3}{8}$	.78	$\frac{3}{8}$
.04	$\frac{1}{2}$	.29	$\frac{1}{2}$	.54	$\frac{1}{2}$	.79	$\frac{1}{2}$
.05	$\frac{5}{8}$	.30	$\frac{5}{8}$	.55	$\frac{5}{8}$	.80	$\frac{5}{8}$
.06	$\frac{3}{4}$	.31	$\frac{3}{4}$	.56	$\frac{3}{4}$	.81	$\frac{3}{4}$
.07	$\frac{7}{8}$	.32	$\frac{7}{8}$	.57	$\frac{7}{8}$	.82	$\frac{7}{8}$
.08	1	.33	4	.58	7	.83	10
.09	$\frac{1}{8}$	.34	$\frac{1}{8}$	.59	$\frac{1}{8}$	.84	$\frac{1}{8}$
.10	$\frac{1}{4}$	.35	$\frac{1}{4}$	.60	$\frac{1}{4}$	.85	$\frac{1}{4}$
.11	$\frac{3}{8}$	.36	$\frac{3}{8}$	.61	$\frac{3}{8}$	.86	$\frac{3}{8}$
.12	$\frac{1}{2}$	.37	$\frac{1}{2}$	.62	$\frac{1}{2}$	.87	$\frac{1}{2}$
.13	$\frac{1}{2}$	.38	$\frac{1}{2}$	.63	$\frac{1}{2}$	.88	$\frac{1}{2}$
.14	$\frac{5}{8}$	.39	$\frac{5}{8}$	.64	$\frac{5}{8}$	.89	$\frac{5}{8}$
.15	$\frac{3}{4}$	.40	$\frac{3}{4}$	.65	$\frac{3}{4}$	.90	$\frac{3}{4}$
.16	$\frac{7}{8}$	.41	$\frac{7}{8}$	.66	$\frac{7}{8}$	.91	$\frac{7}{8}$
.17	2	.42	5	.67	8	.92	11
.18	$\frac{1}{8}$	.43	$\frac{1}{8}$	.68	$\frac{1}{8}$	.93	$\frac{1}{8}$
.19	$\frac{1}{4}$	.44	$\frac{1}{4}$	.69	$\frac{1}{4}$	.94	$\frac{1}{4}$
.20	$\frac{3}{8}$	.45	$\frac{3}{8}$	.70	$\frac{3}{8}$	.95	$\frac{3}{8}$
.21	$\frac{1}{2}$	.46	$\frac{1}{2}$	.71	$\frac{1}{2}$	.96	$\frac{1}{2}$
.22	$\frac{5}{8}$	.47	$\frac{5}{8}$	.72	$\frac{5}{8}$	.97	$\frac{5}{8}$
.23	$\frac{3}{4}$	.48	$\frac{3}{4}$	.73	$\frac{3}{4}$	.98	$\frac{3}{4}$
.24	$\frac{7}{8}$	.49	$\frac{7}{8}$	.74	$\frac{7}{8}$	.99	$\frac{7}{8}$
.25	3	.50	6	.75	9	1.00	12

TABLE VII

Lengths of Circular Arcs for Radius of 1.0

Sec.	Length	Min.	Length.	Deg.	Length.	Deg.	Length.
1	.0000048	1	.0002909	1	.0174533	61	1.0646508
2	.0000097	2	.0005818	2	.0349066	62	1.0821041
3	.0000145	3	.0008727	3	.0523599	63	1.0995574
4	.0000194	4	.0011636	4	.0698132	64	1.1170107
5	.0000242	5	.0014544	5	.0872665	65	1.1344640
6	.0000291	6	.0017453	6	.1047198	66	1.1519173
7	.0000339	7	.0020362	7	.1221730	67	1.1693706
8	.0000388	8	.0023271	8	.1396263	68	1.1868239
9	.0000436	9	.0026180	9	.1570796	69	1.2042772
10	.0000485	10	.0029089	10	.1745329	70	1.2217305
11	.0000533	11	.0031998	11	.1919862	71	1.2391838
12	.0000582	12	.0034907	12	.2094395	72	1.2566371
13	.0000630	13	.0037815	13	.2268928	73	1.2740904
14	.0000679	14	.0040724	14	.2443461	74	1.2915436
15	.0000727	15	.0043633	15	.2617994	75	1.3089969
16	.0000776	16	.0046542	16	.2792527	76	1.3264502
17	.0000824	17	.0049451	17	.2967060	77	1.3439035
18	.0000873	18	.0052360	18	.3141593	78	1.3613568
19	.0000921	19	.0055269	19	.3316126	79	1.3788101
20	.0000970	20	.0058178	20	.3490659	80	1.3962634
21	.0001018	21	.0061087	21	.3665191	81	1.4137167
22	.0001067	22	.0063995	22	.3839724	82	1.4311700
23	.0001115	23	.0066904	23	.4014257	83	1.4486233
24	.0001164	24	.0069813	24	.4188790	84	1.4660766
25	.0001212	25	.0072722	25	.4363323	85	1.4835299
26	.0001261	26	.0075631	26	.4537856	86	1.5009832
27	.0001309	27	.0078540	27	.4712389	87	1.5184364
28	.0001357	28	.0081449	28	.4886922	88	1.5358897
29	.0001406	29	.0084358	29	.5061455	89	1.5533430
30	.0001454	30	.0087266	30	.5235988	90	1.5707963
31	.0001503	31	.0090175	31	.5410521	91	1.5882496
32	.0001551	32	.0093084	32	.5585054	92	1.6057029
33	.0001600	33	.0095993	33	.5759587	93	1.6231562
34	.0001648	34	.0098902	34	.5934119	94	1.6406095
35	.0001697	35	.0101811	35	.6108652	95	1.6580628
36	.0001745	36	.0104720	36	.6283185	96	1.6755161
37	.0001794	37	.0107629	37	.6457718	97	1.6929694
38	.0001842	38	.0110538	38	.6632251	98	1.7104227
39	.0001891	39	.0113446	39	.6806784	99	1.7278760
40	.0001939	40	.0116355	40	.6981317	100	1.7453293
41	.0001988	41	.0119264	41	.7155850	101	1.7627825
42	.0002036	42	.0122173	42	.7330383	102	1.7802358
43	.0002085	43	.0125082	43	.7504916	103	1.7976891
44	.0002133	44	.0127991	44	.7679449	104	1.8151424
45	.0002182	45	.0130900	45	.7853982	105	1.8325957
46	.0002230	46	.0133809	46	.8028515	106	1.8500490
47	.0002279	47	.0136717	47	.8203047	107	1.8675023
48	.0002327	48	.0139626	48	.8377580	108	1.8849556
49	.0002376	49	.0142535	49	.8552113	109	1.9024089
50	.0002424	50	.0145444	50	.8726646	110	1.9198622
51	.0002473	51	.0148353	51	.8901179	111	1.9373155
52	.0002521	52	.0151262	52	.9075712	112	1.9547688
53	.0002570	53	.0154171	53	.9250245	113	1.9722221
54	.0002618	54	.0157080	54	.9424778	114	1.9896753
55	.0002666	55	.0159989	55	.9599311	115	2.0071286
56	.0002715	56	.0162897	56	.9773844	116	2.0245819
57	.0002763	57	.0165806	57	.9948377	117	2.0420352
58	.0002812	58	.0168715	58	1.0122910	118	2.0594885
59	.0002860	59	.0171624	59	1.0297443	119	2.0769418
60	.0002909	60	.0174533	60	1.0471976	120	2.0943951

Add values for degrees, minutes, and seconds of the central angle, and multiply the total by the radius.

Example: Find *L* for a circular curve with $\Delta = 66°18'24''$ and R = 400 ft.

Answer: 1.1519173
                 .0052360
                 .0001164
                 ─────────
                 1.1572697 × 400 = 462.91 ft.

Selected Answers

CHAPTER 1

1. b. 137°
   d. 332°–28′–40″
   f. 198°–56′–15″
   h. 103°–45′–54″

2. b. S 44° E
   d. N 82°–41′–30″ W
   f. N 60°–17′–47″ W
   h. S 7°–32′–20″ E

3. b. N 10°–00′–00″ E   198.82 ft
   d. S 85°–00′–18″ W   285.82 ft

5. b. 1186.05, 1032.81
   d. 1196.60,   710.44

CHAPTER 2

2. 0.011

4. $\dfrac{1}{16,382}$ say $\dfrac{1}{16,400}$ Second order

6. Below Third Order

CHAPTER 3

2. 999.68 ft
4. 186.47 ft

6. 475.95 ft
8. 396.05 ft

CHAPTER 4

4. 153.62

CHAPTER 6

2. b. N 39°–17′–00″ W
      129.19′ using Δ dep
      129.20′ using Δ lat

    d. S 81°–42′–44″ E
      970.97′ using Δ dep
      970.93′ using Δ lat

4. b. 6493.98 S.F.
      0.149 Acre

    d. 52430.46 S.F.
      1.204 Acre

CHAPTER 8

4. 12.17, cut 5.0 ft
6. cut 10.93
   raise 0.07, cut 11.0
   lower 0.93 cut 10.0

CHAPTER 9

2. 2337.23
6. 1′–5″ below
8. 1°–33′

Index